UNITED STATES POSTAL SERVICE

S0-BEC-271

The Postal Service Guide to U.S. Stamps

United States Postal Service
Washington, D.C. 20260-6355

Item No. 927

Important Information

The United States Postal Service sells only the commemoratives released during the past few years and current regular and special stamps and postal stationery.

Prices listed in this book are called "catalog prices" by collectors and serve only as a guide to market prices for Fine specimens when offered by an informed dealer to an informed buyer.

Prices for single unused and used stamps are taken from the latest Brookman Price List (© 1982), whose editors have based these values on the current stamp market. Prices quoted for unused and used stamps are for "Fine" condition, except where Fine is not available. If no value is assigned, market value is individually determined by condition of the stamp, scarcity and other factors.

Prices for Plate Blocks and First Day Covers are taken from Scott's latest published prices (© 1982, Scott U.S. Specialized Catalogue). The Scott numbering system for stamps is used in this book.

Prices for Souvenir Cards have been taken from the Catalog of United States Souvenir Cards, by Franklin R. Bruns, Jr., and James H. Bruns, published by Washington Press.

Prices for American Commemorative Panels are from Frank Riolo, Delray Beach, Florida. Souvenir Pages prices are from Charles D. Simmons of Buena Park, California.

Values for First Day Covers and Plate Blocks from Scott Nos. 230-606 often refer to the latest auction prices or reflect infrequent sales or fluctuating market value. Used and unused values for Newspaper Stamps are from the Scott 1982 U.S. Specialized Catalogue (© 1982).

Note: When minimum price of a used stamp is fixed at 3 cents it reflects dealer's labor and service costs. The sum of these minimum prices does not properly indicate the value of an accumulation of stamps consisting only of cheaper stamps. Prices of actual stamp sales are dependent upon supply and demand, changes in popularity, local custom, quality of the stamp itself and many other factors.

Library of Congress Catalogue Card Number 82-060322
ISBN: 0-9604756-2-1
Printed in the United States of America

Editorial and Design: Mobium Corporation for Design and Communication
Printing: R.R. Donnelley and Sons Co., Crawfordsville, IN
Picture Credits: Bettmann Archive, Inc.

TABLE OF CONTENTS

DEFINITION OF CATALOG PRICES

Stamp collectors use catalog prices as a guide to help them in buying items for their collections or for the purpose of trading stamps with other collectors. The values for the stamps quoted in The Postal Service Guide to U.S. Stamps are taken from the latest available catalogs. These price guides will help you to plan your stamp purchases or to evaluate the stamps that you may come across. However, there are a few things about catalog prices that you must know so you will understand and use them correctly.

Catalog values are simply guidelines to stamp values. Actual stamps may cost more or less than the values shown in the catalog. As you may know, one reason for this is that stamp condition (see pp 18-19) is very important in determining the value of any stamp. The catalog gives a price for both unused (mint) stamps and for those that have been used or cancelled. In each case, the catalog value is for a single stamp (except where prices of blocks or sheets of stamp are specifically noted).

Both the used and unused catalog prices are for a stamp in **Fine Condition** and the catalog price also assumes that the copy has been hinged. If you want a stamp with **Superb** centering and color that has never been hinged, it could cost several times the catalog value. But, stamps in less than **Fine** condition or those that have been heavily hinged may be worth only a small percentage of catalog value.

In the case of used stamps, the catalog price is based on a light cancellation. Heavy cancellations lessen a stamp's value. Sometimes used stamps, however, are worth more than unused stamps. This frequently happens when the cancellation is of a special type or for a significant date. Of course, this could mean that the stamp is worth more **only** if it is still on the original envelope.

So, if you find old envelopes, be sure to have them evaluated before simply, tearing off the stamp and discarding its "cover."

There are other important things that you should know about catalog prices. One is that they are estimates of how much you should expect to pay for a copy of the stamp from a regular dealer. If you should wish to sell the same stamp to a dealer, he may offer you much less than the catalog price. The dealer's quote will be based upon his own interest in owning your stamp: he may have a full supply of this stamp at the moment and he will only buy more at a very low price.

Another point about catalog prices concerns very low priced stamps. Frequently the catalog will show that a stamp is worth a small or "minimum" value, like $.03. This means that a stamp dealer cannot afford to sell you an individual stamp for less than this minimum amount. However, a packet of stamps made up of numerous inexpensive stamps is not necessarily worth the total of their individual catalog values.

As a general rule you should try to collect only the best quality stamps. This practice will result in a hobby that can be enjoyable and rewarding for the rest of your life.

How to Use **The Postal Service Guide to U.S. Stamps**

The Postal Service Guide to U.S. Stamps is a color catalog of postage stamps of the United States. This illustrated catalog has been designed to put all the vital information you need in one, handy reference line.

Each line listing contains the following information:

		Un	U	PB	#	FDC	Q
1183	4¢ Kansas Statehood, May 10	.00	.00	0.00	(6)	0.00	000,000,000

Scott Catalog Number → 1183

Denomination → 4¢

Description / First Day of Issue → Kansas Statehood, May 10

Unused Catalog Price → Un

Used Catalog Price → U

Plate Block Price → PB

in Plate Block* →

First Day Cover Price → FDC

Quantity Issued → Q

1183

*All Plate Blocks are blocks of four unless otherwise indicated in parenthesis.

The Postal Service Guide to U.S. Stamps also lists philatelic details such as watermarks, perforations and years of issue. These will aid you in identifying stamps of similar design. Watermarks (Wmk.) are designs incorporated in the paper on which certain stamps are printed. (Please refer to sample illustrations on this page for stamps marked as Watermark 190 or 191.) Perforations are the number of small holes in a two centimeter space on the edge of the stamp. A stamp which has 12 such holes is listed as Perf. 12 (perforated 12), while a stamp with no perforations is listed as Imperf. (imperforate). Coil stamps are perforated on two sides only, either horizontally or vertically. **When a perforation, year of issue, or watermark is mentioned, the description applies to all succeeding issues until a change is noted.**

Illustration Numbers. Some of the stamps cataloged in this book are not shown. The illustrations on such stamps are identified by a number in parenthesis. For example, in the listings which appear below, Scott No. 247 has the same illustration as Scott No.246.

246   1 ¢ Franklin
247   1 ¢ blue Franklin (246)

How to Order Stamps. When ordering stamps from a dealer, identify items wanted by country of issue, Scott No., and condition (unused or used).

Condition is an important factor of price. Prices are for stamps in fine condition. Off center, heavily cancelled, faded or stained stamps usually sell at large discounts. Values in italics indicate latest auction prices, infrequent sales or fluctuating market values.

INTRODUCTION TO STAMP COLLECTING

The wonderful world of stamp collecting—an activity enjoyed by some 20,000,000 people in the United States and considered to be the world's most popular hobby. Collecting stamps appeals to young and old, rich or poor; it can be pursued alone or shared with family and friends, and it has become known as the hobby of "Kings and Kids." Among many famous collectors were Franklin D. Roosevelt of the United States and King George V of England.

Stamp collecting began in Great Britain shortly after the first postage stamp, the "Penny Black," was issued in 1840. It pictured Queen Victoria and was sold to raise money to insure an effective mail delivery. Soon other countries throughout the world were producing stamps for the same purpose. Since that time, hundreds of thousands of different stamps have been issued. The first two United States stamps appeared on July 1, 1847—they featured Benjamin Franklin and George Washington.

Over the years, the study and collecting of stamps has been a source of pride and fascination to many people. And that's not surprising. Each stamp is a masterpiece in miniature, a mirror reflecting a nation's great people, places and events. Brightly colored and finely designed, each stamp has a story to tell.

As you explore the world of stamps, you will find there is always something new and exciting to learn about them. One of the best introductions to stamp collecting is to read a stamp catalog, such as The Postal Service Guide to U.S. Stamps, which details all pertinent information about specific stamps. A catalog not only identifies a stamp and its major varieties by color and denomination, but also supplies such information as its date of issue and the perforation size and watermark (if any). It identifies the stamp's subject matter and lists the value of the stamp in used and unused condition. The catalog also contains identification numbers for each stamp, which are used by dealers and collectors when they are buying, selling or trading.

Beginning Stamp Collecting: Starting a stamp collection is simple, easy and inexpensive. All you need to begin is a looseleaf notebook and paper, stamp hinges or mounts and a touch of ingenuity and resourcefulness. The best place to start is with U.S. stamps . . . carefully soak stamps off the envelopes your family gets in the daily mail, have your friends and relatives save their stamps and envelopes for you and join a stamp club so you can swap duplicates with other beginning collectors. (When soaking stamps off envelopes, immerse in slightly warm water until the stamp easily lifts off. Then let dry under a weight overnight to have a completely flat specimen.)

Once you get started, you'll find there are many ways to collect. Some people like to collect a specimen of each stamp issued by a country; then they expand on that and collect the different varieties of such stamps. Another very popular form of collecting is "topical." To form this type of collection, you should select topics or subjects that interest you, such as animals, sports, music, space, etc. If you chose some that are broad enough, you will find it quite easy to create a fascinating and personally meaningful collection.

Types of Stamps. You may limit your collection to a simple type of stamp or to stamps of any kind. Stamp issues are normally divided into the following types:

Regular or Definitive Stamps. These are the stamps you'll find on most day-in, day-out mail. They are printed in huge quantities and are kept in use by the post office for sizable stretches of time—several years, usually. Definitives usually appear in a series, with values from 1 cent to higher values, say $5.00, with as many intermediate values as are needed for the postal rates then in effect.

Regular or Definitive

Commemorative Stamps. These are issued to honor an important event, person or special subject. They are usually larger than the definitives, more colorful and are circulated for a limited time. Often they depict famous people, but U.S. stamps never depict a living person.

Coil Stamps. These are stamps issued in rolls, so that each stamp has two straight edges and two perforated edges. Many collectors specialize in this type of stamp.

Coil

Commemorative

Air Mail Stamps. Air Mail stamps are no longer issued for postage within the U.S., Canada and Mexico. Some U.S. Air Mail stamps for use in sending mail overseas are still issued.

Postage Due Stamps. Postage due stamps are affixed to mail at the post office to indicate that the prepaid postage was not enough to carry the letter to its destination and more is to be paid for delivery.

Air Mail   Postage Due

Special Delivery Stamps. These stamps are sold to the sender at a premium price to secure extra-fast delivery for a letter or package.

Special Delivery

Stamp collecting also has its own set of working tools. In addition to a reference catalog, there are six essential tools. Simple and inexpensive, they are:

Stamp Album: An album is a showcase for your stamps, a place to arrange and mount your collection in a systematic way for viewing and studying. Albums on the market are geared for every pocketbook, taste and specialty. It is advisable to select one with looseleaf pages to allow for convenient expansion of your collection.

Tongs or Tweezers: A stamp's value depends on its condition. And because stamps are relatively delicate, they can become damaged easily. Therefore, it is best to handle them with specially designed tongs to prevent unnecessary soiling or tearing.

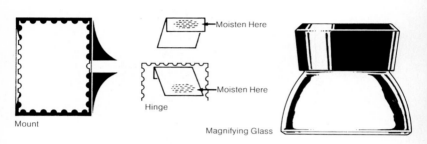

Mount

Moisten Here

Moisten Here

Hinge

Magnifying Glass

Stamp Mounts and Hinges: Mounts are special plastic envelopes that hold a stamp in your album. They should always be used for uncancelled stamps to preserve their value. For less expensive stamps, you can use lower-cost stamp hinges, but it is best not to buy the self-sticking variety as stamps could eventually become stained from the chemical action of these hinges.

Perforation Gauge: The perforations found around the edges of a stamp can often be the sole means of determining the difference between two similar stamps. A gauge to measure the size and number of these perforations is, therefore, a very useful instrument. The gauge also features a millimeter scale so that the dimensions of a stamp can be accurately measured.

Magnifying Glass: To closely examine your stamps, a four- or six-power magnifying glass is recommended. It should be optically correct and large enough so that at least two-thirds of the stamp can be viewed at the same time.

Watermark Detector and Detector Fluid: A watermark is a design or pattern incorporated into the stamp paper during its manufacture. Sometimes the only way you can distinguish the difference between two stamps is by their watermark. Watermarks can often be seen if the stamp is held up to a bright light, but the most accurate method is to use a detector. In its simplest form, a watermark detector is a small tray. The stamp is placed face down in the tray, a few drops of detector fluid (Benzine, Carbon Tetrachloride or lighter fluid) are poured over it and the watermark becomes visible. Be sure to air-dry the stamp before putting it back into your album, and be very careful of fire and ventilation since the fluids are flammable.

With these basic tools, a good stamp catalog and an enthusiasm for stamps, you will be well-equipped for the many joys to be encountered in the wonderful world of stamp collecting.

GLOSSARY OF PHILATELIC TERMS

Adhesive: Those postage stamps made for affixing to mail (as compared to stamps printed on cards and envelopes or hand struck stamps). Adhesive postage stamps were introduced in 1840 by Great Britain.

Aerophilately: Collecting air mail stamps, covers and other postal materials related to mail delivery by balloon, airplane or other types of aircraft.

Aerogramme: A sheet of paper with a stamp printed on it for air mail use. The sheet is folded and sealed with pre-gummed flaps.

Appraisals: A process whereby experts evaluate philatelic materials to ascertain true market value.

APS: Abbreviation for the American Philatelic Society.

Approvals: Stamps sent to a collector for examination. Approvals must be bought or returned to the dealer within a specific time.

A.T.A.: Abbreviation for the American Topical Association.

Autographed Cover: Any cover sheet or envelope signed by a member of the crew of the airplane involved in carrying the material, a postmaster, the artist or even the person sending the letter.

Backprinting: Any printing done on the back of a stamp.

Bar Cancels: Any cancellations formed of bars. Can take the form of ovals, circles or rectangles.

Bisect: Half of a stamp used to pay postage of half the face value of the original stamp. This variety must appear on its original cover with the cancellation or postmark covering the cut.

Block: An attached group of stamps at least two stamps wide and two stamps high.

Booklet Pane: A small pane of stamps especially printed and cut to be sold in booklets.

Cachet: A special handstamp or printed device on a cover to denote the special circumstances in which it was mailed.

Cancellation: A mark placed on a stamp by a postal authority to prevent its reuse. Prior to 1880, postmasters could make their own cancelling devices, some of which were highly decorative.

Cancelled to Order (CTO): Stamps which are cancelled by the postal authorities without being sent through the mails. They are normally less desirable than stamps which have served their postal function.

Catalogs: Postage stamp catalogs which illustrate, list and price stamps. The first postage stamp catalog was published in 1861 in Paris.

Catalog Value: Valuations listed in catalogs. Prices indicated are a guide and do not represent the actual retail or wholesale market value.

C.C. of N.Y.: Abbreviation for the Collectors Club of New York (City).

Centering: Refers to the position of the design in a postage stamp. Perfectly centered stamps have margins of equal width.

Classics: Rare and often beautiful early issues; generally issues of a country before 1870.

Coils: Stamps issued in rolls for use in dispensers, affixers or vending machines.

Color Changeling: A stamp whose color has been changed, either accidentally or intentionally.

Commemoratives: Stamps which honor anniversaries, important people or special events. Commemoratives are usually sold for a specific length of time.

Compound Perforations: A stamp with perforations of different sizes on different sides.

Condition: The state of a stamp in regard to centering, color, freshness, cancellation and other related characteristics.

Cover: The entire wrapping or envelope in which a letter has been sent through the mail.

Cut Square: An envelope stamp cut out with a square margin.

Dead Horse: Refers to the illustration on the 10¢ Trans-Mississippi issue (Scott No. 290) of 1898.

Definitives: Regular issues of stamps as distinct from commemoratives. Usually on sale for long periods of time.

Die: An engraving from which the plates for printing stamps can be made.

Errors: Stamps with accidental mistakes in color, paper, inscription, watermark, etc. Errors also include bicolored stamps with inverted centers.

Essays: Designs submitted in stamp form but not accepted for issuance.

First Day Cover: A cover bearing a new stamp and cancelled with the first day of use, usually at an officially designated location.

Flat Press Stamps: Stamps printed on a flat bed press, as distinguished from a rotary press.

Freaks: Stamps which show conspicuous deviations from the normal caused by shifted perforations, heavy inking, color shifts, or similar accidents during production. Not errors.

Grill: Parallel rows of small pyramids impressed or embossed on the stamp in order to break the fibers of the paper so that the cancellation ink will soak in and make washing for reuse impossible. Used on U.S. stamps from 1867 to 1870.

Gum: The adhesive on the back of the stamp.

Hinges: Small strips of paper gummed on one side and used by collectors to mount their stamps.

Overprint

Precancel

Perforated

Imperforate Stamp

Coils. These stamps are perforated on two sides only.

Surcharge

Cut Square

Perfin

Se-tenant

Souvenir Sheet

Imperforate: Stamps printed in sheet form without perforation or other means of separation, except by the use of knife or scissors. Usually collected in pairs to prove their authenticity.

India Paper: A soft, thin, silky appearing wove paper usually used for proof impressions.

Inverted Center: A stamp with the center appearing to be printed upside down in relation to the rest of the design. (See Scott No. C3a.)

Laid Paper: A paper showing alternate light and dark parallel lines when held to the light or immersed in benzine.

Locals: Stamps issued for use in restricted areas either by government or private carriers.

Margin: The border outside the printed design of a stamp.

Overprint: Any word, inscription, or device placed on a stamp to alter its use or locality, or to serve a special purpose.

Pair: Two attached stamps.

Pane: A portion of the original sheet as cut for sale at the post office.

Part-Perforate: A stamp which has perforations on one, two or three sides.

Pen Cancel: A cancellation supplied to the stamp with pen and ink.

Perfin: Punch-perforated or "branded" stamps.

Perforations: Line of small cuts or holes placed between two rows of stamps to facilitate separation.

Plate: The base from which the stamps are printed.

Plate Number Block: A block of stamps with sheet margin showing a plate number or numbers. Often it is known simply as a plate block.

Postal Stationery: Envelopes, postal cards, aerogrammes, wrappers, etc., which had non-adhesive stamps embossed or printed on them.

Postmark: A mark struck upon envelopes and other mailing pieces, generally to indicate the name of the post office, date of mailing, etc.

Precancels: Stamps with cancellations applied before the mailing of the article on which postage is prepaid.

Proofs: Trial printing of a stamp made from the original die or the plate.

Provisionals: Stamps issued prior to the regular issues or to meet a temporary shortage of regular stamps.

Reissue: An official reprinting of a stamp, or stamps, that had been discontinued.

Remainders: Stocks of stamps on hand after the sale of the issue has been discontinued.

Reprints: Impressions from the original plates taken after the issuance of the stamps to post offices has ceased and their postal use has been voided, usually to satisfy collectors' demands.

Revenue Stamps: Stamps issued for use in collecting special taxes on documents, proprietary articles, products, etc.

Rotary Press Stamps: Stamps printed on a rotary type press from curved plates as compared to stamps printed from flat plates on a flat bed press. They will be slightly larger in one direction than flat press stamps.

Rouletting: Short consecutive cuts in the paper between rows of stamps to facilitate separation. Original rouletting machine was invented by Henry Archer in 1841.

Selvage: The paper around panes or sheets of stamps. Sometimes called marginal paper.

Se-tenant: An attached pair, strip or block of stamps which differ in value, design or surcharge.

Sheet: Complete unseparated group of stamps as originally printed.

Special Printing: Stamps of current design reissued, usually on a better grade of paper and in brilliant colors.

Souvenir Sheets: A sheet containing one or more stamps, often with a commemorative inscription. The first U.S. Souvenir Sheet was issued for the International Philatelic Exhibition of 1926 and consisted of a perforated block of 25 two-cent stamps (Scott No. 630). Recent U.S. issues include the 1966 SIPEX (Scott No. 1311) and the 1976 Bicentennial issue (Scott Nos. 1686-1689).

Stampless Cover: An envelope without stamps generally bearing a postmark and sometimes notations such as "Paid," "Paid 10," etc.

Straight Edge: The imperforate side of a stamp which is otherwise perforate.

Surcharge: An overprint which alters or restates the face value or denomination of the stamp to which it is applied.

Tied On: A stamp is "tied on" when the cancellation or postmark extends from the stamp to the envelope.

Topicals: Area of philately in which emphasis is on the subject portrayed on stamps rather than the stamps themselves.

Unused: A stamp with or without original gum which has no cancellation or other evidence of postal use.

Used: A stamp which has been postally used as evidenced by the cancellation.

Want List: A list of stamp numbers or philatelic items needed by a collector.

Watermark: A design or pattern incorporated into the paper during its manufacture.

Wove Paper: A paper of uniform texture throughout, showing no light or dark patterns when held to the light or immersed in benzine.

STAMP CLUBS

What Are Benjamin Franklin Stamp Clubs?

The United States Postal Service began a stamp club program in elementary schools in 1974-75. Its purpose was to introduce fourth, fifth, and sixth grade students to the educational and enjoyable hobby of stamp collecting. Various stamp club materials, a monthly newsletter, and special student-involvement projects are distributed to these stamp clubs free-of-charge by the Postal Service. To date, more than 65,000 clubs have been established, offering over 1,500,000 young students an opportunity to learn a fun-filled and educational hobby.

Why Are These Clubs Named After Ben Franklin?

You know all about Ben Franklin's key and kite experiment, his Franklin stove, his bifocals and his Poor Richard's Almanac. But did you know that Franklin was also the Father of the Postal Service? That's why it's his face that appears on the first postage stamp the U.S. ever issued. And that's why, when the Postal Service decided to help establish stamp clubs in schools all over the country, it thought of calling them Benjamin Franklin Stamp Clubs.

How Does A Typical Stamp Club Get Started?

Because the clubs are primarily intended for fourth, fifth, and sixth grade students, the first place to get a club started is in the schools. Some clubs, however, are begun and sponsored by local community and service organizations like the YMCA, Boy Scouts, and Girl Scouts. These clubs also contain elementary school students in the fourth to sixth grades.

If you think you'd like to start a stamp club, your first task is to find members. So publicize your club with announcements on your school's bulletin boards and in the school newsletters . . . with posters in the windows of cooperating stores, banks and restaurants . . . with announcements in local newspapers and over local radio stations, if they're willing to carry club activity news without charge.

Your announcements should tell when the club will meet, where, and how a prospective member can get additional information.

You'll want a conveniently located place for your meetings, available at no charge to the club. Usually, this means your school classroom, auditorium or other area in your own elementary school. Sometimes, local libraries, churches, museums, community recreation centers, the "Y" or the homes of club members are more convenient locations because of school and bus schedules.

A *club advisor,* usually an interested school teacher or administrative official, will volunteer to help the new club form and conduct its club meetings. A local Postal Service employee in your area will meet with the advisor and typically make a presentation to interested students. That Postal employee will provide the new club with a full supply of organizing materials, including membership cards and certificates, club by-laws and other educational materials. The Postal Service has prepared a lot of other exciting material to help your club get started and to support its activities. These include color movies, film strips, printed brochures, plus stamp albums. Each members also gets a colorful wallet I.D. card, and membership certificate suitable for framing.

The next step is to elect officers. Initially, the club elects only those officers necessary for the club to function properly. Additional officers can be elected as needed, from the club's expanding membership. The rules to govern the club's activities should be developed by the entire membership as early as possible. These rules can be developed using the sample "by-laws" left with the club advisor.

Another of your early club meetings could consist of a field trip to the local post office. Be sure to telephone the Postmaster in advance to see if he can arrange for a guided tour. While at the post office, have the local Postmaster endorse the club charter to make your club official, if this has not already been done.

How Does A Stamp Club Operate?

The entire membership should participate in planning club activities. And planning should start at the very first meeting. Clubs typically keep the business part of each meeting short, and the pleasure part long.

The pleasure part consists of trading, buying, and selling stamps. Other than that, members can exhibit their collections. Guest speakers can be invited to lecture or conduct questions and answer sessions. Films can be shown. Stamp auctions can be organized. Group discussions can be set up. Club members also enjoy stamp quiz shows—like the quiz shows on television, but with questions that deal exclusively with stamps and collecting.

But with all that going on, how will members ever remember what's coming up and when? They'll read about it in the club newsletter. Many clubs issue a weekly or monthly bulletin to keep members informed. It doesn't have to be an elaborate publication, and the duplication method used can be the least expensive. A single sheet of paper would do very nicely, with pertinent club information on one side and a calendar of meetings and upcoming events on the other.

Does the idea of starting a stamp club sound a little crazy? It shouldn't—not if you organize well, distribute the work fairly, and take things step by step.

So become a member of a stamp club—whether you join a Benjamin Franklin Stamp Club at school or an ongoing stamp club in your community. The joy of collecting is multiplied many times over when you share it.

SPECIALTY COLLECTING

Specialty collecting hasn't anything to do with the subject matter of the stamps you collect. It refers strictly to the form in which you collect them.

Blocks of Four A block of four, with two mint stamps above and two below, can come from anywhere on a sheet of stamps. That makes it the most plentiful form of block and the easiest to come by.

Booklet Panes Stamps booklets were first issued in 1898. On the average, two new booklet panes are issued per year. Most philatelists collect entire panes of entire booklets, just as they came from the post office. The first combination pane, consisting of one 9¢ Freedom to Assemble stamp and seven 13¢ Flag stamps was issued March 11, 1977.

Covers Covers (or envelopes) canceled on a postage stamp's first day of issue are collected with tremendous enthusiasm by a large philatelic audience. On page 15 you'll find a more detailed discussion of first day covers.

Plate Blocks The Postal Service adopted a new plate number system effective January 1, 1981. Except in cases where more than four designs appear in a pane of stamps, the new system establishes a plate block as consisting of four stamps regardless of the number of inks or the press used to print the stamps. The new system permits offset plate numbers to remain on the selvage of panes instead of being trimmed off during production and makes possible the printing of plate numbers on booklet panes and the printing at intervals of plate numbers on coil stamps.

Each color plate or cylinder used initially in the production of a stamp will be designated by the number "1," and the numbers for each plate or cylinder will be grouped in the selvage adjacent to a single stamp. Whenever a plate or a cylinder is replaced during the manufacturing process the number "1" will give way to the number "2" in the color of the plate or cylinder replaced.

"Copyright" Blocks The U.S. Postal Service now copyrights all new stamp designs. The copyright "C" in a circle, followed by "United States Postal Service" or "USPS" and the year, appears in the selvage of each pane. The first copyright inscription appeared January 6, 1978, in the margin of sheets of the Carl Sandburg stamp. Most philatelists collect copyrights in blocks of four.

"Mr. ZIP" Blocks The Zoning Improvement Plan—better known as ZIP Code— was devised to increase postal efficiency. And it succeeded dramatically. A "Mr. ZIP" cartoon and slogan were inaugurated January 10, 1964, with the Sam Houston issue. The cartoon and slogan with adjoining block of four immediately became a popular collectible.

Souvenir Cards In 1938 and 1939, the Postal Office Department Philatelic Truck toured the country distributing souvenir sheets that pictured the White House. They were the forerunners of the modern souvenir card. For more detailed information on souvenir cards, see page 264-267.

FIRST DAY COVERS

A first-day cover is an envelope that bears a new stamp cancelled on the first-day of the issue at the post office designated to conduct the first-day ceremonies.

For each new stamp or postal stationery issue, the Postal Service designates one post office where the item is first placed on sale. Usually it's a post office that is in some way related to the subject the stamp commemorates. Other post offices place the stamp on sale the following day.

Here's how you can secure a first-day cover through the Postal Service:

The date and place of issue of new stamps are announced by the Postal Service in the press and on post office bulletin board posters.

When the stamps go on sale at your post office, you can buy them and affix them to your own envelopes. Your stamped and addressed envelopes (peelable labels are permitted) should be mailed inside another envelope to "Customer Affixed Envelopes," care of the Postmaster of the designated first day city. The post office will cancel the envelope and return it to you through the mail.

Or, you can send your pre-addressed envelope to the name of stamp or postal stationery issue, care of the Postmaster of the designated first day city, and the first-day post office will affix the new stamp. You must include payment to cover the total face value of the stamps that will be affixed. Do not send cash. Payment can be made by check, bank draft, or U.S. Postal money order, payable to the U.S. Postal Service.

The envelope you send for your first-day cover can be plain or cacheted. A cacheted envelope carries a special design at the left. The Postal Service doesn't provide cacheted envelopes, but you can buy them from stamp dealers as well as some department and stationery stores. If you ever receive a damaged first-day cover, though, you can send it right back and it will be replaced.

First-day cover service is one way the Postal Service accommodates collectors, and they spare no effort to get the cover in the mail without delay. But be patient . . . the volume of requests is high and occasionally a post office is completely swamped. The 10¢ Moon Landing Airmail Stamp of 1969, for example, was affixed to 8,700,000 first-day covers. It is anticipated that First-Day Covers for the 1982 state bird and flower issue will exceed the 1969 record.

POSTAL STATIONERY

There are three items in the category of collectibles called postal stationery: (1) embossed stamped envelopes, (2) postal cards and (3) aerogrammes. They're all available at post offices, and the number of Americans who collect them is growing all the time.

Aerogrammes

An aerogramme is a flat sheet of paper that's specially shaped, fold-marked and gummed so that, after the message is written, it can be sealed for privacy in transit. It's letter and envelope in one, it's intended for air mail only, and it carries a message anywhere in the world at a lower postage rate than air mail.

Aerogrammes are produced by the Bureau of Engraving and Printing on a Seven-Color press. It can execute multicolor stamp designs, apply a phosphor tag and gum the sealing flaps.

Just as is the case with stamped envelopes and postal cards, the Postal Service has stepped up its issuance of commemorative aerogrammes in recent years.

Postal Cards

Plain and simple one-color Government postal cards were first issued May 1, 1873. They stayed plain and simple until 1956, when the first U.S. commemorative postal card came out.

"Visit the USA" was the theme of the first pictorial postal card, issued in 1966. Six years later, a series of five picture postal cards hailed "Tourism Year of the Americas." The backs of the cards featured twenty different U.S. scenic attractions.

Postal cards are manufactured at the Government Printing Office in Washington D.C. Regular one-color cards can come off the four high-speed rotary web presses at a rate of 250,000 an hour. The Government Printing Office's two-color sheet-fed offset presses produce the two-color air mail and multi-color commemorative cards. Some 800 million postal cards are issued each year by the Postal Service, accounting for approximately 2,500 tons of paper annually.

Stamped Envelopes

In the case of stamped envelopes, the stamp is embossed and printed right onto the envelope rather than separately affixed. In recent years the number of commemorative stamped envelopes issued by the United States has been on the increase. Multicolor was recently introduced to embossed stamp envelopes.

Stamped envelopes are manufactured for the Postal Service under private contract. They're issued in a number of sizes and styles, including the window type.

Stamped envelopes were first issued in June, 1853. In 1865 envelopes bearing the purchaser's printed return address were authorized by law. The average annual issues of stamped envelopes today is in excess of 1 billion.

The record for the largest number of stamped envelopes manufactured in a single day goes all the way back to 1932. A new postal rate was going into effect, and an enormous quantity of envelopes was needed to stock the post offices of the nation. To meet the monumental need, the contractor produced, in a single day, a total of 19,168,000 stamped envelopes.

See the U.S.A... vacationland of the world!

Aerogramme

Tour
The
United
States

© USPS 1981

USA
30c

AEROGRAMME · VIA AIR MAIL · PAR AVION

② Second fold

③ Seal top flap last

③ Seal top flap last

Do not use tape or stickers to seal—No enclosures permitted

←— ① Fold first at notches —→

Additional message area

Stamped Envelope

USA 20c

USA 13c

La Salle claims Louisiana, 1682

© USPS 1982

Postal Card

17

STAMP CONDITION

Condition, in the philatelic sense, means the state of a stamp—that is, whether it is a superb specimen, a mediocre specimen or a specimen that is below average. A stamp in fine condition is always more valuable than one that has been less well cared for.

When selecting a stamp to be placed in your collection, always make sure that it is the best you can obtain. Unused stamps should, if possible, be well-centered, fresh looking and have the original gum intact. Gum is the proper term for the adhesive applied to the back of the stamp. Remember, too, that unused stamps that have been hinged or with only part of the original gum are priced below a never hinged stamp with its original gum intact. Used stamps should be well-centered, lightly cancelled and never faded, dirty or stained. There should be no thinning of the paper. Thinning often occurs when stamps are improperly removed from envelopes or album pages and part of the stamp is removed as well.

Most dealers designate stamp condition by such term as "Superb," "Fine," and "Good." There are many gradations in the range from "Exceptionally Fine," "Very Fine," and "Very Good," through "Fair," "Poor," and "Spacefiller." However, for our purposes, "Superb," "Fine," and "Good" cover the ground for most newer collectors.

"Superb" means a stamp that is of the finest quality, has perfect centering, brilliant color and perfect gum. Used copies in this category also have perfect centering. They are fresh looking, are lightly cancelled, and are sound of body.

"Fine" means a stamp without flaws, average centering, gum with light hinge marks. Used copies in this category are not quite as fresh, cancels are heavier, and centering is average.

"Good" means stamps that are off-center, but fairly attractive and there may be minor defects such as disturbed gum, tiny thins, heavy hinge marks. Used copies, except for the gum, fall into this classification.

Stamps that fall below these standards should be ignored and are not worth acquiring. Of course, there are exceptions to these rules, but they do not come into the province of a new collector and will not be discussed here.

Superb

Fine

Good

Cancelled, Good

Cancelled, Fine

Lightly Cancelled

STAMPS COLOR GUIDE

A slight difference in the color of a stamp can make it not only a different variety, but sometimes a thing of great rarity. The ability to recognize such color differences requires a practiced eye, but being able to ascertain a valuable shade is one of the real enjoyments of stamp collecting.

The stamp colors we reproduced here are not 100% accurate because printing processes such as the one used in The Postal Guide to U.S. Stamps use different kinds of ink and paper than the original stamps. As a result, the colors shown in the book are not exact reproductions.

In most catalogs the illustrations are only in black and white. The catalog editors use many descriptive phrases to indicate the color of the stamps listed. Below we list some of the more popular names for the colors found on stamps along with some stamps that go with them.

Bright Blue

Blue

Dark Blue

Ultramarine

Purple

Violet

Carmine

Jose Lake

Peach Blossom

Red

Henna Brown

Brown

Bistre Brown

Sepia

Gray Brown

Dark Gray

Black

Light Green

Green

Olive

Light Olive Green

Blue Green

Yellow Gold

Orange

Deep Orange

Yellow-Black-Green

POSTMASTERS GENERAL OF THE UNITED STATES

1789 Samuel Osgood, MA
1791 Timothy Pickering, PA
1795 Joseph Habersham, GA
1801 Gideon Granger, CT
1814 Return J. Meigs, Jr., OH
1823 John McLean, OH
1829 William T. Barry, KY
1835 Amos Kendall, KY
1840 John M. Niles, CT
1841 Francis Granger, NY
1841 Charles A. Wickliffe, KY
1845 Cave Johnson, TN
1849 Jacob Collamer, VT
1850 Nathan K. Hall, NY
1852 Samuel D. Hubbard, CT
1853 James Campbell, PA
1857 Aaron V. Brown, TN
1859 Joseph Holt, KY
1861 Horatio King, ME
1861 Montgomery Blair, DC
1864 William Dennison, OH
1866 Alexander W. Randall, WI
1869 John A. J. Creswell, MD
1874 James W. Marshall, NJ
1874 Marshall Jewell, CT
1876 James N. Tyner, IN
1877 David McK. Key, TN
1880 Horace Maynard, TN
1881 Thomas L. James, NY

1882 Timothy O. Howe, WI
1883 Walter Q. Gresham, IN
1884 Frank Hatton, IA
1885 William F. Vilas, WI
1888 Don M. Dickinson, MI
1889 John Wanamaker, PA
1893 Wilson S. Bissell, NY
1895 William L. Wilson, WV
1897 James A. Gary, MD
1898 Charles Emory Smith, PA
1902 Henry C. Payne, WI
1904 Robert J. Wynne, PA
1905 George B. Cortelyou, NY
1907 George von L. Meyer, MA
1909 Frank H. Hitchcock, MA
1913 Albert S. Burleson, TX
1921 Will H. Hays, IN
1922 Hubert Work, CO
1923 Harry S. New, IN
1929 Walter F. Brown, OH
1933 James A. Farley, NY
1940 Frank C. Walker, PA
1945 Robert E. Hannegan, MO
1947 Jesse M. Donaldson, IL
1953 Arthur E. Summerfield, MI
1961 J. Edward Day, CA
1963 John A. Gronouski, WI
1965 Lawrence F. O'Brien, MA
1968 W. Marvin Watson, TX
1969 Winton M. Blount, AL
1972 E. T. Klassen, MA
1975 Benjamin Franklin Bailar, MD
1978 William F. Bolger, CT

MAJOR U.S. PHILATELIC
SOCIETIES AND PUBLICATIONS

Philatelic Societies

American Air Mail Society
102 Arbor Rd.
Cinnaminson, NJ 08077

Specializes in aerophilately, and periodically presents the Conrath Award to a member of the society in the name of Walter Conrath, one of its founders.

American First Day Cover Society
Mrs. Monte Eiserman
Membership Chairman
14359 Chadbourne
Houston, TX 77079

American Philatelic Society
Box 800
State College, PA 16801

A full complement of services and resources for the philatelist. Membership offers: American Philatelic Research Library; expertizing service; estate advisory service; translation services; a stamp theft committee which functions as a clearing house for stamp theft information; and a speakers' bureau. Society affiliate: Perfins Club, specializing in perfin collection and survey.

American Philatelic Foundation
7219 Hampton Avenue
Los Angeles, CA 90046

A newly-formed postal foundation and museum specializing in the display of U.S. and foreign specialty stamp collections and historical documentation of western usage of stamps and mail.

American Stamp Dealer's Association
840 Willis Ave.
Albertson, NY 11507

Association of dealers engaged in every facet of philately, with eleven regional chapters nationwide. Sponsors national and local shows, seminars for member and non-member dealers, credit information service, monthly newsletter and ASDA membership directory.

American Topical Association
3306 No. 50th Street
Milwaukee, WI 53216

A service organization concentrating on the specialty of topical collecting. Offers handbooks on specific topics; an exhibition award; *Topical Time,* a bi-monthly publication dealing with topical interest areas; a slide and film loan service; information, translation, biography and sales services; and an heirs' and estate service.

Bureau Issues Association
19 Maple Street
Arlington, MA 02174

Collectors Club, Inc.
22 East 35th Street
New York, NY 10016

Regular services include library and reading rooms, a publication and lectures on philatelic subjects. The group also honors a great American collector annually and actively supports national and international exhibitions.

Council of Philatelic Organizations
P.O. Box 3492
North New Hyde Park Station
New Hyde Park, NY 11040

An organization comprised of 175 member philatelic groups. Objectives include: to educate the general public to the many benefits and pleasures of collecting stamps.

Junior Philatelists of America
Box 195
Minetto, NY 13115

Provides an auction department, library service, tape and slide service, stamp identification and translation services. Publishes a bi-monthly, illustrated publication titled the *Philatelic Observer.*

National Association of Precancel Collectors
5121 Park Blvd.
Wildwood, NJ 08260

The Perfin Club
10550 Western Ave.
Stanton, CA 90680

An affiliate of the American Philatelic Society, specializing in the collection and survey of perfins.

Philatelic Foundation
270 Madison Ave.
New York, NY 10016

A non-profit organization known for its excellent expertization service. The Foundation's broad resources, including extensive reference collections, 5,000-volume library and Expert Committee provide collectors with comprehensive consumer protection. It also publishes educational information.

Plate Block Collector Club
Box 937
Homestead, FL 33030

Plate Number Society
9600 Colesville Rd.
Silver Springs, MD 20901

Postal History Society
Box 20
Bayside, NY 11361

Post Mark Collectors Club
Bernice White
3487 Firstenberger Rd.
Marion, OH 43302

Society of Philatelic Americans
Box 9041
Wilmington, DE 19809

An organization with members from all over the world, the Society publishes a monthly journal, provides sales circuits, and services in exchange, expertization, insurance, publications and slide films. It also sponsors numerous philatelic awards.

United Postal Stationery Society
Mrs. J. Thomas
Box 48
Redlands, CA 92373

The United States Possessions Philatelic Society
141 Lyford Drive
Tiburon, CA 94920

The Universal Ship Cancellation Society
P.O. Box 13
New Britain, CT 06050

Catalogs

Brookman Price List of U.S. Stamps
91 South 9th Street
Minneapolis, MN 55402

Brookman's values are used for used and unused single stamp pricing in The Postal Service Guide to U.S. Stamps.

Catalogue of United States Souvenir Cards
The Washington Press
Florham Park, NJ 07932

First Day Cover Catalogue (U.S.-U.N.)
The Washington Press
Florham Park, NJ 07932

Souvenir Pages Price List
(Please send self-addressed stamped envelope to receive current listings.)
Charles D. Simmons
P.O. Box 6238
Buena Park, CA 90622

Stamps of the World 1982 Catalogue
Stanley Gibbons Publications. Available through dealers only. All the stamps of the world from 1840 to date. Over 1,900 pages feature more than 200,000 stamps (47,900 illustrations) from over 200 issuing countries.

Commemorative Panel Price List.
(Please send self-addressed stamped envelope to receive current listings.)
Frank Riolo
P. O. Box 1540
Delray Beach, FL 33444

Fleetwoods Standard First Day Cover Catalog
Unicover Corporation
Cheyenne, WY 82001

Harris Illustrated Postage Stamp Catalog
Boston, MA 02117

Minkus New World Wide Stamp Catalogue
NY

American Air Mail Catalogue
American Air Mail Society
Cinnaminson, NJ 08077

Scott Standard Postage Stamp Catalogue
NY

Magazines and Newspapers

Linn's Stamp News
Box 29
Sidney, OH 45367

Mekeel's Weekly Stamp News
Box 1660
Portland, ME 04104

Minkus Stamp Journal
116 West 32nd Street
New York, NY 10001

Scott's Monthly Stamp Journal
3 East 57th St.
New York, NY 10022

Stamps
153 Waverly Place
New York, NY 10014

Stamp Collector
Box 10
Albany, OR 97321

Stamp Show News & Philatelic Review
1839 Palmer Ave.
Larchmont, NY 10538

Stamp World
P.O. Box 601
Sidney, OH 45365

Monthly publication directed to informational and feature articles on stamp subjects, stamp designs and other general topics.

Philatelic Literature

Brookman, Lester G. *The 19th Century Postage Stamps of the United States* (3 volumes). NY, 1968.

Chase, Carroll C. *The 3¢ Stamps of the United States, 1942.*

Johl, Max G. *The United States Commemorative Stamps of the Twentieth Century, 1947.*

Linn's World Stamp Almanac, Sidney, OH, 1978.

Griffenhagen, G. and Husak, J., *Mini-Adventures in Topical Stamp Collecting,* condensed from ATA Handbook 96. Reference book on "how-to's" of topical collecting.

Mueller, Barbara R. *United States Postage Stamps, 1958.*

Patrick, Douglas and Mary. *The Musson Stamp Dictionary, 1972.*

D.G. Phillips Publ. Co. *The American Stampless Cover Catalog, 1978.*

Scheele, Carl H. *A Short History of the Mail Service, 1970.*

Scott's New Handbook for Philatelists, NY, 1967.

Sutton, R.J., *Stamp Collector's Encyclopedia.*

Allen, J.L. and Silverstone, P.H., *Stamp Collector's Guide to Europe.*

Topical Stamp Publications List, 1982-83, American Topical Association.

Thorp, Prescott H. *Stamped Envelopes and Wrappers of the United States,* Netcong, NJ, 1954.

United Postal Stationery Society. *United States Postal Card Catalog,* Albany, OR, 1975.

United States Postal Service United States Postage Stamps, Pub.9
A popular reference book compiled and produced by the United States Postal Service's Stamps Division. Includes illustrations, background data and technical information (designers, engravers, etc.) on all U.S. postage stamps complete through 1980. Basic book and latest update supplements available through the Superintendent of Documents, Government Printing Office, Washington, D.C. 20402.

FOUR FREEDOMS POSTAGE STAMP—ISSUE OF 1943

This stamp was issued to impress upon the public the necessity of spreading the Four Freedoms throughout the world, and to replace the 1-cent National Defense stamp. The stamp is 35/100 by 30/100 inch in dimensions, arranged vertically. It is printed in green by rotary process and issued in sheets of 100. The central subject, enclosed in an oval-shaped panel, is a reproduction in bas-relief of Liberty holding the lighted Torch of Freedom and Enlightenment. Across the top of the stamp is the inscription reading "U.S. Postage" shown in white architectural Roman on a shaded background. Underneath this inscription, at the left, is the denomination designation "1¢" and in corresponding position but reversed order at the right "¢1". Below the central design is a rectangular plaque with white background, in which appears the wording: "Freedom of Speech and Religion, From Want and Fear," in solid Gothic lettering arranged in five lines. In the space at the right and left of the central oval and plaque are shown conventionalized oak leaves, outlined in white.
The stamp was first placed on sale at Washington, D.C., on February 12, 1943.

OVERRUN COUNTRIES COMMEMORATIVE STAMPS—ISSUE OF 1943-44

387-129"—70——6

107

The Overrun Countries Series is comprised of 13 stamps, issued in tribute to the following countries overrun and occupied by the Axis powers: Poland, Czechoslovakia, Norway, Luxembourg, Netherlands, Belgium, France, Greece, Yugoslavia, Albania, Austria, Denmark, and Korea.
All of these stamps are of 5-cent denomination, 35/100 by 14¼/100 inches in dimension, arranged horizontally, and issued in sheets of 50 stamps each.
The central subjects, which are surface printed, reproduce in natural colors the flags of the respective countries with the name of the country underneath. Rays of light extend from behind the central subjects to the outer frames. The main frames of the stamps, steel engraved, are printed in purple and depict on the left the phoenix, a mythological bird symbolizing the renewal of life, and on the right, in a corresponding position, a kneeling female figure portraying the breaking of the shackles of oppression and enforced servitude. Both figures are supported by pedestals on which, in oval-shaped panels with dark ground, the numeral 5 is indicated in white. These pedestals rest on a panel, in which appears the word "Cents" in white-faced Roman. Immediately back of the wording the panel is of a darker shade fading out at each end. Across the top of the stamps are the words "United States Postage" in white-faced Gothic, within a ruled panel with ornamental scroll ends. The Bureau of Engraving and Printing, Treasury Department, contracted with the American Bank Note Co., New York, N.Y., for printing of these stamps to take advantage of their special multicolor printing equipment.

AIRMAIL STAMP 8-CENT—ISSUE OF 1944

The issuance of this denomination airmail stamp was required to conform to the adjusted airmail rate which became effective March 26, 1944.
The 8-cent airmail stamp is identical in size and design with the 6-cent airmail stamp of the 1941 issue, the only alterations being that of a change in the denomination numeral to "8" and the color to olive-green.
The stamp was first placed on sale at Washington, D.C., on March 21, 1944.

FIRST TRANSCONTINENTAL RAILROAD COMMEMORATIVE STAMP—ISSUE OF 1944

This stamp was issued to commemorate the seventy-fifth anniversary of the completion of the first transcontinental railroad in America.
The stamp is 0.84 by 1.44 inches in dimension, arranged horizontally, printed in purple by the rotary process, and issued in sheets of 50. The colorful subject depicts the celebration ceremonies which took place at Promontory, Utah, on May 10, 1869, on the occasion of the driving of the last spike in the completion of the transcontinental railroad. The design is enclosed in an arch, at the base of which, in white Gothic, is the title, "Completion of the First Transcontinental Railroad." The wording, "United States of America," in dark Roman letters, appears in a white ribbon panel, with scroll ends, along the lower edge of the stamp. Within shields, ornamented with laurel leaves, in the upper corners at the left are the dates "1869" and "1944," in dark numerals, ar-

Subject	Color of flag	Issued
Poland	White and red.	Chicago, Ill., June 22, 1943.
Czechoslovakia	Red, white, and blue.	Washington, D.C., July 12, 1943.
Norway	Red, white, and blue.	Washington, D.C., July 27, 1943.
Luxembourg	Red, white, and blue.	Washington, D.C., Aug. 10, 1943.
Netherlands	Red, white, and blue.	Washington, D.C., Aug. 24, 1943.
Belgium	Black, yellow, and red.	Washington, D.C., Sept. 14, 1943.
France	Blue, white, and red.	Washington, D.C., Sept. 28, 1943.
Greece	Blue and white.	Washington, D.C., Oct. 12, 1943.
Yugoslavia	Blue, white, and red.	Washington, D.C., Oct. 26, 1943.
Albania	Red field, with black emblem.	Washington, D.C., Nov. 9, 1943.
Austria	Red, white, and red.	Washington, D.C., Nov. 25, 1943.
Denmark	Red and white.	Washington, D.C., Dec. 7, 1943.
Korea	White, blue, and red.	Washington, D.C., Nov. 2, 1944.

108

Selected pages from the USPS Publication 9 covering U.S. stamps.

PRICE TRENDS OF SELECTED STAMP ISSUES

As the price of goods and services continues to spiral, there is comfort in knowing that the value of your stamp collection is more than keeping pace. In many cases, stamp values outdistance most other investments, providing an invaluable safeguard against rising costs.

This chart gives you a good idea of how selected issues have increased over the past year. The stamp issues listed represent a broad range of stamps purchased by U.S. collectors. Also, the prices of classic U.S. issues have tended to hold up better than similar issues of other countries. In the past year, newer issues have tended to stabilize. Keep in mind, too, that many issues have out-performed those shown here, while still others have shown negligible increases. Overall, though, the trend in stamp values has been upward.

If you began your collection a few years ago, and have made wise choices since then, it is very possible that your stamps today may be worth several times the amount of your initial investment. And, of course, it's impossible to even put a price tag on the hours of enjoyment that stamp collecting provides.

Through the decade of the 1970s, stamp values more than held their own compared to a significant increase in our cost of living. If that performance continues during the 1980s, stamps will most certainly continue to be a fine investment value. In fact, the chart data shown here include only stamp types listed in The Postal Service Guide to U.S. Stamps. If other, higher value issues were included, stamp values would likely reflect an even greater increase.

It's important to remember two things. First, the primary purpose of stamp collecting is the enjoyment of the hobby, with value increases being an occasional benefit. Some stamps, in fact, do not increase in monetary value, yet are still fun to acquire and display. Secondly, the amount of gain indicated by stamp price comparisons in catalogs is overstated; catalog prices are what you must pay to purchase a copy of the stamp. When you wish to sell your copy to another collector or a stamp dealer, you should expect to sacrifice anywhere between 10% and 50% of the current catalog value.

The prices for these stamps have been taken from The Harris Postage Stamp Price Index, 1982 Edition (© 1981 by H.E. Harris & Co., Inc.) and are reprinted by permission of the publisher. Prices refer to the market price for the issue in average condition in that year. Prices refer to uncancelled stamps.

Harris Postage Stamp Price Index

Scott #	Description	1950	1960	1970	1980	1981	%*
112	1869 Pictorial	6.00	10.85	37.50	220.00	250.00	13.6
230	Columbian	.40	1.10	2.75	35.00	42.50	21.4
285	Trans-Mississippi	.60	1.65	4.50	32.50	42.50	30.8
294	Pan-American	.40	1.00	2.40	32.50	37.50	15.4
300	1902 Regular	.14	.40	.70	8.00	9.50	18.8
401	1915 Panama-Pacific	1.00	2.10	4.35	30.00	37.50	25.0
523	1918 $2 Franklin	45.00	47.50	85.00	1100.00	1650.00	50.0
551	1922 Regular	.02	.04	.05	.25	.25	0.0
910	Overrun Countries — Czechoslovakia	.10	.10	.12	.35	.35	0.0
1039	Liberty Issue		.08	.12	.45	.50	11.1
1178	Civil War 100th Anniversary Issue			.10	.27	.27	0.0
1229	5¢ Washington			.10	1.30	1.30	0.0
1374	6¢ John Wesley Powell			.09	.27	.27	0.0
1460	1972 Olympic Games Issue				.22	.22	0.0
1529	10¢ Skylab II				.30	.30	0.0
C1	First Airmail	2.25	3.95	14.50	160.00	235.00	46.9
C4	Second Airmail	3.75	6.00	21.50	225.00	110.00	46.7
C13	Graf Zeppelin	14.50	22.75	90.00	1075.00	975.00	0.9
E1	1885 Special Delivery	4.50	8.35	25.00	240.00	300.00	25.0
J1	Postage Due	.30	.60	1.50	16.00	18.50	15.6

*Refers to percentage increase between 1980 and 1981.

230

1039

1178

C1

C4

C13

E1

SOUVENIR SHEETS

A sheet of stamps designed to call attention to an event or reason for the issue is called a souvenir sheet. With a few expensive exceptions, souvenir sheets make affordable and interesting collectibles.

As one might expect, the very first U.S. souvenir sheet sells today at elevated prices. It was issued for the International Philatelic Exhibition of 1926 held in New York City—it was a perforated block of 25 two-cent stamps (Scott No. 630). Other popular U.S. souvenir sheets were issued to commemorate the American Philatelic Society (Scott Nos. 730, 731) in 1933 and (#735, 750) in 1934, the National Stamp Exhibition (#734) in 1934, the Third International Philatelic Exhibition (#778) in 1936 and the Society of Philatelic Americans (#797) in 1937.

Foreign governments also issue souvenir sheets, usually to celebrate philatelic or patriotic events. Czechoslovakia's 1934 national anthem souvenir is one of the most famous. It contains 15 stamps with appropriate titles and borders, plus the musical score and words of the national anthem, "Kde domov muj." Belgium issued one of the world's most unusual sheets in 1941—nine different value stamps in full color, each picturing a different Belgian city's coat of arms. South Africa's 1936 Johannesburg Philatelic Exhibition sheets are perhaps the only ones with postal and commercial advertising tabs on the stamps.

It is quite possible to put together a complete collection of U.S. souvenir sheets. Since many of these commemorate philatelic exhibitions and conventions, they have a special attraction for collectors. More recent U.S. souvenir sheets have included the Sixth International Philatelic Exhibitions Issue (#1311) in 1966 and the popular American Bicentennial Issues (#1686-1689) which depicted the Surrender of Cornwallis at Yorktown, the Declaration of Independence, Washington Crossing the Delaware and Washington Reviewing the Army at Valley Forge.

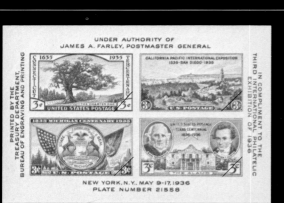

UNDER AUTHORITY OF
JAMES A. FARLEY, POSTMASTER GENERAL

PRINTED BY THE TREASURY DEPARTMENT,
BUREAU OF ENGRAVING AND PRINTING

IN COMPLIMENT TO THE TRANS-MISSISSIPPI
PHILATELIC EXPOSITION AND CONVENTION,

OMAHA, NEBRASKA, OCTOBER, 1934.
PLATE NUMBER 21341

UNDER AUTHORITY OF JAMES A. FARLEY, POSTMASTER GENERAL AT A CENTURY OF PROGRESS

PRINTED BY THE TREASURY DEPARTMENT, BUREAU OF ENGRAVING AND PRINTING

IN COMPLIMENT TO THE AMERICAN PHILATELIC SOCIETY FOR ITS CONVENTION AND EXHIBITION

CHICAGO, ILLINOIS, AUGUST 1933. PLATE NO. 21160

CONFEDERATE PHILATELY

No period of American philatelic history is more dramatic than the Civil War. Letters originated from training and prisoner camps, battlefields and occupied regions. Some traveled by flag of truce. Others reached their destination by kite!

When the Civil War broke out, propaganda envelopes carrying patriotic messages and designs appeared both in the North and South. Among the most interesting Confederate envelopes are those that show the rebel flag in various stages as extra stars were added for new Confederate states.

As the war progressed, and material shortages increased, envelopes were turned and used a second time. Some were even made of wallpaper or ledger paper from old account books. Letters were not handled as carefully as they are today. Envelopes were stuffed into saddlebags and jolted along rural roads for mile after mile before they reached their final destination. This accounts for the poor condition of most surviving Civil War covers.

Collectors of Confederate stamps are faced with a bewildering range of varieties. This can be traced to the fact that prior to June 1861, when the Confederate Postal Service came into being, no postage stamp had ever been printed in the states south of New York.

The Richmond firm of Hoyer and Ludwig printed an emergency stamp early in the war. But the firm evidently took no greater pains with engraving, transferring and printing than they did with a regular order for commercial labels, except to account for waste sheets. They did the best they could with the available materials, but there is no end to the "freaks" that developed.

In one instance, a 17-year-old boy was relieved of his field duties and put in charge of an old Washington hand press. The blue ink he used was made of home-ground pigment and boiled linseed oil. Given these handicaps, young Frank Baptist succeeded remarkably well.

The variations among Confederate stamps are one of the chief attractions of this area of specialty. In the words of one eminent philatelist, "We are grateful for these shortcomings. Perfect stamps hold no lure to the student, and there is no story behind them."

PERFINS

Perfins are stamps with small holes punched in them to form initials or various designs, such as a crown. Private firms, universities and various governments have punched-perforated stamps since the late 1860s to prevent theft or to advertise.

In the wake of the theft of 8,000 postage stamps from a large firm, Great Britain issued a patent to Joseph Sloper in 1868 for a punch-perforation machine. Demand for the machine soon spread to other European countries. British Guiana and Paraguay issued punched stamps as regular postal issues in the late 1800s. Australia, Canada and other countries followed suit.

United States regulations require that a punched design not exceed a half-inch square, with perforations no larger than 1/32 of an inch across. There is no record of the number of designs that have been used in the history of perfins, but some collections contain more than 3,500 different types. One collector has reported 170 branch office identifications of a single large life insurance company.

The Perfins Club of the United States Cataloging Committee has developed ten symbols and a few rules to govern the cataloging of U.S. and most foreign perfins. The ten symbols cover designs arranged in one, two, and three lines, as well as perfins consisting of fancy monograms or letters within letters. The rules concern perfin measurement.

Perfin collectors are usually more interested in the perfin than they are in the stamp itself. According to the Perfins Club, which began researching perfins in 1943, there are almost as many ways to collect perfins as there are perfins. Most collectors begin by gathering **types** of perfins. They try to collect one example of each different perfin pattern, regardless of the stamp on which it appears. Many collectors seek **covers** that carry corner cards identifying the owners of the patterns. **Strips**—the top two inches of an envelope, showing the corner card, perfin and postmark—are a substitute for covers. **Topical** perfin collecting is also very popular. Owners specialize in perfins used by banks, or auto companies, or perfins that spell a word.

Though postage meters have replaced perfins at a rapid rate, one confident collector predicts, "As long as there are stamps, we can be reasonably sure there will be perfins."

PONY EXPRESS

"Wanted—Young, skinny, wiry fellows not over 18. Must be expert riders willing to risk death daily. Orphans preferred." Thus William Hepburn Russell, organizer of the Pony Express, advertised along the frontier for young men to work for what became one of the most dependable private mail services ever operated in the United States.

Russell and his partners had only 60 days to stock and man 190 stations—with 500 horses, plus station keepers, stock tenders, riders and supplies. The difficulties of holding to a tight schedule across 1,966 miles without direct communication were incredible. Yet for the most part the system worked remarkably well. During the service's 19 months of operation, only one saddlebag was lost—a casualty of Indian disturbances.

The route began in St. Joseph, Missouri, and cut across northeastern Kansas into Nebraska, following the Platte Valley to Fort Laramie. From there it ran through the South Pass of the Rocky Mountains to Fort Bridger, Salt Lake City, and across the alkali flats of Nevada to Carson City and Lake Tahoe. It climbed the high passes of the Sierra and dropped to Sacramento, where a final, easy boat ride completed the journey to San Francisco.

The first Pony Express riders left the eastern and western terminals on April 3, 1860. On the evening of April 14, San Franciscans learned by telegraph that the first delivery from the East was steaming toward the Golden Gate—having cut in half the regular delivery time of the Butterfield Overland Mail. A noisy torchlight parade greeted young Billy Hamilton as he rode his horse off the steamboat Antelope, and a band played "See, the Conquering Hero Comes."

The completion of the first transcontinental telegraph line cut short the life of the Pony Express Service, but did not dim its accomplishments. Lincoln's inaugural speech, warning the Southern states that they could not legally secede from the Union, crossed the West by Pony Express in seven days, seventeen hours and helped the President hold California in the Union. The service also proved the superiority of the central route across the West and set the route for the first transcontinental railroad.

On October 26, 1861, the Pony Express was discontinued. That day the Sacramento Bee published a farewell tribute: "Thou staunch, wilderness-overcoming, swift-footed messenger . . . were the pioneer of a continent in the rapid transmission of intelligence . . . Rest upon your honors; be satisfied with them, your destiny has been fulfilled—a new and higher power has superseded you."

UNITED STATES POSTAL SERVICE

1982 Commemorative and Definitive Stamps

A complete listing of stamps issued during 1982 including technical and other pertinent information about the stamps and stamp subjects.

The Postal Service Guide to U.S. Stamps

Igor Stravinsky (2¢)

Type: Definitive (Great Americans Series)
Designer: Burt Silverman
Printing: Intaglio
Colors: Brown

Other information not available at press time.

The 1982 stamp in the Great American Series pays tribute to composer Igor Stravinsky. The definitive issue was designed by Burg Silverman and modeled by Clarence Holbert. Gary J. Slaught engraved the lettering while Gary M. Chaconas was responsible for the vignette. There is one plate number.

Ralph Bunche (20¢, #1852)

Type: Definitive (Great Americans Series)
Date of Issue: January 12, 1982
Place of Issue: New York, New York
Designer: Jim Sharpe
Printing: Intaglio
Color: Maroon

The Great Americans Series—initiated in 1980—is devoted to the life and good works of outstanding U.S. citizens. The fifth stamp in this category pays tribute to Dr. Ralph J. Bunche (1904-1971), grandson of a former slave and the first black in history to win the Nobel Peace Prize. This widely known international civil servant was a man of many accomplishments. From the days when he starred in football and basketball at the University of California in the late 1920s to his outstanding academic life in the 1930s, and during his distinguished 25-year career (1946-1971) with the United Nations, he brought a special brilliance and expertise to the task at hand. Dr. Bunche assisted Count Folke Bernadotte of Sweden in mediating the Israel-Arab warfare in Palestine and later supervised the truce and armistice agreements. It was for this and other efforts in behalf of the U.N. that Dr. Bunche received the Nobel Peace Prize in 1950. Dr. Bunche later went on to direct peace keeping efforts in the Suez (1956), the Congo (1960) and Cyprus (1964). He became Undersecretary for the United Nations in 1957 and served in that capacity until shortly before his death on December 9, 1971. His diplomatic skill, a masterpiece in the practical application of psychology, has become legendary in the annals of American history.

The stamp, featuring a portrait of Dr. Bunche, was designed by Jim Sharpe of Westport, Connecticut. His artistic rendering captures the great man's compassion and love of humanity. Artist Sharpe also designed stamps in the Performing Arts Series: Jimmie Rodgers (#1755), George M. Cohan (#1756), Will Rogers (#1801), W.C. Fields (#1803) and the 1982 Barrymores. For the Dr. Bunche stamp, Sharpe was assisted by three members of the Bureau of Engraving and Printing: modeler Clarence Holbert; and engravers Kenneth Kipperman (vignette) and Gary J. Slaght (lettering and numerals). The sheet stamp was issued in panes of 100 with one group of plate numbers.

Crazy Horse (13¢, #1847)

Type: Definitive
Date of Issue: January 15, 1982
Place of Issue: Crazy Horse, South Dakota
Designer: Brad Holland
Printing: Intaglio
Color: Maroon

The most recent stamp to be issued in the Great Americans Series is dedicated to Crazy Horse, the revered leader of the Oglala Sioux Indians. The Crazy Horse stamp was designed by New York artist Brad Holland. His portrait was patterned on studies made by Korczak Ziolkowski, the prominent sculptor who is creating a gigantic memorial in honor of the Sioux Indian. Because Crazy Horse was never photographed, Ziolkowski interviewed survivors of the Battle of Little Big Horn to get their first hand impressions of the great Indian. Therefore, the Ziolkowski studies are the only likeness of Crazy Horse, and Holland's portrait seeks to capture the Sioux leader as remembered by his fellowmen. The stamp is produced 100 stamps to the pane with one plate number.

Bighorn Sheep (20¢, #1949)

Type: Definitive
Date of Issue: January 8, 1982
Place of Issue: Bighorn Montana
Photographer: Jim Brandenberg
Printing: Intaglio
Color: Dark Blue

Formerly featured in the 1981 Wildlife Issue (see Scott #1880-89), the bighorn sheep in a revised version is the sole subject for this year's stamp booklet and contains two panes of ten stamps each. In accordance with the new plate numbering system, the top pane displays a single-digit plate number printed on the tab which attaches the pane to the booklet.

The stamp was engraved from a photograph taken by Jim Brandenburg of Minneapolis, Minnesota. The bighorn sheep stamp and booklet cover were modeled by Esther Porter; stamp engravers were Gary M. Chaconas (vignette), and Robert G. Culin, Sr., lettering and numerals). All are members of the Bureau of Engraving and Printing staff.

Franklin D. Roosevelt (20¢, #1950)

Type: Commemorative
Date of Issue: January 30, 1982
Place of Issue: Hyde Park, New York
Designer: Clarence Holbert
Printing: Intaglio
Color: Blue

This 1982 commemorative stamp is indeed a fitting tribute to celebrate the centennial of Franklin D. Roosevelt's birth. Not only was FDR an avid stamp collector, but he also assisted in the design of numerous stamps during his four-term office. Designed and modeled by Clarence Holbert, an engraver for the Bureau of Engraving and Printing, the stamp is based on a famous UPI photograph of Roosevelt which was taken on July 4, 1937. The late President is pictured in his touring car while showing reporters the tree plantings on the grounds of his Hyde Park estate. Assisting Mr. Holbert in the production of the stamp were Thomas R. Hipschen who engraved the vignette and Thomas J. Bakos who handled the lettering and numerals. There are 48 stamps per pane and a single-digit plate number.

Love (20¢, #1951)

Type: Definitive
Date of Issue: February 1, 1982
Place of Issue: Boston, Massachusetts
Designer: Mary Faulconer
Printing: Gravure
Colors: Yellow, Green, Red, Purple, Blue

Designed by artist Mary Faulconer of New York City, the "LOVE" stamp visually embraces the warmth and joy of the very word itself. To symbolize "LOVE", gaily colored flowers were selected to create each letter, "to give form to the word and convey a sense of its meaning, delicacy and strength at the same time," according to the artist. The letter "L" is formed by miniature red poppies; the "O" by painted daisies and Johnny-jump-ups (miniature pansies): the "V" by cornflowers (or bachelor's buttons); and the "E" was created from coralbells.
Mary Faulconer also created the 1978 Rose booklet stamps (see Scott #1737) and was awarded the distinguished gold medal by the American Rose Society for her artistic endeavors.

  Although the 1982 "LOVE" stamp was released in time for Valentine's Day, it was designed to be appropriate for mailing on many other occasions such as birthdays, anniversaries, and weddings, or simply for sending sentiments to someone special. Therefore, this popular stamp—designed in response to thousands of requests for a new love stamp—is a definitive issue. It is offered in panes of 50 with one group of five plate numbers. Peter Cocci of the Bureau of Engraving and Printing modeled the stamp.

Bicycle (5.9¢, #1898)

Type: Definitive (Transportation Series)
Date of Issue: February 17, 1982
Place of Issue: Wheeling, West Virginia
Designer: David Stone
Printing: Intaglio
Color: Blue

Designed by David Stone of Port Washington, New York, the bicycle stamp was fashioned after pictures of the "highwheeler" or "ordinary" bike, which was first introduced to the United States at the Philadelphia Centennial Exposition in 1876. The stamp was printed in coils of 500 and 3,000 with a plate number on every 24th stamp. It was engraved by Gary M. Chaconas (vignette) and Thomas Bakos (lettering and numerals); and modeled by Clarence Holbert. All three are with the Bureau of Engraving and Printing.

Hansom Cab (10.9¢, #1901)

Type: Definitive (Transportation Series)
Date of Issue: March 26, 1982
Place of Issue: Chattanooga, Tennessee
Designer: David Stone
Printing: Intaglio
Color: Purple

Designer David Stone patterned his drawing of the hansom cab after a photograph that originally appeared in an 1892 edition of The Hub Magazine. Mr. Stone also designed the Bicycle and Locomotive stamps for the Transportation Series, as well as the 1970 Ft. Snelling (#1409) and 1974 Ft. Harrod (#1542) stamps. Stamps are printed in coils of 500 and 3,000, with one plate number appears on every 24th stamp. The Bureau of Engraving and Printing modeler was Clarence Holbert; engravers were Edward P. Archer and Thomas Bakos.

Locomotive (2¢, #1897)

Type: Definitive (Transportation Series)
Date of Issue: May 20, 1982
Place of Issue: Chicago, Illinois
Designer: David Stone
Printing: Intaglio
Color: Black

Veteran stamp designer David Stone used several Currier and Ives prints–including the American Express Train (1864)—as reference sources to create his illustration. Three staff members of the Bureau of Engraving and Printing were involved: Clarence Holbert modeled the stamp, John S. Wallace cut the vignette, and Robert G. Culin, Sr., engraved the lettering and numerals. Stamps are printed in coils of 500 and 3,000; there is one plate number at every 24-stamp interval.

Stagecoach (4¢)

Type: Definitive, Coil (Transportation Series)
Date of Issue: August 19, 1982
Place of Issue: Milwaukee, Wisconsin
Designer: Jim Schleyer
Color: Brown

George Washington (20¢, #1952)

Type: Commemorative
Date of Issue: February 22, 1982
Place of Issue: Mount Vernon, Virginia
Designer: Mark English
Printing: Gravure
Colors: Yellow, Magenta, Cyan, Black, Gold Type, and Blue Type

To honor the 250th anniversary of George Washington's birth a commemorative stamp, bearing our first President's portrait, was issued at his Mount Vernon estate in Virginia. Going back to July 1, 1847 (when Washington was featured on a 10-cent stamp, one of the first two stamps issued by the United States) to the present, Washington has appeared on more U.S. stamps than any other individual. This most recent Washington stamp was designed by the prominent illustrator Mark English of Kansas City, Missouri, and represents a modernistic approach with a stylized profile against a black backdrop with a flag of the era. To render the profile, English worked from a replica of a Washington "life mask," originally made by French sculpture Jean Antoine Houdon in 1785. Esther Porter of the Bureau of Engraving and Printing prepared the model for this commemorative stamp. There are 50 stamps per pane and each pane displays a multicolored six digit plate number.

Netherlands (20¢, #2003)

Type: Commemorative
Date of Issue: April 20, 1982
Place of Issue: Washington, D.C.
Designer: Heleen Tigler Wybrandi-Raue
Printing: Gravure
Colors: Red, blue black

1982 marked the 200th anniversary of diplomatic recognition of the United States by the Netherlands and the longest continuously peaceful diplomatic relations of the U.S. with any foreign power. To honor the occasion, a commemorative stamp was simultaneously issued in the United States and the Netherlands. The design of the stamp for both countries was created by artist Heleen Tigler Wybrandi-Raue of Studio Dumbar in the Netherlands. When the stamp was issued on April 20th in the United States, Queen Beatrix and her husband, His Royal Highness Prince Claus of the Netherlands, came to our nation's capital for the 1982 bilateral bicentennial celebrations. Peter Cocci of the Bureau of Engraving and Printing modeled the U.S. stamp.

State Birds and Flowers (20¢, #1953-2002)

Type: Commemorative
Date of Issue: April 14, 1982
Place of Issue: Washington, D.C.
Designers: Arthur and Alan Singer
Printing: Gravure
Colors: Yellow, Magenta, Cyan, Black Tone and Black Line

When the State Bird and Flower stamps were introduced in the spring of 1982, they were enthusiastically received by the general public as well as the serious collector. This unique pane of 50 commemorative stamps features the official birds and flowers of our 50 states. Created by a father and son team—a first for the United States Postal Service—each stamp is a masterpiece in miniature. The father, Arthur Singer, designed the birds while son Alan rendered the flowers. In bringing the designs to life, the Singers strove for high artistic quality as well as authenticity of subject matter. Although several states claim the same bird or flower as an official emblem (i.e. seven states have the cardinal for their state bird), no two stamps in the series are alike. Each one is the result of individual treatment and the successful collaboration of two extraordinary talents—both Singers are highly regarded in the field of wildlife art. The pane of stamps was modeled by Peter Cocci of the Bureau of Engraving and Printing. The stamps are sold in full panes of 50 and are arranged in alphabetical order—starting with Alabama in the upper left hand corner and ending with Wyoming in the lower right hand side. Individual states and their official bird and flower, as featured on each stamp, are as follows:

Hawaii
USA 20c

Hawaiian Goose & *Hibiscus*

Idaho
USA 20c

Mountain Bluebird & *Syringa*

Illinois
USA 20c

Cardinal & *Violet*

Indiana
USA 20c

Cardinal & *Peony*

Iowa
USA 20c

Eastern Goldfinch & *Wild Rose*

Kansas
USA 20c

Western Meadowlark & *Sunflower*

Kentucky
USA 20c

Cardinal & *Goldenrod*

Louisiana
USA 20c

Brown Pelican & *Magnolia*

Maine
USA 20c

Chickadee & *White Pine Cone and Tassel*

Maryland
USA 20c

Baltimore Oriole & *Black-Eyed Susan*

Massachusetts
USA 20c

Black-Capped Chickadee & *Mayflower*

Michigan
USA 20c

Robin & *Apple Blossom*

Minnesota
USA 20c

Common Loon & *Showy Lady Slipper*

Mississippi
USA 20c

Mockingbird & *Magnolia*

Missouri
USA 20c

Eastern Bluebird & *Red Hawthorn*

Montana
USA 20c

Western Meadowlark & *Bitterroot*

Nebraska
USA 20c

Western Meadowlark & *Goldenrod*

Nevada
USA 20c

Mountain Bluebird & *Sagebrush*

New Hampshire
USA 20c

Purple Finch & *Lilac*

New Jersey
USA 20c

American Goldfinch & *Violet*

New Mexico
USA 20c
Roadrunner &

New York
USA 20c
Eastern Bluebird & Rose

North Carolina
USA 20c
Cardinal & Flowering Dogwood

North Dakota
USA 20c
Western Meadowlark & Wild Prairie Rose

Ohio
USA 20c
Cardinal & Red Carnation

Oklahoma
USA 20c
Scissor-tailed Flycatcher & Mistletoe

Oregon
USA 20c
Western Meadowlark & Oregon Grape

Pennsylvania
USA 20c
Ruffed Grouse & Mountain Laurel

Rhode Island
USA 20c
Rhode Island Red & Violet

South Carolina
USA 20c
Carolina Wren & Carolina Jessamine

South Dakota
USA 20c
Ring-Necked Pheasant & Pasqueflower

Tennessee
USA 20c
Mockingbird & Iris

Texas
USA 20c
Mockingbird & Bluebonnet

Utah
USA 20c
California Gull & Sego Lily

Vermont
USA 20c
Hermit Thrush & Red Clover

Virginia
USA 20c
Cardinal & Flowering Dogwood

Washington
USA 20c
American Goldfinch & Rhododendron

West Virginia
USA 20c
Cardinal & Rhododendron Maximum

Wisconsin
USA 20c
Robin & Wood Violet

Wyoming
USA 20c
Western Meadowlark & Indian Paintbrush

Library of Congress (20¢, #2004)

Type: Commemorative
Date of Issue: April 21, 1982
Place of Issue: Washington, D.C.
Designer: Bradbury Thompson
Printing: Intaglio
Colors: Black and Red

Bradbury Thompson of Riverside, Connecticut, based his design for the Library of Congress stamp on a photograph of the Thomas Jefferson Building taken by the Detroit Publishing Company in 1898. The Jefferson Building is one of three—and the oldest—structures that make up the Library of Congress complex. Upon its completion in 1897, it was heralded as the largest and costliest library in the world.

Members of the Bureau of Engraving and Printing staff assisted in the production of the stamp: Clarence Holbert prepared the model; Robert C. Culin, Sr., engraved the vignette. There are 50 stamps per pane and a two-digit plate number.

Knoxville's World Fair
(20¢, #2006-2009)

Type: Commemorative
Date of Issue: April 29, 1982
Place of Issue: Knoxville, Tennessee
Designer: Charles Harper
Printing: Gravure
Colors: Yellow, Magenta, Cyan, Black Tone and Black Line

A block of four stamps was issued to commemorate the 1982 Knoxville World's Fair and its theme "Energy." Artist Charles Harper of Cincinnati, Ohio, designed the stamp quartet which symbolically represents four important energy sources: solar, synthetic fuel, nuclear breader reactor and fossil fuel. Individual stamps portray each of the energy themes in a contemporary and colorful manner. Clarence Holbert of the Bureau of Engraving and Printing modeled the stamps which were printed in panes of 50 with one group of plate numbers.

Wolf Trap (20¢)

Type: Commemorative
Designer: Richard Schlecht
Printing: Gravure
Colors: Yellow, Magenta, Cyan, Black Tone, Black Line

Other information not available at press time.

For more than ten years, Wolf Trap Farm, in the foothills of the Virginia Blue Ridge Mountains, has been a national summer center for the performing arts. Thanks to the recent addition of the "Barns"—two buildings as old as they are new—Wolf Trap now functions year 'round.

The Barns, which date from before the Revolutionary War, originally stood in New York State. Both buildings were dismantled by Richard Babcock of Hancock, Massachusetts, and reconstructed in Vienna, Virginia.

Though he did the work in 1980, Babcock used nothing but eighteenth-century techniques to get it done—block and tackles, gin poles and pulleys, and man power. He reconstructed the barns from the inside out, carefully designing modern additions to complement the hand-cut timbers and weathered boarding of the original buildings.

In the great tradition of barn-raising, the newest addition to Wolf Trap Farm functions as an informal, congenial site for dance, music, film, opera, theater, conferences and conversation. The Barns are a promise to the community of creative abundance and a symbol of Wolf Trap's legacy. One group of five plate numbers.

Dr. Robert A. Millikan (37¢, #1860)

Type: Definitive (Great American Series)
Date of Issue: January 26, 1982
Place of Issue: Pasadena, California
Designer: Roy Andersen
Printing: Intaglio
Color: Blue

This, the seventh stamp to be issued in the Great Americans Series, honors the eminent scientist, professor and administrator and a key figure in the development of Caltech, the famous California Institute of Technology. Dr. Millikan was a Nobel prizewinning physicist. During the years 1912 to 1916, he tested more precisely the quantum theory of radiation that had been expounded by Einstein in 1905. Dr. Millikan's findings confirmed Einstein's equation and accurately measured a second basic constant in atomic physics. In 1923, he received the Nobel prize for this and for previous work in this field.

Ronald C. Sharpe modelled the stamp and the engravers were Joseph S. Creamer, Jr. (vignette) and Robert C. Culin, Sr. (lettering and numerals). The sheet stamp was issued in panes of 100 with one plate number.

Consumer Education (20¢, #2005)

Type: Definitive
Date of Issue: April 27, 1982
Place of Issue: Washington, D.C.
Designer: John Boyd
Printing: Intaglio
Color: Blue

The Consumer Education definitive stamp was issued during National Consumers Week in April and printed in coils of 100, 500 and 3,000 with a single digit plate number appearing on every 24th stamp. When the stamp was introduced, Postmaster General William F. Bolger noted, "Each of the Consumer Education stamps produced will serve to bring national and worldwide attention to consumer education efforts by educators, government agencies, consumer organizations, business, labor organizations and the media." The engravers from the Bureau of Engraving and Printing were Joseph S. Creamer, Jr., and Albert Saavedra.

America's Libraries
(20¢, #2015)

Type: Commemorative
Date of Issue: July 13, 1982
Place of Issue: Philadelphia, Pennsylvania
Designer: Bradbury Thompson
Printing: Intaglio
Colors: Black and Red

The Libraries of America stamp commemorates the good works and services that these institutions have provided throughout the course of our nation's history. The Bureau of Engraving and Printing engraver was Robert C. Culin, Sr.; the modeler was Clarence Holbert. This issue features a single digit plate number and there are 50 stamps per pane.

Aging Together (20¢, #2011)

Type: Commemorative
Date of Issue: May 21, 1982
Place of Issue: Sun City, Arizona
Designer: Paul Calle
Printing: Intaglio
Color: Brown

Introduced during Older Americans Month (May 1982), the Aging Together commemorative stamp was issued to herald our older citizens as highly valued Americans who have enriched society with their wealth of experience and creative energies. Aging Together was created by veteran stamp designer Paul Calle of Stamford, Connecticut. The model was prepared by Frank J. Waslick; and the stamp was engraved by John S. Wallace (vignette) and Robert G. Culin, Jr. (lettering and numerals). All three are with the Bureau of Engraving and Printing. There are 50 stamps per pane and one plate number.

Horatio Alger
(20¢, 2010)

Type: Commemorative
Date of Issue: April 30, 1982
Place of Issue: Willow Grove, Pennsylvania
Designer: Robert Hallock
Printing: Intaglio
Colors: Red, Black line, on Tan Stock

Introduced on the 150th anniversary of Horatio Alger's birth, this stamp recognizes his contribution to 19th-century children's literature. Alger's "rags to riches" characters serve as the stamp's theme. From left to right, they are: Ben, the luggage boy; Ragged Dick, a bootblack; the newsboy Rufus, known as "Rough and Ready"; and Mark, the match boy. The design, by Robert Hallock, was adapted from the frontispiece of Ragged Dick—a series of six books that brought Alger national prominence in 1867 and 1868. The stamp's engraved vignette and typeface appropriately reflect the historical period of Alger's works. Hallock's design was modeled by Clarence Holbert, and engraved by Gary H. Slaght (lettering and numerals), and Gary M. Chaconas who crafted the vignette.

Dr. Mary Walker (20¢, #2013)

Type: Commemorative
Date of Issue: June 10, 1982
Place of Issue: Oswego, New York
Designer: Glenora Richards
Printing: Gravure
Colors: Yellow, Magenta, Cyan, Black Tone,
Blue Line and Black Line

The Dr. Mary Walker commemorative stamp honors the life and humanitarian acts of this remarkable woman. She treated the sick and wounded during the Civil War, often at the risk of her own safety.

For her patriotism and loyalty to our country, she was awarded the Medal of Honor by President Andrew Johnson on November 11, 1865. Fifty-one years later an act of Congress changed the criteria for awarding the Medal and Dr. Walker, along with 910 others, was disqualified. She refused to return the Medal and made repeated, yet unsuccessful, attemps to have the decision changed. She faithfully wore the Medal every day until her death in 1919. It would have been a source of great satisfaction for this determined woman to know that in 1977 the Secretary of Army signed an order to reinstate Dr. Walker's Medal of Honor and correct the official records.

For the stamp, artist Glenora Richards of New Canann, Connecticut, portrayed Dr. Walker in watercolors on a piece of antique ivory. Mrs. Richards is noted for her miniature paintings and used the same techniques that she applied to her other stamp design—the 1981 Edna St. Vincent Millay issue. The Bureau of Engraving and Printing modeler was Ronald C. Sharpe. There are 50 stamps to a pane with a single six-digit plate number.

The Barrymores (20¢, #2012)

Type: Commemorative
Date of Issue: June 8, 1982
Place of Issue: New York, New York
Designer: Jim Sharpe
Printing: Gravure
Colors: Yellow, Red, Cyan, Brown,
Dark Blue, and Black

Fifth in the Performing Arts Series is a commemorative stamp honoring the Barrymores, America's distinguished theatrical family. The stamp spotlights a family portrait of Lionel, Ethel and John Barrymore, superimposed on a blue background. It was designed by Jim Sharpe of Westport, Connecticut, who was also responsible for creating the other four stamps in the Performing Arts Series. The series was introduced in 1978 and has featured stamps celebrating Jimmie Rodgers (#1755), George M. Cohan (#1756), Will Rogers (#1801) and W.C. Fields (#1803). In preparing the design for the Barrymore stamp, Sharpe reviewed many photographs of the three actors to create a composite image—not a portrait based on any specific likeness. The Bureau of Engraving and Printing modeler for the stamp, who shares the same last name with the designer, was Ronald C. Sharpe. There are 50 stamps per pane and one group of six plate numbers.

International Peace Garden (20¢, #2014)

Type: Commemorative
Date of Issue: June 20, 1982
Place of Issue: Dunseith, North Dakota
Designer: Gyo Fujikawa
Printing: Offset/Intaglio
Colors (Offset): Yellow, Red, Green and Black
Colors (Intaglio): Black, Brown and Green

To celebrate the 50th anniversary (1932-1982) of the International Peace Garden, a commemorative stamp was issued on the grounds of the Garden, which covers 2,300 acres between the state of North Dakota and the province of Manitoba, Canada. In 1929, Dr. Henry J. Moore conceived the idea of the gardens to be a place "where the people of two countries could share the glories found in a garden and the pleasures found in warm friendships." Today the International Peace Gardens symbolize the harmony of the two nations which live along the longest unfortified boundary in the world. The stamp was designed by New York artist Gyo Fujikawa; engraved by Kenneth Kipperman and James L. Goodbody. There are 50 stamps to a pane with two groups of plate numbers—a four-digit number representing the offset plates and a three-digit number representing the intaglio plates.

Jackie Robinson (20¢)

Type: Definitive
Date of Issue: August 2, 1982
Place of Issue: Cooperstown, New York
Designer: Jerry Pinkney
Printing: Gravure
Colors: Yellow, Magenta, Cyan,
Black and Ochre

Jackie Robinson, the legendary Brooklyn Dodger, is the subject for this commemorative stamp in the 1982 Black Heritage Series. Designed by Jerry Pinkney, the stamp focuses on the athlete in action—catching and stealing bases, for which he was so famous—with a portrait of Robinson in the background. Frank J. Waslick of the Bureau of Engraving and Printing was the modeler. The stamp has five plate numbers.

Touro Synagogue (20¢)

Type: Commemorative
Date of Issue: August 22, 1982
Place of Issue: Newport, Rhode Island
Printing: Gravure/Intaglio
Colors: Yellow, Magenta, Cyan, Black/Black, Brown

The Touro Synagogue commemorative stamp honors this venerable landmark not only as an historic American building but also as a symbol of our country's tradition of religious freedom. The oldest existing synagogue in America, Touro was built in 1763 by Sephardic Jews who fled Spain and Portugal during the Inquisition and found religious freedom in Rhode Island. The stamp features a view of the synagogue plus the words of George Washington, "To bigotry, no sanction. To persecution, no assistance." The design of the stamp was a joint effort by two artists: the portrait of the building is from a painting by Donald Moss; the typography is the work of Bradbury Thompson. Both men are from Connecticut and have previously designed many U.S. issues for the Postal Service. Modeler was Peter Cocci; engraver was John C. Masure. There are six plate numbers.

Francis of Assisi (20¢)

Type: Commemorative
Date of Issue: October 7, 1982
Place of Issue: San Francisco, California
Designer: Ned Seidler
Printing: Gravure
Colors: Violet, Flesh Tone, Brown, Ochre, Red, Black

This commemorative stamp honors a man with a deep sense of brotherhood. Born in 1181/1182 at Assisi in Umbria, Italy, Francis renounced material goods and family ties to embrace a life of poverty, marked by a love of nature, mankind and all creatures on earth. One group of six plate numbers.

Ponce de Leon (20¢)

Type: Commemorative
Date of Issue: October 12, 1982
Place of Issue: San Juan, Puerto Rico
Designer: Richard Schlecht
Printing: Gravure

Other information not available at press time.

In the popular imagination, Juan Ponce de Leon often appears as a doddering old Spaniard stumbling about the New World in a desperate search for a mythical Fountain of Youth. The evidence of history, however, provides a dramatically different portrait.

Juan Ponce de Leon was born to a noble family and fought against the Moors as a youth. At nineteen he shipped to the New World on Columbus's second voyage of 1493. The fleet anchored for a time on the western coast of Puerto Rico, which Ponce de Leon conquered early in the next century. First, however, he fought to conquer the native kingdom of Higuey in what is now the Dominican Republic and Haiti.

Ponce de Leon was rewarded with the governorship of that province. But rumors of gold sent him sailing to Puerto Rico in 1506 at the head of 100 Spanish soldiers. The conquistadores prevailed against the natives, and in 1509 Ponce became the governor of Puerto Rico. He also retained control of most other government offices and left Puerto Rico a very rich man indeed. During his brief reign as governor he demonstrated considerable administrative skills. Among his other achievements, he established a splendid capital at San Juan.

He became the first to discover the mighty Gulf Stream, knowledge of which proved invaluable to Spanish fleets returning to Spain. Believing himself to have landed on an island he called Bimini, Ponce also became the first European to reach the Yucatan and the great Empire of Mexico.

A royal grant to colonize the "islands" of Florida and Bimini ultimately proved fatal to the ambitious explorer. On his second and last trip to Florida he received a serious arrow wound, from which he died in Havana at the age of 47. Floating plate number.

Contemporary Christmas

Type: Commemorative
Date of Issue: October 28, 1982
Place of Issue: Snow, Oklahoma
Designer: Dolli Tingle
Printing: Gravure
Colors: Yellow, Magenta, Cyan, Black

Christmas is a time for children sets the theme for the 1982 Contemporary Christmas Series. The quartet of stamps shows colorful renderings of children at play in the snow: sledding, building a snowman, skating, and decorating a Christmas tree. "Season's Greetings" runs on the lower border of each stamp. One group of four plate numbers.

Traditional Christmas

Type: Commemorative
Date of Issue: October 28, 1982
Place of Issue: Washington, D.C.
Designer: Bradbury Thompson
Printing: Gravure
Colors: Yellow, Magenta, Cyan,
Black Tone and Black Line, and Red Line

The 1982 Traditional Christmas stamp highlights a painting of the Madonna and Child, created by Tiepolo. The original 18th century masterpiece now hangs in the National Gallery of Art in Washington, D.C. Floating plate number.

Kitten and Puppy (13¢)

Type: Definitive
Date of Issue: November 3, 1982
Designer: Chuck Ripper

Other information not available at press time.

Architecture (20¢)

Type: Commemorative
Date of Issue: September 24, 1982
Place of Issue: Washington, D.C.
Designer: Walter Richards
Printing: Intaglio
Colors: Brown and Black

Walter Richards created a quartet of stamps to commemorate American Architecture. Each stamp depicts a different example of architecture by four 20th-century architects. From upper left hand corner to the lower right, they are: Frank Lloyd Wright's Fallingwater Mill Run; Mies van der Rohe's Illinois Institute of Technology; the Gropius House by Walter Gropius; and Eero Saarinen's Dulles Airport. Bureau of Engraving and Printing modeler Esther Porter and six engravers assisted in the production of this stamp. There is a single digit plate number with 40 stamps to each pane.

		Un	U

Issues of 1847 to 1894 are Unwatermarked, Issue of 1847, Imperf.

1	5¢ Benjamin		
	Franklin, July 1	3,750.00	1,100.00
2	10¢ George		
	Washington,		
	July 1	16,500.00	3,000.00

Issue of 1875, Reproductions of 1 & 2

| 3 | 5¢ Franklin | 2,500.00 | — |
| 4 | 10¢ Washington | 3,100.00 | — |

Reproductions. The letters R. W. H. & E. at the bottom of each stamp are less distinct on the reproductions than on the originals.

5¢. On the original the left side of the white shirt frill touches the oval on a level with the top of the "F" of "Five." On the reproduction it touches the oval about on a level with the top of the figure "5."

10¢. On the reproduction, line of coat at left points to right of "X" and line of coat at right points to center of "S" of CENTS. On the original, line of coat points to "T" of TEN and between "T" and "S" of CENTS.

On the reproduction the eyes have a sleepy look, the line of the mouth is straighter, and in the curl of hair near the left cheek is a strong black dot, while the original has only a faint one.

Issue of 1851-56, Imperf.

| 5 | 1¢ Franklin, type I | — | — |
| 5A | 1¢ Same, type Ib | — | 3,000.00 |

Nos. 6-9: Franklin (5)

6	1¢ dark blue,		
	type Ia	—	3,750.00
7	1¢ blue, type II	550.00	115.00
8	1¢ blue, type III	—	1,300.00
8A	1¢ pale blue,		
	type IIIA	1,500.00	675.00
9	1¢ blue, type IV	335.00	110.00
10	3¢ orange brown Washington,		
	type I (11)	1,350.00	85.00
11	3¢ Washington, type I	150.00	8.50

		Un	U
12	5¢ Jefferson, type I	—	1,250.00
13	10¢ green Washington,		
	type I (15)	—	725.00
14	10¢ green, type II (15)	1,350.00	340.00
15	10¢ Washington, type III	1,450.00	340.00
16	10¢ green, type IV (15)	—	1,500.00
17	12¢ Washington	—	275.00

		Un	U

Issue of 1857-61, Perf. 15

Nos. 18-24: Franklin (5)

18	1¢ blue, type I	750.00	385.00
19	1¢ blue, type Ia	—	1,250.00
20	1¢ blue, type II	475.00	170.00
21	1¢ blue, type III	—	1,000.00
22	1¢ blue, type IIIa	600.00	250.00
23	1¢ blue, type IV	—	300.00
24	1¢ blue, type V	145.00	42.50

		Un	U

Nos. 25-26: Washington (11)

| 25 | 3¢ rose, type I | 675.00 | 33.50 |
| 26 | 3¢ dull red, type II | 75.00 | 4.25 |

Nos. 27-29: Jefferson (12)

27	5¢ brick red, type I	—	975.00
28	5¢ red brown, type I	—	340.00
28A	5¢ Indian red, type I	—	1,375.00
29	5¢ brown, type I	775.00	250.00
30	5¢ orange brown		
	Jefferson, type II (30A)	800.00	900.00
30A	5¢ Jefferson, type II	425.00	190.00

Nos. 31-35: Washington (15)

31	10¢ green, type I	—	525.00
32	10¢ green, type II	1,475.00	190.00
33	10¢ green, type III	1,475.00	190.00
34	10¢ green, type IV	—	1,250.00
35	10¢ green, type V	215.00	100.00
36	12¢ black Washington		
	(17)	340.00	110.00
37	24¢ Washington	775.00	250.00
38	30¢ Franklin	900.00	340.00
39	90¢ Washington	1,700.00	—
	90¢ Same, with pen cancel	—	—

Note: Beware of forged cancellations of No. 39. Genuine cancellations are rare.

1875: Government Reprints, Perf. 12, White Paper, Without Gum

40	1¢ bright blue Franklin (5)	—	—
41	3¢ scarlet Washington (11)	—	—
42	5¢ orange brown		
	Jefferson (30A)	—	—
43	10¢ blue green		
	Washington (15)	—	—

2　　　　3　　　　4

5　　　　11

2　　15　　17　　30A　　38　　39

45   55   56   57   58   59

62   63   64   67   68   69

70   71   72   73   77

		Un	U
1875 continued			
44	12¢ greenish black		
	Washington (17)	—	—
45	24¢ blackish violet		
	Washington (37)	—	—
46	30¢ yel. org. Franklin		
	(38)	—	—
47	90¢ deep blue		
	Washington (39)	—	—

Issue of 1861, Perf. 12

Following the outbreak of the Civil War, the U.S. Government demonetized all previous issues.

		Un	U
55	1¢ Franklin	—	—
56	3¢ Washington	875.00	—
57	5¢ brown Jefferson	—	—
58	10¢ Washington	—	—
59	12¢ Washington	—	—
60	24¢ dk. vio. Washington		
	(70)	4,750.00	—
61	30¢ red org. Franklin		
	(71)	14,000.00	—
62	90¢ dull blue		
	Washington (72)	18,000.00	—
62B	10¢ dark green		
	Washington (58)	—	600.00

Nos. 55-62 were not used for postage and do not exist in a cancelled state. The paper they were printed on is thin and semi-transparent, that of the following issues is more opaque.

Issue of 1861-62, Perf. 12

		Un	U
63	1¢ Franklin	135.00	25.00
64	3¢ Washington	—	350.00
65	3¢ rose Washington (64)	60.00	1.70
66	3¢ lake Washington (64)	—	—
67	5¢ Jefferson	—	400.00
68	10¢ Washington	240.00	30.00
69	12¢ Washington	475.00	55.00
70	24¢ Washington	550.00	80.00
71	30¢ Franklin	515.00	85.00
72	90¢ Washington	1,100.00	275.00

Issue of 1861-66, Perf. 12

		Un	U
73	2¢ Andrew Jackson		
	("Black Jack")	160.00	33.50

		Un	U
74	3¢ scarlet Washington		
	(64)	—	—
75	5¢ red brown Jefferson		
	(67)	1,250.00	220.00
76	5¢ brn. Jefferson (67)	275.00	60.00
77	15¢ Abraham Lincoln	550.00	85.00
78	24¢ lilac Washington (70)	250.00	50.00

No. 74 was not regularly issued.

Grills on U.S. Stamps

Between 1867 and 1870, postage stamps were embossed with grills to prevent people from re-using cancelled stamps. The pyramid-shaped grills absorbed cancellation ink, making it virtually impossible to remove a postmark chemically.

Issue of 1867, With Grills, Perf. 12

Grills A, B, C: Points Up

A. Grill Covers Entire Stamp

		Un	U
79	3¢ rose Washington		
	(64)	—	500.00
80	5¢ brn. Jefferson (67)	—	—
81	30¢ org. Franklin (71)	—	—

B. Grill about 18x15 mm.

		Un	U
82	3¢ rose Washington (64)	—	—

C. Grill about 13x16 mm.

		Un	U
83	3¢ rose Washington (64)	1,500.00	335.00

Grills, D, Z, E, F: Points Down

D. Grill about 12x14 mm.

		Un	U
84	2¢ blk. Jackson (73)	—	800.00
85	3¢ rose Washington (64)	1,100.00	340.00

Z. Grill about 11x14 mm.

		Un	U
85A	1¢ bl. Franklin (63)	—	—
85B	2¢ blk. Jackson (73)	1,100.00	300.00
85C	3¢ rose Washington (64)	—	675.00
85D	10¢ green Washington		
	(68)	—	—
85E	12¢ black Washington		
	(69)	1,600.00	500.00
85F	15¢ blk. Lincoln (77)	—	—

E. Grill about 11x13 mm.

		Un	U
86	1¢ blue Franklin (63)	635.00	200.00
87	2¢ black Jackson (73)	300.00	70.00
88	3¢ rose Washington (64)	220.00	10.00
89	10¢ grn. Washington (68)	1,150.00	145.00
90	12¢ blk. Washington (69)	1,250.00	145.00

		Un	U
	1867 continued		
91	15¢ black Lincoln (77)	2,350.00	335.00
	F. Grill about 9x13 mm.		
92	1¢ blue Franklin (63)	300.00	95.00
93	2¢ black Jackson (73)	295.00	31.50
94	3¢ red Washington (64)	100.00	4.25
95	5¢ brown Jefferson (67)	875.00	225.00
96	10¢ yellow green		
	Washington (68)	600.00	85.00
97	12¢ black Washington		
	(69)	635.00	85.00
98	15¢ black Lincoln (77)	675.00	97.50
99	24¢ gray lilac		
	Washington (70)	1,375.00	475.00
100	30¢ orange Franklin (71)	1,450.00	365.00
101	90¢ blue Washington		
	(72)	3,350.00	900.00
	Reissues of 1861-66 in 1875, Without Grill, Perf. 12		
102	1¢ blue Franklin (63)	—	—
103	2¢ black Jackson (73)	—	—
104	3¢ brown red		
	Washington (64)	—	—
105	5¢ brown Jefferson (67)	—	—
106	10¢ grn. Washington (68)	—	—
107	12¢ blk. Washington		
	(69)	—	—
108	15¢ black Lincoln (77)	—	—
109	24¢ deep violet		
	Washington (70)	—	—
110	30¢ brownish orange		
	Franklin (71)	—	—
111	90¢ blue Washington		
	(72)	—	—
	Issue of 1869, With Grill Measuring 9½x9 mm., Perf. 12		
112	1¢ Franklin	275.00	85.00
113	2¢ Post Horse & Rider	190.00	30.00
114	3¢ Locomotive	170.00	7.50
115	6¢ Washington	875.00	100.00
116	10¢ Shield and Eagle	975.00	115.00
117	12¢ S.S. Adriatic	850.00	110.00
118	15¢ Columbus		
	Landing, type I	2,000.00	335.00

		Un	U
119	15¢ brown and blue		
	Columbus Landing,		
	type II (118)	1,000.00	135.00
119b	Center		
	inverted	—	—
120	24¢ Declaration of		
	Independence	2,750.00	585.00
120b	Center		
	inverted	—	—
121	30¢ Shield, Eagle		
	and Flags	2,500.00	300.00
121b	Flags inverted	—	—
122	90¢ Lincoln	7,500.00	1,450.00
	Reissues of 1869 in 1875, Without Grill, Hard White Paper, Perf. 12		
123	1¢ buff (112)	375.00	250.00
124	2¢ brown (113)	415.00	375.00
125	3¢ blue (114)	—	—
126	6¢ blue (115)	—	—
127	10¢ yellow (116)	—	—
128	12¢ green (117)	—	—
129	15¢ brown and blue		
	Columbus Landing,		
	type III (118)	—	—
130	24¢ grn. & vio. (120)	—	—
131	30¢ bl. & car. (121)	—	—
132	90¢ car. & blk. (122)	—	—
	Reissues of 1869 in 1880, Soft, Porous Paper, Perf. 12		
133	1¢ buff (112)	250.00	210.00
	Issue of 1870-71, With Grill, White Wove Paper, Perf. 12		
134	1¢ Franklin	500.00	62.50
135	2¢ Jackson	335.00	33.50
136	3¢ Washington	250.00	8.50
137	6¢ Lincoln	1,350.00	275.00
138	7¢ Edwin M. Stanton	1,100.00	235.00
139	10¢ Jefferson	1,500.00	425.00
140	12¢ Henry Clay	—	—
141	15¢ Daniel Webster	—	675.00
142	24¢ General Winfield		
	Scott	—	—

It is generally accepted as fact that the Continental Bank Note Co. printed and delivered a quantity of 24¢ stamps. They are impossible to distinguish from those printed by the National Bank Note Co.

112   113   114   115   116

117   118   120   121   122

34   135   136   137   138

39   140   141   142

43   144   156   157   158   159

60   161   162   163   179

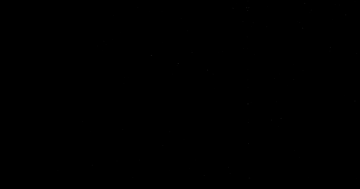

Watermark 191

		Un	U
1870-71 continued			
143	30¢ Alexander		
	Hamilton	—	1,000.00
144	90¢ Commodore Perry	—	675.00
	Without Grill, White Wove Paper, Perf. 12		
145	1¢ ultra. Franklin (134)	150.00	7.00
146	2¢ red brn. Jackson		
	(135)	67.50	5.75
147	3¢ green Washington		
	(136)	100.00	.50
148	6¢ carmine Lincoln (137)	215.00	11.00
149	7¢ verm. Stanton (138)	335.00	53.50
150	10¢ brown Jefferson (139)	235.00	14.50
151	12¢ dull violet Clay (140)	550.00	50.00
152	15¢ bright orange Webster		
	(141)	500.00	53.50
153	24¢ purple W. Scott (142)	575.00	70.00
154	30¢ black Hamilton (143)	1,000.00	100.00
155	90¢ carmine Perry (144)	1,150.00	210.00

Issue of 1873, Without Grill, Perf. 12, White Wove Paper, Thin to Thick

		Un	U
156	1¢ Franklin	65.00	2.50
157	2¢ Jackson	150.00	7.50
158	3¢ Washington	50.00	.17
159	6¢ Lincoln	185.00	10.00
160	7¢ Stanton	415.00	57.50
161	10¢ Jefferson	210.00	11.00
162	12¢ Clay	625.00	57.50
163	15¢ Webster	525.00	25.00
165	30¢ Hamilton (143)	525.00	50.00
166	90¢ Perry (144)	1,150.00	200.00

Issue of 1875, Special Printing, Hard, White Wove Paper, Without Gum

		Un	U
167	1¢ ultra. Franklin (156)	—	—
168	2¢ dark brown		
	Jackson (157)	—	—
169	3¢ blue green		
	Washington (158)	—	—
170	6¢ dull rose Lincoln		
	(159)	—	—
171	7¢ reddish vermilion		
	Stanton (160)	—	—
172	10¢ pale brown		

		Un	U
	Jefferson (161)	—	—
173	12¢ dark violet Clay		
	(162)	—	—
174	15¢ bright orange		
	Webster (163)	—	—
175	24¢ dull purple		
	W. Scott (142)	—	—
176	30¢ greenish black		
	Hamilton (143)	—	—
177	90¢ violet car. Perry		
	(144)	—	—

Although perforated, these stamps were usually cut apart with scissors. As a result, the perforations are often much mutilated and the design is frequently damaged.

		Un	U
	Yellowish Wove Paper		
178	2¢ vermilion Jackson		
	(157), June 21	165.00	4.50
179	5¢ Zachary Taylor,		
	June 21	165.00	9.00

Special Printing, Hard, White Wove Paper, Without Gum

		Un	U
180	2¢ carmine verm.		
	Jackson (157)	—	—
181	5¢ bright blue Taylor		
	(179)	—	—

Issue of 1879. Printed by the American Bank Note Company. Soft, Porous Paper Varying from Thin to Thick.

		Un	U
182	1¢ dark ultramarine		
	Franklin (156)	125.00	1.50
183	2¢ vermilion Jackson		
	(157)	75.00	1.65
184	3¢ green Washington		
	(158)	57.50	.17
185	5¢ blue Taylor (179)	185.00	8.00
186	6¢ pink Lincoln (159)	500.00	12.75
187	10¢ brown Jefferson (139)		
	(no secret mark)	675.00	15.00
188	10¢ brown Jefferson (161)		
	(with secret mark)	415.00	16.50
189	15¢ red orange		
	Webster (163)	165.00	18.50
190	30¢ full black Hamilton		
	(143)	500.00	27.50
191	30¢ carmine Perry (144)	1,050.00	185.00

		Un	U
	Issue of 1880, Special Printing, Soft, Porous Paper, Without Gum		
192	1¢ dark ultramarine		
	Franklin (156)	—	—
193	2¢ black brown		
	Jackson (157)	—	—
194	3¢ blue green		
	Washington (158)	—	—
195	6¢ dull rose Lincoln		
	(159)	—	—
196	7¢ scarlet vermilion		
	Stanton (160)	—	—
197	10¢ deep brown		
	Jefferson (161)	—	—
198	12¢ blackish purple		
	Clay (162)	—	—
199	15¢ orange Webster		
	(163)	—	—
200	24¢ dark violet		
	W. Scott (142)	—	—
201	30¢ greenish black		
	Hamilton (143)	—	—
202	90¢ dull car. Perry (144)	—	—
203	2¢ scarlet vermilion		
	Jackson (157)	—	—
204	5¢ deep blue Taylor		
	(179)	—	—
	Issue of 1882		
205	5¢ Garfield, Apr. 10	115.00	4.85
	Special Printing. Soft, Porous Paper, Without Gum		
205C	5¢ gray brown (205)	—	—
	Issue of 1881-82, Designs of 1873 Re-engraved.		
206	1¢ Franklin	36.50	.60
207	3¢ Washington	45.00	.25
208	6¢ Lincoln	285.00	48.50
209	10¢ Jefferson	80.00	2.85
	Issue of 1883		
210	2¢ Washington, Oct. 1	32.50	.14
211	4¢ Jackson, Oct. 1	155.00	8.75
	Special Printing. Soft, Porous Paper.		
211B	2¢ pale red brown		
	Washington (210)	—	—

		Un	U
211D	4¢ deep blue green		
	Jackson (211) no gum	—	—
	Issue of 1887		
212	1¢ Franklin	56.50	.75
213	2¢ green Washington		
	(210)	22.00	.12
214	3¢ vermilion		
	Washington (207)	60.00	36.50
	Issue of 1888, Perf. 12		
215	4¢ carmine Jackson		
	(211)	145.00	13.00
216	5¢ indigo Garfield (205)	137.50	6.50
217	30¢ orange brown		
	Hamilton (143)	400.00	80.00
218	90¢ purple Perry (144)	800.00	180.00
	Issue of 1890-93, Perf. 12		
219	1¢ Franklin	23.50	.15
219D	2¢ Washington	135.00	.60
220	2¢ carmine (219D)	19.00	.09
	1890-93 continued		
221	3¢ Jackson	85.00	5.00
222	4¢ Lincoln	85.00	2.10
223	5¢ Ulysses S. Grant	85.00	2.10
224	6¢ Garfield	85.00	19.00
225	8¢ William T. Sherman	60.00	12.00
226	10¢ Webster	135.00	2.25
227	15¢ Clay	215.00	22.50
228	30¢ Jefferson	295.00	27.50
229	90¢ Perry	475.00	125.00

05 206 207 208 209

210 211 212 219 219D

221 222 223 224 225 226

27 228 229

**1¢ Franklin Types I-IV of
1851-56**

5

Bust of **5**

Detail of **7** Type II
Lower scrollwork incomplete
(lacks little balls).
Side ornaments are complete.

11

Bust of **5**

Detail of **6** Type Ia
Top ornaments and outer line
partly cut away.
Lower scrollwork is complete.

Bust of **5**

Detail of **8** Type III
Outer lines broken in the
middle.
Side ornaments are complete.

Detail of **8A** Type IIIa
Outer lines broken top or
bottom but not both.

Detail of **11**
THREE CENTS.
Type I. There is an outer frame
line at top and bottom.

Bust of **5**

Detail of **5** Type I
Has curved, unbroken lines
outside labels.
Scrollwork is complete, forms
little balls at bottom.

Detail of **5A** Type Ib
Lower scrollwork is incomplete,
the little balls are not so clear.

Bust of **5**

Detail of **9** Type IV
Outer lines recut top, bottom,
or both.

12

Detail of **12**
FIVE CENTS.
Type I. There are projections on
all four sides.

10¢ Washington Types I-IV of 1855

15

Bust of **15** ↓

Detail of 16
Type IV. The outer lines have been recut at top or bottom or both.
Types I, II, III and IV have complete ornaments at the sides of the stamps and three pearls at each outer edge of the bottom panel.

30A

Detail of 30A
FIVE CENTS JEFFERSON
Type II. The projections at top and bottom are partly cut away.

Bust of **15** ↓   ↓

↑   ↑

Detail of 13
Type I. The "shells" at the lower corners are practically complete. The outer line below the label is very nearly complete. The outer lines are broken above the middle of the top label and the "X" in each upper corner.

Bust of **5**

Detail of 24
ONE CENT FRANKLIN
Type V. Similar to Type III of 1851-56 but with side ornaments partly cut away.

Detail of 35
TEN CENTS WASHINGTON
(Two typical examples).
Type V. Side ornaments slightly cut away. Outer lines complete except over right X.

Bust of **15** ↓

 ←

Detail of 14
Type II. The design is complete at the top. The outer line at the bottom is broken in the middle. The shells are partly cut away.

Bust of **11**

↑

Detail of 26
THREE CENTS WASHINGTON
Type II. The outer frame line has been removed at top and bottom. The side frame lines were recut so as to be continuous from the top to the bottom of the plate.

↓

 ←

Detail of 15
Type III. The outer lines are broken above the top label and the "X" numerals. The outer line at the bottom and the shells are partly cut away, as in Type II.

55   **57**

Detail of **67**
5¢. A leaflet has been added to the foliated ornaments at each corner.

Detail of **64**
3¢. Ornaments at corners have been enlarged and end in a small ball.

Issue of 1861

Detail of **55**

Detail of **57**

56   **58**

68   **69**

Detail of **56**

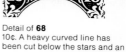

Detail of **68**
10¢. A heavy curved line has been cut below the stars and an outer line has been added to the ornaments above them.

63   **67**

Detail of **58**

Detail of **69**
12¢. Ovals and scrolls have been added to the corners.

Issue of 1861-62

Detail of **63**
1¢. A dash has been added under the tip of the ornament at right of the numeral in upper left corner.

62   **64**

72

Detail of **62**

Detail of **72**
90¢. Parallel lines from an angle above the ribbon with "U.S. Postage"; between these lines a row of dashes has been added and a point of color to the apex of the lower pair.

118

Detail of **118**
FIFTEEN CENTS.
Type I. Picture unframed.

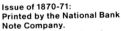

Detail of **119**
Type II. Picture framed.
Type III. Same as Type I but without fringe of brown shading lines around central vignette.

Issue of 1870-71:
Printed by the National Bank Note Company.
Issued without secret marks (see Nos. 156-163).

134

Detail of **134**

Detail of **138**

135　　　**136**　　　**139**　　　**140**

Detail of **135**

Detail of **139**

Detail of **136**

Detail of **140**

137　　　**138**　　　**141**

Detail of **137**

Detail of **141**

1873: Printed by the Continental Bank Note Co.

Designs of the 1870-71 Issue with secret marks on the values from 1¢ to 15¢ as described and illustrated below.

159   **160**

Detail of **159**
6¢. The first four vertical lines of the shading in the lower part of the left ribbon have been strengthened.

Detail of **160**
7¢. Two small semi-circles are drawn around the ends of the lines which outline the ball in the lower right hand corner.

161   **162**

Detail of **161**
10¢. There is a small semi-circle in the scroll, at the right end of the upper label.

Detail of **162**
12¢. The balls of the figure "2" are crescent shaped.

163

Detail of **163**
15¢. In the lower part of the triangle in the upper left corner two lines have been made heavier forming a "V". This mark can be found on some of the Continental and American (1879) printings, but not all stamps show it.
Secret marks were added to the dies of the 24¢, 30¢ and 90¢ but new plates were not made from them. The various printings of these stamps can be distinguished only by the shades and paper.

206   **207**

Detail of **206**
1¢. Upper vertical lines have been deepened, creating a solid effect in parts of background. Upper arabesques have lines of shading.

Detail of **207**
3¢. Shading at sides of central oval is half its previous width. A short horizontal dash has been cut below the "TS" of "CENTS".

208   **209**

Detail of **208**
6¢. Has three vertical lines instead of four between the edge of the panel and the outside of the stamp.

Detail of **209**
10¢. Has four vertical lines instead of five between left side of oval and edge of the shield. Horizontal lines in lower part of background have been strengthened.

$1 Perry
Types of 1894

261

283

2¢ Washington
Types I-III of 1894

Triangle of **248-250**
Type I. Horizontal lines of uniform thickness run across the triangle.

Detail of **261**
Type I. The circles enclosing $1 are broken.

Detail of **261A**
Type II. The circles enclosing $1 are complete.

Detail of **283**
Type II. The lips of the ornaments break the curved line below the "E" of "TEN" and the "T" of "CENTS."

282C

251

Triangle of **251**
Type II. Horizontal lines cross the triangle, but are thinner within than without.

Watermark **191**

USPS
Watermark **190**

USPS
Watermark **191**

Detail of **282C**
TEN CENTS
Type I. The tips of the foliate ornaments do not impinge on the white curved line below "TEN CENTS."

Triangle of **252**
Type III. The horizontal lines do not cross the double frame lines of the triangle.

230   231   232

233   234   235

236   237   238

239   240   241

242   243   244

245

		Un	U	PB	#	FDC	Q
	Columbian Exposition Issue, 1893, Perf. 12						
230	1¢ Columbus Sights Land	37.50	.45	600.00	(6)	2,500.00	449,195,550
231	2¢ Landing of Columbus	33.50	.10	550.00	(6)	1,900.00	1,464,588,750
232	3¢ The Santa Maria	80.00	21.00	1,000.00	(6)	5,250.00	11,501,250
233	4¢ Fleet of Columbus ultramarine	100.00	8.50	1,300.00	(6)	5,250.00	19,181,550
233a	4¢ blue (error) (233)	—	—				
234	5¢ Columbus Seeking Aid	125.00	8.75	1,750.00	(6)	5,500.00	35,248,250
235	6¢ Columbus at Barcelona	120.00	30.00	1,600.00	(6)	6,000.00	4,707,550
236	8¢ Columbus Restored to Favor	85.00	11.00	1,000.00	(6)	6,000.00	10,656,550
237	10¢ Columbus Presenting Indians	185.00	9.50	3,750.00	(6)	7,000.00	16,516,950
238	15¢ Columbus Announcing						
	His Discovery	325.00	85.00	5,750.00	(6)		1,576,950
239	30¢ Columbus at La Rabida	425.00	125.00	8,500.00	(6)		617,250
240	50¢ Recall of Columbus	550.00	2.10	12,000.00	(6)		243,750
241	$1 Isabella Pledging Her Jewels	1,650.00	7.50	23,500.00	(6)		55,050
242	$2 Columbus in Chains	1,850.00	625.00	25,000.00	(6)	14,000.00	45,550
243	$3 Columbus Describing His						
	Third Voyage	3,350.00	1,100.00	55,000.00	(6)		27,650
244	$4 Isabella and Columbus	4,500.00	1,600.00	110,000.00	(6)		26,350
245	$5 Portrait of Columbus	5,000.00	1,850.00	120,000.00	(6)		27,350

CHICAGO WORLD'S FAIR

Nearly 100 years afterwards, the Chicago World's Fair of 1893 is still recalled as "magnificent." Officially the fair was known as the World's Columbian Exposition, and, although it was a year off schedule, its purpose was to commemorate the 400th anniversary of Columbus' first voyage to America.

Among the attractions was the world's first Midway. It gave visitors the first Ferris wheel, Thomas Edison's revolutionary Kinetoscope—a "moving pictures" machine—and, reputedly, Little Egypt's scandalous shimmy dance. To see everything at the fair, a visitor needed about three weeks and the stamina to cover 150 miles of zig-zag paths.

Certainly the single most impressive aspect of this fair was the grand scale of its classically-inspired architecture.

All 200 buildings were created under the general direction of the famed architectural firm of Daniel Burnham and John Root. Every building was spray-painted white, and as a group they will forever be known as the "White City" style.

Sadly, disastrous fires destroyed many of the buildings and others were subsequently torn down. Only one important building remains: The Charles B. Atwood-designed Palace of Fine Arts, which today houses Chicago's famed Museum of Science and Industry. See Scott Nos. 230-245.

		Un	U	PB	#	FDC	Q

Bureau Issues

Starting in 1894, the Bureau of Engraving and Printing at Washington has produced all U.S. postage stamps except Nos. 909-921 (Overrun Countries), 1335 (Eakins painting), 1355 (Disney), 1410-1413 (Anti-Pollution), 1414-1418 (Christmas, 1970),1789 (John Paul Jones), 1804 (Benjamin Banneker), 1825 (Veterans Administration) and 1833 (American Education).

		Un	U	PB	#	FDC	Q
	Issue of 1894, Perf. 12, Unwmkd.						
246	1¢ Franklin	22.50	3.75	325.00	(6)		
247	1¢ blue Franklin (246)	55.00	2.15	625.00	(6)		
248	2¢ Washington, type I	19.50	2.40	210.00	(6)		
	Nos. 249-252: Washington (248)						
249	2¢ carmine lake, type I	135.00	1.50	1,250.00	(6)		
250	2¢ carmine, type I	25.00	.30	325.00	(6)		
251	2¢ carmine, type II	190.00	3.00	2,500.00	(6)		
252	2¢ carmine, type III	100.00	3.35	1,200.00	(6)		
253	3¢ Jackson	85.00	8.00	950.00	(6)		
254	4¢ Lincoln	100.00	3.00	1,250.00	(6)		
255	5¢ Grant	67.50	4.25	800.00	(6)		
256	6¢ Garfield	125.00	17.00	1,600.00	(6)		
257	8¢ Sherman	100.00	12.50	950.00	(6)		
258	10¢ Webster	200.00	7.50	2,750.00	(6)		
259	15¢ Clay	300.00	50.00	4,250.00	(6)		
260	50¢ Jefferson	400.00	85.00	7,000.00	(6)		
261	$1 Commodore Perry, type I	1,100.00	250.00	15,000.00	(6)		
261A	$1 black Perry, type II (261)	2,000.00	485.00	25,000.00	(6)		
262	$2 James Madison	2,500.00	635.00	40,000.00	(6)		
263	$5 John Marshall	4,250.00	1,200.00	12,000.00	(6)		
	Issue of 1895, Perf. 12, Wmkd. 191						
264	1¢ blue Franklin (264)	6.75	.10	185.00	(6)		
	Nos. 265-267: Washington (248)						
265	2¢ carmine, type I	32.50	.75	375.00	(6)		
266	2¢ carmine, type II	40.00	3.15	450.00	(6)		
267	2¢ carmine, type III	6.00	.09	150.00	(6)		
268	3¢ purple Jackson (253)	37.50	1.20	650.00	(6)		
269	4¢ dk. brown Lincoln (254)	37.50	1.35	650.00	(6)		
270	5¢ chocolate Grant (255)	33.50	2.10	650.00	(6)		
271	6¢ dull brn. Garfield (256)	75.00	4.25	1,100.00	(6)		
272	8¢ vio. brn. Sherman (257)	33.50	1.20	700.00	(6)		
273	10¢ dk. green Webster (258)	67.50	1.35	1,300.00	(6)		
274	15¢ dark blue Clay (259)	210.00	10.00	3,500.00	(6)		
275	50¢ orange Jefferson (260)	300.00	25.00	6,000.00	(6)		
276	$1 black Perry, type I (261)	750.00	75.00	11,500.00	(6)		
276A	$1 blk. Perry, type II (261)	1,700.00	135.00	22,500.00	(6)		
277	$2 brt. blue Madison (262)	1,100.00	310.00	21,000.00	(6)		
278	$5 dk. grn. Marshall (263)	2,250.00	415.00	60,000.00	(6)		

253 254 255 256

259 260 261 262

82 C · · · · · · · 283

85 · · · · · · · 286 · · · · · · · 287

88 · · · · · · · 289 · · · · · · · 290

91 · · · · · · · 292 · · · · · · · 293

94 · · · · · · · 294a · · · · · · · 295 · · · · · · · 295a

96 · · · · · · · 296a · · · · · · · 297

		Un	U	PB	#	FDC	Q
	Issue of 1898, Perf. 12						
279	1¢ dp. green Franklin (246)	11.50	.10	200.00	(6)		
279B	2¢ red Washington, type III (248)	11.00	.09	175.00	(6)		
279Be	Booklet pane of 6	—	—				
280	4¢ rose brn. Lincoln (254)	33.50	.85	650.00	(6)		
281	5¢ dark blue Grant (255)	37.50	.75	775.00	(6)		
282	6¢ lake Garfield (256)	50.00	2.50	1,200.00	(6)		
282C	10¢ Webster, type I	170.00	2.75	3,000.00	(6)		
283	10¢ Webster, type II	125.00	2.25	1,800.00	(6)		
284	15¢ olive green Clay (259)	150.00	9.50	2,500.00	(6)		
	Trans-Mississippi Exposition Issue, June 17, Perf. 12						
285	1¢ Marquette on the Mississippi	37.50	6.75	350.00		5,250.00	70,993,400
286	2¢ Farming in the West	36.00	1.85	325.00		4,500.00	159,720,800
287	4¢ Indian Hunting Buffalo	200.00	30.00	1,900.00			4,924,500
288	5¢ Frémont on the Rocky Mts.	165.00	25.00	1,800.00		5,500.00	7,694,180
289	8¢ Troops Guarding Train	250.00	50.00	2,850.00		8,000.00	2,927,200
290	10¢ Hardships of Emigration	265.00	27.50	3,350.00			4,629,760
291	50¢ Western Mining Prospector	950.00	200.00	21,000.00		9,250.00	530,400
292	$1 Western Cattle in Storm	2,250.00	70.00	45,000.00			56,900
293	$2 Mississippi River Bridge						
	at St. Louis	3,500.00	950.00	100,000.00			56,200
	Pan-American Exposition Issue, 1901, May 1, Wmkd. 191						
294	1¢ Great Lakes Steamer	33.50	5.25	400.00	(6)	3,500.00	91,401,500
294a	Center inverted	—	—				
295	2¢ An Early Locomotive	33.50	1.50	400.00	(6)	3,000.00	209,759,700
295a	Center inverted	—	—				
296	4¢ Closed Coach Automobile	150.00	25.00	3,400.00	(6)	4,250.00	5,737,100
296a	Center inverted	—	—				
297	5¢ Bridge at Niagara Falls	150.00	25.00	3,650.00	(6)	4,500.00	7,201,300
298	8¢ Sault Ste. Marie Canal Locks	210.00	75.00	6,750.00	(6)		4,921,700
299	10¢ American Line Steamship	310.00	41.50	4,500.00	(6)		5,043,700

		Un	U	PB	#	FDC	Q
	Regular Issue of 1902-03, Perf. 12, Wmkd. 191						
300	1¢ Franklin, 1903	12.00	.09	200.00	(6)	2,750.00	
300b	Booklet pane of 6	—	—				
301	2¢ Washington, 1903	13.50	.10	225.00	(6)	2,750.00	
301c	Booklet pane of 6	—	—				
302	3¢ Jackson, 1903	75.00	3.00	1,100.00	(6)	2,750.00	
303	4¢ Grant, 1903	75.00	1.25	1,100.00	(6)	2,750.00	
304	5¢ Lincoln, 1903	80.00	1.25	1,250.00	(6)	3,000.00	
305	6¢ Garfield, 1903	85.00	3.00	1,250.00	(6)	3,000.00	
306	8¢ Martha Washington, 1902	47.50	2.50	950.00	(6)	3,250.00	
307	10¢ Webster, 1903	95.00	1.60	1,500.00	(6)	3,250.00	
308	13¢ Benjamin Harrison, 1902	50.00	10.00	775.00	(6)		
309	15¢ Clay, 1903	225.00	7.50	4,500.00	(6)		
310	50¢ Jefferson, 1903	675.00	33.50	9,500.00	(6)		
311	$1 David G. Farragut, 1903	1,200.00	63.50	18,500.00	(6)		
312	$2 Madison, 1903	1,500.00	240.00	27,500.00	(6)		
313	$5 Marshall, 1903	3,250.00	750.00	70,000.00	(6)		
	For listings of 312 and 313 with Perf. 10, see Nos. 479 and 480.						
	Issues of 1906-08, Imperf.						
314	1¢ blue green Franklin (300),-06	40.00	25.00	325.00	(6)		
314A	4¢ brown Grant (303), 1908	—	—				
315	5¢ blue Lincoln (304), 1908	900.00	350.00	6,500.00	(6)	·	
	No. 314A was issued imperforate, but all copies were privately perforated with large oblong perforations at the sides. (Schermack type III).						
	Coil Stamps, Perf. 12 Horizontally						
316	1¢ blue green pair						
	Franklin (300), 1908	—	—				
317	5¢ blue pair Lincoln (304),-08	—	—				
	Perf. 12 Vertically						
318	1¢ blue green pair Franklin						
	(300), 1908	—	—				
	Issue of 1903, Perf. 12, Shield-shaped Background						
319	2¢ Washington, Nov. 12	10.00	.09	135.00	(6)		
319g	Booklet pane of 6	—	—				
	Issue of 1906, Nos. 320-322: Washington (319), Imperf.						
320	2¢ carmine, Oct 2	40.00	20.00	375.00	(6)		
	Issue of 1908, Coil Stamps, Perf. 12, Horizontally						
321	2¢ carmine pair	—	—				
	Perf. 12 Vertically						
322	2¢ carmine pair	—	—				
	Issue of 1904, Perf. 12, Louisiana Purchase Exposition Issue, Apr. 30						
323	1¢ Robert R. Livingston	46.50	5.25	135.00		3,500.00	79,779,200
324	2¢ Thomas Jefferson	37.50	1.90	125.00		3,250.00	192,732,400
325	3¢ James Monroe	125.00	45.00	425.00		3,750.00	4,542,600
326	5¢ William McKinley	165.00	29.50	550.00		4,750.00	6,926,700

300 301 302 303 304

305 306 307 308 309 310

311 312 313 319

323 324 325 326

327 328 329 330

331 332 333 334

335 336 337 338 342

	1904 continued	Un	U	PB	#	FDC	Q
327	10¢ Map of Louisiana Purchase	335.00	45.00	1,250.00		7,000.00	4,011,200
	Issue of 1907, Perf. 12, Jamestown Exposition Issue						
328	1¢ Captain John Smith	35.50	7.50	385.00	(6)	2,250.00	77,728,794
329	2¢ Founding of Jamestown	40.00	5.00	525.00	(6)	2,250.00	149,497,994
330	5¢ Pocahontas	180.00	45.00	3,750.00	(6)		7,980,594
	Regular Issues of 1908-09, Perf. 12, Wmkd. 191						
331	1¢ Franklin, 1908	11.00	.09	950.00	(6)	1,000.00	
331a	Booklet pane of 6	190.00	—				
332	2¢ Washington, 1908	11.00	.09	80.00	(6)	1,000.00	
332a	Booklet pane of 6	150.00	—				
333	3¢ Washington, type I, 1908	33.50	3.35	375.00	(6)		
	Nos. 334-342: Washington (333)						
334	4¢ orange brown, 1908	33.50	1.25	400.00	(6)		
335	5¢ blue, 1908	45.00	2.25	600.00	(6)	1,750.00	
336	6¢ red orange, 1908	58.50	5.00	800.00	(6)	1,750.00	
337	8¢ olive green, 1908	37.50	2.95	550.00	(6)	1,750.00	
338	10¢ yellow, 1909	75.00	1.65	1,000.00	(6)	2,000.00	
339	13¢ blue green, 1909	45.00	29.50	550.00	(6)	2,100.00	
340	15¢ pale ultramarine, 1909	80.00	6.75	750.00	(6)	2,450.00	
341	50¢ violet, 1909	375.00	16.50	8,000.00	(6)		
342	$1 violet brown, 1909	525.00	85.00	11,000.00	(6)		
	Imperf.						
343	1¢ green Franklin (331), 1908	11.00	2.75	110.00	(6)	1,000.00	
344	2¢ car. Washington (332), 1908	15.00	3.35	190.00	(6)		
	Nos. 345-347: Washington (333)						
345	3¢ deep violet, type I, 1909	30.00	17.00	350.00	(6)		
346	4¢ orange brown, 1909	75.00	23.50	550.00	(6)		
347	5¢ blue, 1909	110.00	40.00	900.00	(6)		
	Coil Stamps of 1908-10						
	Nos. 350-351, 354-356: Washington (333), Perf. 12 Horizontally						
348	1¢ green Franklin (331), 1908	27.50	19.50				
349	2¢ car. Washington (332), 1909	60.00	7.50				
350	4¢ orange brown, 1910	150.00	75.00				
351	5¢ blue, 1909	165.00	100.00				
	1909, Perf. 12 Vertically						
352	1¢ green Franklin (331), 1909	75.00	22.50			1,000.00	
353	2¢ car. Washington (332), 1909	67.50	7.50				
354	4¢ orange brown, 1909	150.00	60.00				
355	5¢ blue, 1909	165.00	85.00				
356	10¢ yellow, 1909	1,350.00	500.00				
	Issues of 1909, Bluish Paper, Perf. 12						
	Nos. 359-366: Washington (333)						
357	1¢ green Franklin (331)	125.00	110.00	1,250.00	(6)		
358	2¢ car. Washington (332)	120.00	85.00	1,250.00	(6)		

	1909 continued	Un	U	PB	#	FDC	Q
359	3¢ deep violet, type I	1,650.00	1,100.00	15,000.00	(6)		
360	4¢ orange brown	—	—				
361	5¢ blue	3,750.00	—	35,000.00	(6)		
362	6¢ red orange	1,100.00	675.00	10,500.00	(6)		
363	8¢ olive green	—	—		(6)		
364	10¢ yellow	1,150.00	750.00	11,000.00	(6)		
365	13¢ blue green	2,500.00	1,250.00	17,500.00	(6)		
366	15¢ pale ultramarine	1,000.00	675.00	9,500.00	(6)		
	Lincoln Memorial Issue, Feb. 12						
367	2¢ Lincoln, Perf. 12	11.00	3.35	250.00	(6)	450.00	148,387,191
368	2¢ Lincoln, Imperf.	80.00	33.50	550.00	(6)	1,900.00	1,273,900
369	2¢ Lincoln, Perf. 12, Bluish Paper	375.00	250.00	4,750.00	(6)		637,000
	Alaska-Yukon Exposition Issue						
370	2¢ William Seward, Perf. 12	15.00	2.50	400.00	(6)	2,100.00	152,887,311
371	2¢ William Seward, Imperf.	87.50	40.00	625.00	(6)	2,750.00	525,400
	Hudson-Fulton Celebration Issue, Sep. 25						
372	2¢ Half Moon and Clermont, Perf. 12	18.50	5.00	450.00	(6)	950.00	72,634,631
373	2¢ Half Moon and Clermont, Imperf.	110.00	40.00	750.00	(6)	2,350.00	216,480
	Issues of 1910-13, Perf. 12, Wmkd. 190						
	Nos. 376-382: Washington (333)						
374	1¢ green Franklin (331), 1910	10.00	.10	95.00	(6)		
374a	Booklet pane of 6	165.00	—				
375	2¢ car. Washington (332), 1910	8.50	.09	85.00	(6)		
375a	Booklet pane of 6	140.00	—				
376	3¢ deep violet, type I, 1911	20.00	2.00	175.00	(6)		
377	4¢ brown, 1911	22.50	.65	225.00	(6)		
378	5¢ blue, 1911	22.50	.60	325.00	(6)		
379	6¢ red orange, 1911	41.50	.90	600.00	(6)		
380	8¢ olive green, 1911	135.00	15.00	1,500.00	(6)		
381	10¢ yellow, 1911	110.00	5.00	1,500.00	(6)		
382	15¢ pale ultramarine, 1911	250.00	15.00	2,750.00	(6)		
	Imperf.						
383	1¢ green Franklin (331), 1911	5.75	3.00	100.00	(6)		
384	2¢ car. Washington (332), 1911	9.00	2.00	250.00	(6)		
	Coil Stamps, Perf. 12 Horizontally						
385	1¢ green Franklin (331), 1910	29.50	15.00				
386	2¢ car. Washington (332), 1910	41.50	13.50				
	Perf. 12 Vertically						
387	1¢ green Franklin (331), 1910	95.00	25.00				
388	2¢ car. Washington (332), 1910	625.00	85.00				
389	3¢ dp. vio. Washington,						
	type I (333), 1911	—	—				
	Perf. 8½ Horizontally						
390	1¢ green Franklin (331), 1910	5.75	3.65				

367   368   370   371

372   373

ROBERT FULTON

Robert Fulton was 44 years old when he gave the world his most famous invention, the steamboat. It was a young age for so great an achievement, but Fulton had been a precocious youth.

Fulton's genius for drawing was apparent by the time he was ten, and so was his inventive mind. He made his own pencils by hammering the lead out from scrap sheet metal. As a teenager he enjoyed fishing but could not be bothered with poling a boat. So he devised a set of hand-cranked paddle wheels to make the job easier.

The public was widely skeptical of Fulton's plan to sail the world's first steamboat up the Hudson River in August 1807. To the average citizen, it was unthinkable that a vessel could move except under sail or by oars. Those who knew Fulton had a higher opinion of his scheme. But they could hardly have anticipated the reaction of terror that greeted the steamboat's maiden voyage.

Like a floating volcano, the Clermont's belching smokestack sprayed the night sky with sparks. One of the farmers who saw it raced home, barred the doors and announced to his astonished family that Lucifer himself was going to Albany in a sawmill! See Scott Nos. 372-273, 1270.

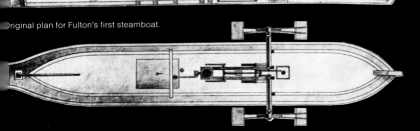

Original plan for Fulton's first steamboat.

397 398 399 400

405 406 414 420

VASCO NUNEZ de BALBOA

The great Spanish explorer Vasco Nunez de Balboa actually began his career as a stowaway. After sailing once with the explorer Bastidas, Balboa, a man of humble origins, found himself in Santo Domingo, broke and pursued by creditors. With no other resources than his wits on which to call, Balboa hid himself in a provision cask ready to be loaded on a ship bound for the Spanish colony on the Gulf of Darien.

It was a few years later, in 1513, that Balboa set out on his famous crossing of the cordillera, across the isthmus of Panama. Though the mountains were not particularly high at that point, the tropical rain forest was thick and heavy, the many swamps and lakes all but impassable. For two long weeks, the party of 190 Spaniards and several hundred native guides hacked and waded their way across just 45 territory. Then, on September 25, "silent upon a peak at Darien," Balboa sighted the great body of water he called "el mar del sur"—the Pacific Ocean.

Balboa actually reached the waters four days later. But he was not the first. A man named Alonso Martin, now all but forgotten by history, had reached the ocean the day before, paddled out in a dugout, and laid claim to the first European sailing of the Pacific. See Scott No. 397-400.

		Un	U	PB	#	FDC	Q
	1910-13 continued						
391	2¢ car. Washington (332), 1910	48.50	9.75				
	Perf. 8½ Vertically, Nos. 394-396: Washington (333)						
392	1¢ green Franklin (331), 1910	28.50	19.50				
393	2¢ car. Washington (332), 1910	56.50	6.50				
394	3¢ deep violet, type I, 1911	65.00	32.50			1,350.00	
395	4¢ brown, 1912	68.50	32.50				
396	5¢ blue, 1913	68.50	32.50				
	Panama Pacific Exposition Issue, 1913, Perf. 12						
397	1¢ Balboa	27.50	2.10	250.00	(6)	3,500.00	167,398,463
398	2¢ Locks, Panama Canal	33.50	.75	450.00	(6)	3,500.00	251,856,543
399	5¢ Golden Gate	135.00	12.75	3,350.00	(6)		14,544,363
400	10¢ Discovery						
	of San Francisco Bay	250.00	33.50	4,500.00	(6)	5,500.00	8,484,182
400A	10¢ orange (400)	375.00	22.50	13,000.00	(6)		
	1914-15, Perf. 10						
401	1¢ green Balboa (397), 1914	37.50	7.50	550.00	(6)	1,350.00	167,398,463
402	2¢ carmine Canal Locks (398),-15	125.00	2.00	2,850.00	(6)		251,856,543
403	5¢ blue Golden Gate (399),-15	295.00	21.00	6,250.00	(6)	3,250.00	14,544,363
404	10¢ orange Discovery of						
	San Francisco Bay (400), 1915	2,000.00	82.50	23,000.00	(6)		8,484,182
	Issues of 1912-14						
	Nos. 405-413: Washington (333), Perf. 12						
405	1¢ green, 1912	8.00	.10	120.00	(6)	1,400.00	
405b	Booklet pane of 6	75.00	—				
406	2¢ carmine, type I, 1912	7.50	.09	135.00	(6)	1,000.00	
406a	Booklet pane of 6	78.50	—				
407	7¢ black, 1914	110.00	8.35	1,400.00	(6)	1,350.00	
408	1¢ green, Imperf., 1912	1.60	.75	35.00	(6)	875.00	
409	2¢ carmine, type I, Imperf., 1912	2.00	.80	65.00	(6)	875.00	
	Coil Stamps, Perf. 8½ Horizontally						
410	1¢ green, 1912	8.25	4.15				
411	2¢ carmine, type I, 1912	10.00	4.65				
	Perf. 8½ Vertically						
412	1¢ green, 1912	29.00	6.50				
413	2¢ carmine, type I, 1912	57.50	.75			1,100.00	
	Perf. 12, Nos. 415-421: Franklin (414)						
414	8¢ Franklin, 1912	37.50	1.85	550.00	(6)	1,500.00	
415	9¢ salmon red, 1914	46.50	16.00	725.00	(6)	1,250.00	
416	10¢ orange yellow, 1912	36.00	.30	600.00	(6)	1,500.00	
417	12¢ claret brown, 1914	37.50	4.85	475.00	(6)	1,400.00	
418	15¢ gray, 1912	78.50	3.75	825.00	(6)	1,850.00	
419	20¢ ultramarine, 1914	200.00	16.50	2,350.00	(6)	2,000.00	
420	30¢ orange red, 1914	150.00	18.50	2,150.00	(6)	2,250.00	

	Un	U	PB	#	FDC	Q
1912-14 continued						
421 50¢ violet, 1914	625.00	16.50	9,000.00	(6)		
Nos. 422-423: Franklin (414), Perf. 12						
422 50¢ violet, Feb. 12, 1912	335.00	16.50	6,000.00	(6)		
423 $1 violet brown, Feb. 12, 1912						
Wmkd. 191	665.00	83.50	11,000.00	(6)		
Issues of 1914-15, Perf. 10, Wmkd. 190						
Nos. 424-430: Washington (333)						
424 1¢ green, 1914	4.50	.10°	65.00	(6)		
424d Booklet pane of 6	5.85	—				
425 2¢ rose red, type I, 1914	3.25	.09	50.00	(6)		
425e Booklet pane of 6	22.50	—				
426 3¢ deep violet, type I, 1914	15.00	1.55	135.00	(6)		
427 4¢ brown, 1914	36.50	.50	450.00	(6)		
428 5¢ blue, 1914	29.50	.50	350.00	(6)		
429 6¢ red orange, 1914	48.50	1.30	325.00	(6)		
430 7¢ black, 1914	92.50	5.00	1,050.00	(6)		
Nos. 431-440: Franklin (414)						
431 8¢ pale olive green, 1914	45.00	1.60	400.00	(6)		
432 9¢ salmon red, 1914	60.00	9.75	525.00	(6)		
433 10¢ orange yellow, 1914	53.50	.35	550.00	(6)		
434 11¢ dark green, 1915	32.50	7.25	195.00	(6)		
435 12¢ claret brown, 1914	28.50	4.50	235.00	(6)		
437 15¢ gray, 1914	145.00	6.85	900.00	(6)		
438 20¢ ultramarine, 1914	265.00	4.85	3,200.00	(6)		
439 30¢ orange red, 1914	325.00	14.50	4,850.00	(6)		
440 50¢ violet, 1914	850.00 '	18.50	10,500.00	(6)		
Coil Stamps, Perf. 10, 1914						
441 1¢ green	1.45	1.00				
442 2¢ carmine, type I	11.00	7.25				
443 1¢ green	24.00	6.00				
444 2¢ carmine, type I	43.50	1.20				
445 3¢ violet, type I	265.00	120.00				
446 4¢ brown	195.00	36.00				
447 5¢ blue	60.00	24.00				
Coil Stamps, Washington (333), 1915-16, Perf. 10 Horizontally						
448 1¢ green, 1915	7.25	4.00				
449 2¢ red, type I, 1915	—	150.00				
450 2¢ carmine, type III, 1916	13.00	3.65				
1914-16, Perf. 10 Vertically						
452 1¢ green, 1914	12.00	1.75				
453 2¢ red, type I, 1914	145.00	4.00				
454 2¢ carmine, type II, 1915	175.00	14.50				
455 2¢ carmine, type III, 1915	14.00	1.15				

		Un	U	PB	#	FDC	Q
	1914-16 continued						
456	3¢ violet, type I, 1916	325.00	105.00				
457	4¢ brown	37.50	17.50				
458	5¢ blue	42.50	17.50				
	Issue of 1914 Washington (333), Imperf., Coil						
459	2¢ carmine, type I, June 30	550.00	—				
	Issues of 1915, Perf. 10, Wmkd. 191						
460	$1 violet black Franklin						
	(414), Feb. 8	950.00	95.00	11,000.00	(6)		
	Perf. 11						
461	2¢ pale carmine red, type I.						
	Washington (333), June 17	95.00	72.50	950.00	(6)		
	Privately perforated copies of No. 409 have been made to resemble No. 461.						
	From 1916 all postage stamps except Nos. 519 and 832b are on unwatermarked paper.						
	Issues of 1916-17, Perf. 10						
	Nos. 462-469: Washington (333)						
462	1¢ green, 1916	8.00	.30	150.00	(6)		
462a	Booklet pane of 6	12.50	—				
463	2¢ carmine, type I, 1916	4.85	.15	115.00	(6)		
463a	Booklet pane of 6	90.00	—				
464	3¢ violet, type I, 1916	85.00	13.00	1,350.00	(6)		
465	4¢ orange brown, 1916	52.50	1.80	850.00	(6)		
466	5¢ blue, 1916	85.00	1.60	1,100.00	(6)		
467	5¢ car. (error in plate of 2¢), 1917	1,050.00	—				
468	6¢ red orange, 1916	95.00	7.25	1,050.00	(6)		
469	7¢ black, 1916	110.00	14.00	1,450.00	(6)		
470	8¢ olive green, 1916	56.50	5.75	600.00	(6)		
471	9¢ salmon red, 1916	56.50	17.50	700.00	(6)		
472	10¢ orange yellow, 1916	120.00	1.10	1,600.00	(6)		
473	11¢ dark green, 1916	29.50	19.50	325.00	(6)		
474	12¢ claret brown, 1916	48.50	6.00	600.00	(6)		
475	15¢ gray, 1916	180.00	12.00	2,500.00	(6)		
476	20¢ light ultramarine, 1916	295.00	13.00	3,250.00	(6)		
476A	30¢ orange red, 1916	—	—		(6)		
477	50¢ light violet, 1917	1,375.00	72.50	21,000.00	(6)		
478	$1 violet black, 1916	950.00	20.00	11,000.00	(6)		
	Issues of 1917, Perf. 10, Mar. 22						
479	$2 dark blue Madison (312), 1917	675.00	52.50	7,500.00	(6)		
480	$5 light green Marshall (313), 1917	565.00	57.50	6,250.00	(6)		
	Issues of 1916-17, Washington (333), Imperf.						
481	1¢ green, 1916	1.20	.80	18.50	(6)	1,000.00	
482	2¢ carmine, type I, 1916	1.90	1.50	40.00	(6)		
482A	2¢ carmine, type Ia, 1916	—	—				
483	3¢ violet, type I, 1917	20.00	8.75	225.00	(6)		

		Un	U	PB	#	FDC	Q
	1916-17 continued						
484	3¢ violet, type II, 1917	12.75	4.75	175.00	(6)		
485	5¢ car. (error in plate of 2¢),-17	—	—				
	Coil Stamps, Washington (333), 1916-19, Perf. 10 Horizontally						
486	1¢ green, 1918	1.20	.20			625.00	
487	2¢ carmine, type II, 1919	21.50	3.25				
488	2¢ carmine, type III, 1917	4.35	1.60				
489	3¢ violet, type I, 1917	6.00	1.45				
	1916-22, Perf. 10 Vertically						
490	1¢ green, 1916	.80	.20				
491	2¢ carmine, type II, 1916	—	225.00				
492	2¢ carmine, type III, 1916	12.00	.20				
493	3¢ violet, type I, 1917	45.00	2.85				
494	3¢ violet, type II, 1918	24.00	.95				
495	4¢ orange brown, 1917	18.50	4.00				
496	5¢ blue, 1919	4.85	.80				
497	10¢ orange yellow Franklin						
	(414), 1922	32.50	10.50			1,250.00	
	Issues of 1917-19, Perf. 11						
	Nos. 498-507: Washington (333)						
498	1¢ green, 1917	.80	.08	18.00	(6)	1,050.00	
498e	Booklet pane of 6	2.75	—				
498f	Booklet pane of 30	—	—				
499	2¢ rose, type I, 1917	.80	.08	14.00	(6)	1,050.00	
499e	Booklet pane of 6	3.35	—				
499f	Booklet pane of 30	—	—				
500	2¢ deep rose, type Ia, 1917	335.00	140.00	2,750.00	(6)		
501	3¢ light violet, type I, 1917	18.00	.13	175.00	(6)	1,050.00	
501b	Booklet pane of 6	95.00	—				
502	3¢ dark violet, type II, 1917	20.00	.35	235.00	(6)		
502b	Booklet pane of 6, 1918	62.50	—				
503	4¢ brown, 1917	16.00	.25	190.00	(6)	1,050.00	
504	5¢ blue, 1917	12.00	.13	165.00	(6)	1,100.00	
505	5¢ rose (error in plate of 2¢),-17	725.00	—				
506	6¢ red orange, 1917	19.50	.35	250.00	(6)	1,100.00	
507	7¢ black, 1917	36.50	1.20	400.00	(6)	1,200.00	
	Nos. 508-518: Franklin (414)						
508	8¢ olive bistre, 1917	20.00	.80	225.00	(6)	1,200.00	
509	9¢ salmon red, 1917	21.50	2.40	285.00	(6)	1,200.00	
510	10¢ orange yellow, 1917	24.00	.15	325.00	(6)	1,350.00	
511	11¢ light green, 1917	12.00	3.65	150.00	(6)	1,350.00	
512	12¢ claret brown, 1917	14.50	.65	150.00	(6)	1,350.00	
513	13¢ apple green, 1919	20.00	8.00	165.00	(6)		
514	15¢ gray, 1917	65.00	1.20	900.00	(6)	1,350.00	

	Un	U	PB	#	FDC	Q
1917-19 continued						
515 20¢ light ultramarine, 1917	80.00	.35	950.00	(6)	1,550.00	
516 30¢ orange red, 1917	65.00	1.05	800.00	(6)	1,750.00	
517 50¢ red violet, 1917	120.00	.75	2,000.00	(6)	2,250.00	
518 $1 violet brown, 1917	145.00	1.95	1,800.00	(6)	4,750.00	
Issue of 1917, Perf. 11, Wmkd. 191						
519 2¢ carmine Washington						
(332), Oct. 10	225.00	200.00	2,350.00	(6)		
Privately perforated copies of No. 344 have been made to resemble No. 519.						
Issues of 1918, Unwmkd., Perf. 11						
523 $2 orange red and black						
Franklin (547), Aug. 19	1,950.00	200.00	30,000.00	(8)		
524 $5 deep green and black						
Franklin (547), Aug. 19	725.00	28.50	12,500.00	(8)	8,750.00	
Issues of 1918-20, Washington (333)						
Perf. II						
525 1¢ gray green, 1918	3.00	.80	35.00	(6)	775.00	
526 2¢ carmine, type IV, 1920	36.50	4.00	275.00	(6)	825.00	
527 2¢ carmine, type V, 1920	22.00	.95	165.00	(6)		
528 2¢ carmine, type Va, 1920	10.50	.20	75.00	(6)		
528A 2¢ carmine, type VI, 1920	55.00	1.15	400.00	(6)		
528B 2¢ carmine, type VII, 1920	26.50	.16	185.00	(6)		
529 3¢ violet, type III, 1918	3.25	.13	70.00	(6)	575.00	
530 3¢ purple, type IV, 1918	1.35	.10	70.00	(6)	575.00	
Imperf.						
531 1¢ green, 1919	13.50	7.50	15.00	(6)	675.00	
532 2¢ car. rose, type IV, 1919	47.50	26.50	450.00	(6)	775.00	
533 2¢ carmine, type V, 1919	300.00	65.00	2,750.00	(6)		
534 2¢ carmine, type Va, 1919	22.50	9.00	150.00	(6)		
534A 2¢ carmine, type VI, 1919	50.00	23.50	500.00	(6)		
534B 2¢ carmine, type VII, 1919	1,750.00	450.00	15,500.00	(6)		
535 3¢ violet, type IV, 1918	15.00	6.00	100.00	(6)	775.00	
Issues of 1919						
Perf. 12½						
536 1¢ gray green Washington						
(333), Aug. 15	16.50	15.00	200.00	(6)	625.00	

		Un	U	PB	#	FDC	Q
	1919 continued						
	Perf. 11						
537	3¢ Allied Victory, Mar. 3	14.50	4.85	200.00	(6)	700.00	99,585,200
	Nos. 538-546: Washington (333), 1919, Perf. 11x10						
538	1¢ green	11.50	10.00	100.00		675.00	
539	2¢ carmine rose, type II	—	800.00	16,000.00			
540	2¢ carmine rose, type III	11.50	10.50	110.00			
541	3¢ violet, type II	45.00	40.00	500.00		775.00	
	1920, Perf. 10x11						
542	1¢ green, May 26	8.00	1.10	135.00	(6)	525.00	
	1921, Perf. 10						
543	1¢ green	.60	.11	20.00			
	1921, Perf. 11						
544	1¢ green, 19x22½mm	—	—				
545	1¢ green, 19½—20mmx22mm	180.00	110.00	1,100.00			
546	2¢ carmine rose, type III	130.00	80.00	900.00			
	Issues of 1920, Perf. 11						
547	$2 Franklin	600.00	36.50	14,000.00	(8)		
	Pilgrims 300th Anniv. Issue, Dec. 21						
548	1¢ Mayflower	9.50	3.35	95.00	(6)	700.00	137,978,207
549	2¢ Pilgrims Landing	13.50	2.50	125.00	(6)	625.00	196,037,327
550	5¢ Signing of Compact	85.00	20.00	1,000.00	(6)		11,321,607
	Issues of 1922-25, Perf. 11						
551	½¢ Nathan Hale, 1925	.23	.10	8.50	(6)	25.00	
552	1¢ Franklin (19x22mm), 1923	2.75	.10	35.00	(6)	37.50	
552a	Booklet pane of 6	6.50	—				
553	1½¢ Harding, 1925	4.50	.23	55.00	(6)	40.00	
554	2¢ Washington, 1923	2.50	.08	35.00	(6)	50.00	
554c	Booklet pane of 6	8.00	—				
555	3¢ Lincoln, 1923	30.00	1.10	300.00	(6)	42.50	
556	4¢ Martha Washington, 1923	26.50	.23	325.00	(6)	55.00	
557	5¢ Theodore Roosevelt, 1922	25.00	.12	325.00	(6)	125.00	
558	6¢ Garfield, 1922	45.00	.85	750.00	(6)	200.00	
559	7¢ McKinley, 1923	13.50	.75	95.00	(6)	125.00	
560	8¢ Grant, 1923	67.50	.85	1,250.00	(6)	120.00	
561	9¢ Jefferson, 1923	18.75	1.15	260.00	(6)	120.00	
562	10¢ Monroe, 1923	26.50	.12	475.00	(6)	125.00	
563	11¢ Rutherford B. Hayes, 1922	2.50	.30	65.00	(6)	600.00	
564	12¢ Grover Cleveland, 1923	11.50	.12	110.00	(6)	170.00	
565	14¢ American Indian, 1923	7.50	1.00	95.00	(6)	375.00	
566	15¢ Statue of Liberty, 1922	30.00	.10	325.00	(6)	375.00	
567	20¢ Golden Gate, 1923	35.00	.12	350.00	(6)	425.00	
568	25¢ Niagara Falls, 1922	35.00	.55	350.00	(6)	625.00	
569	30¢ Buffalo, 1923	55.00	.40	675.00	(6)	750.00	

537   547   548   549   550

551   552   553   554   555

556   557   558   559   560

561   562   563   564   565   566

567   568   569

570   571   572   573

610   611

		Un	U	PB#		FDC	Q
	1922-25 continued						
570	50¢ Arlington Amphitheater, 1922	100.00	.18	1,650.00	(6)	950.00	
571	$1 Lincoln Memorial, 1923	90.00	.45	825.00	(6)	4,750.00	
572	$2 U.S. Capitol, 1923	225.00	10.00	2,750.00	(6)	9,500.00	
573	$5 Head of Freedom,						
	Capitol Dome, 1923	525.00	15.00	9,250.00	(8)	15,000.00	
	Issues of 1923-25, Imperf.						
575	1¢ green Franklin (552), 1923	13.00	3.25	175.00	(6)		
576	1½¢ yellow brown Harding (553),-25	2.60	1.65	65.00	(6)	50.00	
577	2¢ carmine Washington (554)	2.90	1.75	55.00	(6)		
	For listings of other perforated stamps of issues 551-573 see:						
	Nos. 578 and 579	Perf. 11x10					
	Nos. 581 to 591	Perf. 10					
	Nos. 594 and 595	Perf. 11					
	Nos. 622 and 623	Perf. 11					
	Nos. 632 to 642, 653, 692 to 696	Perf. 11x10½					
	Nos. 697 to 701	Perf. 10½x11					
	Perf. 11x10						
578	1¢ green Franklin (552)	100.00	75.00	850.00			
579	2¢ carmine Washington (554)	60.00	55.00	450.00			

		Un	U	PB	#	FDC	Q
	Issues of 1923-26, Perf. 10						
581	1¢ green Franklin (552), 1923	6.50	.75	90.00		1,900.00	
582	1½¢ brown Harding (553), 1925	5.65	.75	50.00		52.50	
583	2¢ carmine Washington (554), 1924	2.65	.09	35.00		50.00	
583a	Booklet pane of 6	100.00	—				
584	3¢ violet Lincoln (555), 1925	36.50	2.00	350.00		62.50	
585	4¢ yellow brown						
	M. Washington (556)	21.50	.50	200.00		62.50	
586	5¢ blue T. Roosevelt (557), 1925	21.50	.30	200.00		62.50	
587	6¢ red orange Garfield (558), 1925	10.50	.50	75.00		77.50	
588	7¢ black McKinley (559), 1926	13.00	5.65	120.00		75.00	
589	8¢ olive green Grant (560), 1926	40.00	3.25	350.00		80.00	
590	9¢ rose Jefferson (561), 1926	9.50	2.65	50.00		85.00	
591	10¢ orange Monroe (562), 1925	80.00	.10	750.00		110.00	
	Perf. 11						
594	1¢ green Franklin,						
	19¾x22¼mm (552)	—	—				
595	2¢ carmine Washington,						
	19¾x22¼mm (554)	250.00	165.00	1,750.00			
596	1¢ green Franklin,						
	19¼x22¾mm (552)	—	—				
	Coil Stamps 1923-29, Perf. 10 Verically						
597	1¢ green Franklin (552), 1923	.50	.09			450.00	
598	1½¢ brown Harding (553), 1925	1.00	.12			60.00	
599	2¢ carmine Washington,						
	type I (554), 1929	.50	.08			700.00	
599A	2¢ carmine Washington,						
	type II (554), 1929	200.00	12.00				
600	3¢ violet Lincoln (555)	8.75	.11			80.00	
601	4¢ yellow brown						
	M. Washington (556), 1923	4.75	.45			60.00	
602	5¢ dark blue						
	Theodore Roosevelt (557), 1924	1.80	.20			85.00	
603	10¢ orange Monroe (562), 1924	5.00	.15			105.00	
	Coil Stamps 1923-25 Perf. 10 Horizontally						
604	1¢ yellow green Franklin (552), 1924	.30	.12			92.50	
605	1½¢ yellow brown Harding (553), 1925	.35	.20			60.00	
606	2¢ carmine Washington (554), 1923	.40	.15			90.00	
	Harding Memorial Issue, 1923, Flat Plate Printing (19¼x22¼mm)						
610	2¢ Harding, Perf. 11, Sept. 1	1.15	.13	45.00	(6)	50.00	1,459,487,085
611	2¢ Harding Imperf., Nov. 15	20.00	5.25	210.00	(6)	115.00	770,000
	Rotary Press Printing (19¼x22¾mm)						
612	2¢ black, Perf. 10 (610), Sept. 12	28.50	2.15	450.00		130.00	99,950,300
613	2¢ black Perf. 11 (610)	—	—				

		Un	U	PB	#	FDC	Q
	Huguenot-Walloon 300th Anniv. Issue, 1924, May 1						
614	1¢ Ship *New Netherland*	8.00	5.25	80.00	(6)	65.00	51,378,023
615	2¢ Landing at Fort Orange	12.75	3.35	150.00	(6)	85.00	77,753,423
616	5¢ Huguenot Monument, Florida	71.50	25.00	675.00	(6)	150.00	5,659,023
	Lexington-Concord Issue, 1925, Apr. 4						
617	1¢ Washington at Cambridge	7.50	6.50	80.00	(6)	60.00	15,615,000
618	2¢ Birth of Liberty	13.50	7.50	165.00	(6)	75.00	26,596,600
619	5¢ Statue of Minute Man	67.50	22.50	575.00	(6)	135.00	5,348,800
	Norse-American Issue, 1925, May 18						
620	2¢ Sloop *Restaurationen*	13.00	5.25	450.00	(8)	45.00	9,104,983
621	5¢ Viking Ship	45.00	26.50	1,400.00	(8)	80.00	1,900,983
	Issues of 1925-26						
622	13¢ Benjamin Harrison, 1926	22.50	.60	265.00	(6)	35.00	
623	17¢ Woodrow Wilson, 1925	30.00	.38	275.00	(6)	35.00	
	Issues of 1926						
627	2¢ Independence,						
	150th Anniv., May 10	6.00	.70	90.00	(6)	25.00	307,731,900
628	5¢ Ericsson Memorial, May 29	16.50	5.65	145.00	(6)	40.00	20,280,500
629	2¢ Battle of White Plains, Oct. 18	3.75	2.65	90.00	(6)	8.00	40,639,485

HUGUENOTS

It's not surprising that so many of the great patriots of America's early years were descendants of a small band of French Protestants, the Huguenots. Their ancestors saw in America a haven from a history of religious persecution found in their native land.

The Huguenots founded one of the earliest European settlements in America. Arriving in Florida in 1562, they built Fort Caroline at the mouth of the St. John's River, near what is today Jacksonville. The settlers discovered a fruitful land, "so pleasant that those which are melancholic would be enforced to change their humor."

But the settlement soon met with tragedy. Disorganization and disease plagued the Huguenots and they found themselves close to starvation. An even greater danger was the presence of Spaniards who regarded Florida as their domain and the Huguenots as their religious and political enemies. When the King of Spain learned of Fort Caroline, he dispatched his best military leader, Pedro Menendez de Aviles, to destroy the settlement. The Huguenots, led by Jean Ribaut, tried to fight the Spanish but were overwhelmed and slaughtered.

Fortunately, the next wave of Huguenot immigrants fared better than their predecessors. Denied religious freedom by Louis XIV, they arrived in America in the late seventeenth century and settled primarily in the English colonies of New England and the Carolinas. These well-educated and highly cultured refugees brought with them remarkable skills in commerce; they soon prospered. Their love of liberty took them to the forefront of the American independence movement, and Huguenot names like Revere, Cabot, Jay, Laurens and Bowdoin have become part of our history. See Scott No. 616.

614 615 616

617 618 619

620 621 622 623

627 628 629

631   633   643

644   645   646   647   648

649   650

654

651

		Un	U	PB	#	FDC	Q
	International Philatelic Exhibition Issue, Oct. 18, Souvenir Sheet						
630	2¢ car. rose, sheet of 25 with						
	selvage inscription (629)	675.00	—			1,400.00	107,398*
	Imperf.						
631	1½¢ Harding, Aug. 27,						
	18½–19mm x 22mm	4.75	—	90.00		40.00	
	Issues of 1926-27, Perf. 11x10½						
632	1¢ green Franklin (552), 1927	.23	.08	3.50		60.00	
632a	Booklet pane of 6, 1927	5.00	—				
633	1½¢ Harding, 1927	4.15	.12	115.00		60.00	
634	2¢ carmine Washington,						
	type I (554), 1956	.18	.08	1.20		62.50	
634d	Booklet pane of 6, 1927	2.00	—				
634A	2¢ carmine Washington,						
	type II (554), 1926	475.00	16.50	2,500.00			
635	3¢ violet Lincoln (555), 1957	.65	.08	9.00		52.50	
636	4¢ yellow brown						
	M. Washington (556), 1927	5.65	.12	140.00		60.00	
637	5¢ dark blue T. Roosevelt (557),-27	5.65	.08	35.00		60.00	
638	6¢ red orange Garfield (558), 1927	5.65	.08	35.00		72.50	
639	7¢ black McKinley (559), 1927	5.65	.11	35.00		75.00	
640	8¢ olive green, Grant (560), 1927	5.65	.08	35.00		77.50	
641	9¢ orange red Jefferson (561), 1927	5.65	.08	35.00		95.00	
642	10¢ orange Monroe (562), 1927	9.00	.08	55.00		100.00	
	Issues of 1927, Perf. 11						
643	2¢ Vermont 150th Anniversary, Aug. 3	2.00	1.85	80.00	(6)	6.50	39,974,900
644	2¢ Burgoyne Campaign, Aug. 3	7.50	4.50	90.00	(6)	25.00	25,628,450
	Issues of 1928						
645	2¢ Valley Forge, May 26	1.50	.75	65.00	(6)	5.75	101,330,328
	Perf. 11x10½						
646	2¢ Battle of Monmouth, Oct. 20	2.25	2.15	85.00		22.50	9,779,896
647	2¢ carmine (648)	9.00	6.50	275.00		25.00	5,519,897
648	5¢ Hawaii 150th Anniv., Aug. 13	32.50	24.00	550.00		47.50	1,459,897
	Aeronautics Conference Issue, Dec. 12, Perf. 11						
649	2¢ Wright Airplane	2.50	1.50	30.00	(6)	12.00	51,342,273
650	5¢ Globe and Airplane	12.75	5.75	145.00	(6)	18.00	10,319,700
	Issues of 1929						
651	2¢ George Rogers Clark, Feb. 25	1.05	1.00	20.00	(6)	7.00	16,684,674
	Perf. 11x10½						
653	½¢ olive brown Nathan Hale (551)	.11	.08	1.00		30.00	
	Electric Light Jubilee Issue, Perf. 11						
654	2¢ Edison's First Lamp, June 5	1.15	1.15	55.00	(6)	12.50	31,679,200
	Perf. 11x10½						
655	2¢ carmine rose (654), June 11	1.10	.30	85.00		77.50	210,119,474

*Sheets of 25

		Un	U	PB	#	FDC	Q
	1929 continued						
	Coil Stamp, Perf. 10 Vertically						
656	2¢ carmine rose (654), June 11	24.00	1.80			100.00	133,530,000
	Perf. 11						
657	2¢ Sullivan Expedition, June 17	1.00	.95	50.00	(6)	4.50	51,451,880
	Regular Issue of 1926-27						
	Perf. 11x10½, 658-668 Overprinted Kansas						
658	1¢ green Franklin (552)	2.50	1.90	35.00		27.50	13,390,000
659	1½¢ brown Harding (553)	4.65	3.35	55.00		27.50	8,240,000
660	2¢ carmine Washington (554)	4.15	.75	55.00		27.50	87,410,000
661	3¢ violet Lincoln (555)	22.50	16.50	200.00		30.00	2,540,000
662	4¢ yellow brown						
	M. Washington (556)	25.00	8.50	210.00		32.50	2,290,000
663	5¢ deep blue T. Roosevelt (557)	18.75	12.50	185.00		35.00	2,700,000
664	6¢ red orange Garfield (558)	37.50	16.50	550.00		42.50	1,450,000
665	7¢ black McKinley (559)	39.50	27.50	475.00		42.50	1,320,000
666	8¢ olive green Grant (560)	110.00	85.00	850.00		80.00	1,530,000
667	9¢ light rose Jefferson (561)	16.75	12.50	225.00		72.50	1,130,000
668	10¢ orange yellow Monroe (562)	29.50	12.50	385.00		80.00	2,860,000
	669-679 Overprinted Nebraska						
669	1¢ green Franklin (552)	2.75	2.65	35.00		27.50	8,220,000
670	1½¢ brown Harding (553)	3.75	3.15	50.00		25.00	8,990,000
671	2¢ carmine Washington (554)	2.75	1.00	35.00		25.00	73,220,000
672	3¢ violet Lincoln (555)	16.75	12.50	250.00		32.50	2,110,000
673	4¢ yellow brown						
	M. Washington (556)	25.00	15.00	250.00		37.50	1,600,000
674	5¢ deep blue T. Roosevelt (557)	25.00	16.00	250.00		37.50	1,860,000
675	6¢ red orange Garfield (558)	41.50	25.00	575.00		55.00	980,000
676	7¢ black McKinley (559)	27.50	19.50	265.00		57.50	850,000
677	8¢ olive green Grant (560)	39.50	29.50	375.00		60.00	1,480,000
678	9¢ light rose Jefferson (561)	50.00	29.50	475.00		62.50	530,000
679	10¢ orange yellow Monroe (562)	135.00	25.00	1,000.00		70.00	1,890,000
	Warning: Excellent forgeries of the Kansas and Nebraska overprints exist.						
	Perf. 11						
680	2¢ Battle of Fallen Timbers,						
	Sept. 14	1.60	1.40	60.00	(6)	4.25	29,338,274
681	2¢ Ohio River Canal, Oct. 19	1.00	1.00	45.00	(6)	4.00	32,680,900
	Issues of 1930						
682	2¢ Mass. Bay Colony, Apr. 8	.95	.65	65.00	(6)	3.25	74,000,774
683	2¢ Carolina-Charleston, Apr. 10	2.00	1.90	100.00	(6)	3.50	25,215,574
	Perf. 11x10½						
684	1½¢ Warren G. Harding	.60	.08	1.50		4.00	
685	4¢ William H. Taft	1.00	.09	10.00		8.00	

656 (Coil Pair)   657   669   680

681   682   683   684   685

688

689

690

702

703

704

705

706

707

708

709

710

711

712

713

714

715

716

717

	1930 continued	Un	U	PB	#	FDC	Q
	Coil Stamps, Perf. 10 Vertically						
686	1½¢ brown Harding (684)	2.50	.09			6.75	
687	4¢ brown Taft (685)	3.35	.45			27.50	
	Perf. 11						
688	2¢ Braddock's Field, July 9	1.60	1.60	75.00	(6)	5.25	25,609,470
689	2¢ Von Steuben, Sept. 17	.85	.70	45.00	(6)	5.00	66,487,000
	Issues of 1931						
690	2¢ Pulaski, Jan. 16	.35	.22	32.50	(6)	4.00	96,559,400
	Perf. 11x10½						
692	11¢ light blue Hayes (563)	5.25	.14	28.50		90.00	
693	12¢ brown violet Cleveland (564)	8.25	.09	45.00		90.00	
694	13¢ yellow green Harrison (622)	3.50	.18	28.50		95.00	
695	14¢ dark blue Indian (565)	6.25	.40	35.00		95.00	
696	15¢ gray Statue of Liberty (566)	16.50	.09	80.00		105.00	
	Perf. 10½x11						
697	17¢ black Wilson (623)	8.50	.30	50.00		1,750.00	
698	20¢ car. rose Golden Gate (567)	22.50	.08	100.00		180.00	
699	25¢ blue green Niagara						
	Falls (568)	20.00	.11	85.00		1,750.00	
700	30¢ brown Buffalo (569)	27.00	.11	160.00		275.00	
701	50¢ lilac Amphitheater (570)	97.50	.11	500.00		400.00	
	Perf. 11						
702	2¢ Red Cross, May 21	.18	.18	2.50		3.00	99,074,600
	The American Red Cross was founded by Clara Barton in 1881.						
703	2¢ Yorktown, Oct. 12	.45	.45	4.00		4.00	25,006,400
	Issues of 1932. Perf. 11x10½, Washington Bicentennial Issue, Jan. 1						
704	½¢ Portrait by Charles W. Peale	.10	.10	4.50		5.00	87,969,700
705	1¢ Bust by Jean Antoine Houdon	.18	.08	5.50		5.50	1,265,555,100
706	1½¢ Portrait by Charles W. Peale	.70	.15	25.00		5.50	304,926,800
707	2¢ Portrait by Gilbert Stuart	.13	.08	1.75		5.50	4,222,198,300
708	3¢ Portrait by Charles W. Peale	.95	.10	22.50		5.75	456,198,500
709	4¢ Portrait by Charles P. Polk	.55	.11	7.00		5.75	151,201,300
710	5¢ Portrait by Charles W. Peale	4.00	.15	27.50		6.00	170,565,100
711	6¢ Portrait by John Trumbull	8.00	.13	100.00		6.75	111,739,400
712	7¢ Portrait by John Trumbull	.70	.24	8.50		6.75	83,257,400
713	8¢ Portrait by Charles B.J.F.						
	Saint Memin	10.50	1.30	115.00		6.75	96,506,100
714	9¢ Portrait by W. Williams	7.50	.30	75.00		7.75	75,709,200
715	10¢ Portrait by Gilbert Stuart	36.50	.15	200.00		10.00	147,216,000
	Perf. 11						
716	2¢ Olympic Games, Jan. 25	.50	.28	20.00	(6)	5.00	51,102,800
	Perf. 11x10½						
717	2¢ Arbor Day, Apr. 22	.20	.12	12.50		2.75	100,869,300

		Un	U	PB	#	FDC	Q
	1932 continued						
	10th Olympic Games Issue, June 15						
718	3¢ Runner at Starting Mark	1.40	.09	35.00		5.75	168,885,300
719	5¢ Myron's Discobolus	2.25	.28	50.00		7.00	52,376,100
720	3¢ Washington, June 16	.25	.08	1.50		8.00	
720b	Booklet pane of 6	52.50	—				
	Coil Stamps, Perf. 10 Vertically						
721	3¢ deep violet (720), June 24	4.25	.09			17.50	
	Perf. 10 Horizontally						
722	3¢ deep violet (720), Oct 12	2.35	.55			17.50	
	Perf. 10 Vertically						
723	6¢ red orange Garfield						
	(558), Aug. 18	25.00	.25			17.50	
	Perf. 11						
724	3¢ William Penn, Oct. 24	.45	.25	22.50	(6)	2.50	49,949,000
725	3¢ Daniel Webster, Oct. 24	.65	.35	40.00	(6)	2.50	49,538,500
	Issues of 1933						
726	3¢ Georgia 200th Anniv., Feb. 12	.45	.25	27.50	(6)	2.35	61,719,200
	Perf. 10½x11						
727	3¢ Peace of 1783, Apr. 19	.17	.12	7.00		2.75	73,382,400
	Century of Progress Issue, May 25						
728	1¢ Restoration of Ft. Dearborn	.15	.09	3.00		2.00	348,266,800
729	3¢ Fed. Building at Chicago 1933	.22	.08	4.00		2.00	480,239,300
	American Philatelic Society Issue, Souvenir Sheets, Aug. 25, Without Gum, Imperf.						
730	1¢ deep yellow green						
	sheet of 25 (728)	60.00	45.00			150.00	456,704
730a	Single stamp	1.20	.50			2.75	11,417,600
731	3¢ deep violet, sheet of 25 (729)	50.00	35.00			150.00	441,172
731a	Single stamp	1.10	.50			2.75	11,029,300
	Perf. 10½x11						
732	3¢ NRA, Aug. 15	.16	.08	2.00		2.50	1,978,707,300
	Perf. 11						
733	3¢ Byrd's Antarctic Expedition,						
	Oct. 9	1.00	1.00	30.00	(6)	7.00	5,735,944
734	5¢ Tadeusz Kosciuszko, Oct. 13	.85	.45	65.00	(6)	6.25	45,137,700
	Issues of 1934, National Stamp Exhibition Issue, Souvenir Sheet,						
	Feb. 10, Without Gum, Imperf.						
735	3¢ dk. blue sheet of 6 (733)	35.00	27.50			67.50	811,404
735a	Single stamp	5.00	2.50			6.75	4,868,424
	Perf. 11						
736	3¢ Maryland 300th Anniversary,						
	Mar. 23	.20	.20	15.00	(6)	1.40	46,258,300
	Mothers of America Issue, May 2, Perf. 11x10½						
737	3¢ Whistler's Mother	.17	.09	1.75		1.35	193,239,100

718   719   720   723

724   725   726

727   728   729   732

733

734
736
737

39

741

740

42

743

745

744

46

748

	Un	U	PB	#	FDC	Q
1934 continued						
Perf. 11						
738 3¢ deep violet (737)	.25	.25	7.25	(6)	2.00	15,432,200
739 3¢ Wisconsin 300th Anniversary,						
July 7	.21	.14	7.00	(6)	1.60	64,525,400
National Parks Issue						
740 1¢ El Capitan, Yosemite, Calif.	.12	.12	1.50	(6)	2.25	84,896,350
741 2¢ Grand Canyon, Arizona	.17	.14	2.00	(6)	2.25	74,400,200
742 3¢ Mt. Rainier and Mirror Lake,						
Washington	.25	.12	3.50	(6)	2.50	95,089,000
743 4¢ Mesa Verde, Colorado	.70	.65	12.00	(6)	3.25	19,178,650
744 5¢ Old Faithful, Yellowstone,						
Wyoming	1.70	1.10	14.50	(6)	3.25	30,980,100
745 6¢ Crater Lake, Oregon	2.50	1.50	30.00	(6)	4.00	16,923,350
746 7¢ Great Head, Acadia Park,						
Maine	1.40	1.30	20.00	(6)	4.00	15,988,250
747 8¢ Great White Throne,						
Zion Park, Utah	3.50	2.85	35.00	(6)	4.25	15,288,700
748 9¢ Mt Rockwell and Two Medicine						
Lake, Glacier National Park,						
Montana	3.75	1.00	32.50	(6)	4.50	17,472,600
749 10¢ Great Smoky Mountains,						
North Carolina	6.75	1.40	57.50	(6)	7.50	18,874,300
American Philatelic Society Issue, Souvenir Sheet, Imperf.						
750 3¢ deep violet sheet of six						
(742), Aug. 28	55.00	50.00			65.00	511,391
750a Single stamp	6.50	4.50			7.00	3,068,346
Trans-Mississippi Philatelic Issue						
751 1¢ green sheet of six (740), Oct. 10	20.00	18.50			45.00	793,551
751a Single stamp	3.00	1.60			4.50	4,761,306
Special Printing (Nos. 752 to 771 inclusive), Issued March 15, 1935, Without Gum						
Issues of 1935, Perf. 10½x11						
752 3¢ violet Peace of 1783 (727)						
Issued in sheets of 400, Mar. 15	.17	.17	17.50		13.00	3,274,556
Perf. 11						
753 3¢ dk. blue Byrd's Antarctic						
Expedition (733)	.60	.60	25.00	(6)	15.00	2,040,760
Imperf.						
754 3¢ dp. vio. Whistler's Mother (737)	1.10	.60	45.00	(6)	15.00	2,389,288
755 3¢ deep violet Wisconsin						
300th Anniversary (739)	1.10	.60	45.00	(6)	15.00	2,294,948
756 1¢ green Yosemite (740)	.25	.25	7.50	(6)	15.00	3,217,636
757 2¢ red Grand Canyon (741)	.35	.35	9.50	(6)	15.00	2,746,640
758 3¢ dp. vio. Mt. Rainier (742)	.90	.80	27.50	(6)	16.00	2,168,088

	1935 continued	Un	U	PB	#	FDC	Q
759	4¢ brown Mesa Verde (743)	2.25	1.25	35.00	(6)	16.00	1,822,684
760	5¢ blue Yellowstone (744)	3.25	1.75	45.00	(6)	16.00	1,724,576
761	6¢ dk. blue Crater Lake (745)	4.50	2.00	60.00	(6)	16.50	1,647,696
762	7¢ black Acadia (746)	3.50	1.85	55.00	(6)	16.50	1,682,948
763	8¢ sage green Zion (747)	3.65	2.00	75.00	(6)	17.00	1,638,644
764	9¢ red orange Glacier Nat'l Park						
	(748)	4.00	2.00	75.00	(6)	18.00	1,625,224
765	10¢ gray black Smoky Mts. (749)	8.00	4.50	100.00	(6)	20.00	1,644,900
766	1¢ yellow green (728)	—	—				98,712
	Pane of 25 from sheet of 225 (9 panes)						
766a	Single stamp	1.10	.50			11.00	2,467,800
767	3¢ violet (729)	—	—				85,914
	Pane of 25 from sheet of 225 (9 panes)						
767a	Single stamp	1.00	.50			11.00	2,147,850
768	3¢ dark blue (733)	—	—				267,200
	Pane of 6 from sheet of 150 (25 panes)						
768a	Single stamp	5.25	2.50			13.00	1,603,200
769	1¢ green (740)	—	—				279,960
	Pane of 6 from sheet of 120 (20 panes)						
769a	Single stamp	1.75	1.75			8.00	1,679,760
770	3¢ deep violet (742)	—	—				215,920
	Pane of 6 from sheet of 120 (20 panes)						
770a	Single stamp	5.00	5.00			10.00	1,295,520
771	16¢ dark blue Seal of U.S. (CE2),						
	issued in sheets of 200	5.25	4.00	175.00	(6)	25.00	1,370,560
	Perf. 11x10½						
772	3¢ Connecticut 300th Anniv., Apr. 26	.18	.10	2.00		8.50	70,726,800
773	3¢ California-Pacific Exposition,						
	May 29	.13	.09	2.00		8.50	100,839,600
	Perf. 11						
774	3¢ Boulder Dam, Sep. 30	.13	.09	2.50	(6)	11.00	73,610,650
	Perf. 11x10½						
775	3¢ Michigan 100th Anniv., Nov. 1	.13	.10	2.00		8.00	75,823,900
	Issues of 1936						
776	3¢ Texas 100th Anniv., Mar. 2	.13	.09	2.00		8.00	124,324,500
	Perf. 10½x11						
777	3¢ Rhode Island 300th Anniv., May 4	.18	.09	2.00		8.00	67,127,650
	Third International Philatelic Exhibition Issue, Souvenir Sheet, Imperf.						
778	Violet, sheet of 4 different stamps						
	(772, 733, 775 and 776), May 9	4.00	4.00			15.00	2,809,039
	Perf. 11x10½						
782	3¢ Arkansas 100th Anniv., June 15	.13	.09	2.00		8.00	72,992,650
783	3¢ Oregon Territory, July 14	.13	.09	2.00		8.00	74,407,450
784	3¢ Susan B. Anthony, Aug. 26	.13	.08	.75		12.00	269,522,200

772

773

774

775

776

777

782

783

784

785

786

787

788

789

790

791

792

793

794

795

796

798

799

800

801

802

		Un	U	PB	#	FDC	Q
	Issues of 1936-37						
	Army Issue						
785	1¢ George Washington						
	and Nathanael Greene, 1936	.11	.09	1.00		6.00	105,196,150
786	2¢ Andrew Jackson and						
	Winfield Scott, 1937	.15	.09	1.10		6.00	93,848,500
787	3¢ Generals Sherman,						
	Grant and Sheridan, 1937	.25	.10	1.50		6.00	87,741,150
788	4¢ Generals Robert E. Lee						
	and "Stonewall" Jackson, 1937	.65	.27	13.00		6.75	35,794,150
789	5¢ U.S. Military Academy,						
	West Point, 1937	1.25	.27	15.00		8.00	36,839,250
	Navy Issue						
790	1¢ John Paul Jones						
	and John Barry, 1936	.11	.09	1.00		6.00	104,773,450
791	2¢ Stephen Decatur						
	and Thomas MacDonough, 1937	.15	.09	1.10		6.00	92,054,550
792	3¢ Admirals David G. Farragut						
	and David D. Porter, 1937	.25	.10	1.50		6.00	93,291,650
793	4¢ Admirals William T. Sampson,						
	George Dewey and Winfield						
	S. Schley, 1937	.65	.27	13.00		6.75	34,552,950
794	5¢ Seal of U.S. Naval Academy						
	and Naval Cadets, 1937	1.25	.27	15.00		8.00	36,819,050
	Issues of 1937						
795	3¢ Northwest Ordinance						
	150th Anniversary, July 13	.13	.09	2.00		7.50	84,825,250
	Perf. 11						
796	5¢ Virginia Dare, Aug. 18	.35	.28	11.50	(6)	8.50	25,040,400
	Society of Philatelic Americans, Souvenir Sheet, Imperf.						
797	10¢ blue green (749), Aug. 26	1.20	.85			7.25	5,277,445
	Perf. 11x10½						
798	3¢ Constitution 150th Anniv.,						
	Sept. 17	.15	.09	1.65		7.75	99,882,300
	Territorial Issues, Perf. 10½x11						
799	3¢ Hawaii, Oct. 18	.15	.10	2.00		8.50	78,454,450
	Perf. 11x10½						
800	3¢ Alaska, Nov. 12	.15	.10	2.00		8.50	77,004,200
801	3¢ Puerto Rico, Nov. 25	.15	.10	1.75		8.50	81,292,450
802	3¢ Virgin Islands, Dec. 15	.15	.10	2.00		8.50	76,474,550

		Un	U	PB	#	FDC	Q
	Presidential Issue, 1938						
803	½¢ Benjamin Franklin	.08	.08	.50		1.25	
804	1¢ George Washington	.09	.08	.30		1.35	
804b	Booklet pane of 6	2.10	—				
805	1½¢ Martha Washington	.09	.08	.35		1.35	
806	2¢ John Adams	.09	.08	.35		1.65	
806b	Booklet pane of 6	5.25	—				
807	3¢ Thomas Jefferson	.11	.08	.50		1.65	
807a	Booklet pane of 6	10.50	—				
808	4¢ James Madison	.45	.08	2.00		1.65	
809	4½¢ White House	.20	.11	2.00		2.25	
810	5¢ James Monroe	.40	.08	2.00		2.25	
811	6¢ John Q. Adams	.40	.08	2.00		2.25	
812	7¢ Andrew Jackson	.45	.08	2.25		2.50	
813	8¢ Martin Van Buren	.55	.08	2.50		2.50	
814	9¢ William H. Harrison	.60	.08	2.50		2.65	
815	10¢ John Tyler	.45	.08	2.25		2.75	
816	11¢ James K. Polk	1.10	.10	4.50		2.75	
817	12¢ Zachary Taylor	1.65	.09	6.25		3.00	
818	13¢ Millard Filmore	1.60	.11	6.00		3.00	
819	14¢ Franklin Pierce	1.60	.12	6.00		3.25	
820	15¢ James Buchanan	.80	.08	4.00		3.25	
821	16¢ Abraham Lincoln	1.85	.55	7.50		3.50	
822	17¢ Andrew Johnson	1.65	.12	7.50		3.75	
823	18¢ Ulysses S. Grant	3.00	.11	10.00		4.25	
824	19¢ Rutherford B. Hayes	2.00	.55	8.00		4.25	
825	20¢ James A. Garfield	1.20	.08	5.50		4.00	
826	21¢ Chester A. Arthur	2.00	.14	9.50		5.00	
827	22¢ Grover Cleveland	2.00	.70	11.00		5.25	
828	24¢ Benjamin Harrison	7.00	.25	25.00		5.25	
829	25¢ William McKinley	1.60	.08	8.00		6.50	
830	30¢ Theodore Roosevelt	10.75	.08	42.50		10.00	
831	50¢ William Howard Taft	16.00	.09	60.00		17.50	
	Perf. 11						
832	$1 Woodrow Wilson	23.50	.12	85.00		60.00	
832b	Wmkd. USIR	300.00	.80				
833	$2 Warren G. Harding	50.00	6.00	245.00		125.00	
834	$5 Calvin Coolidge	185.00	5.50	925.00		200.00	

This series was in use for approximately 16 years when the Liberty Series began replacing it. Various shades of these stamps are in existence due to the numerous reprintings.

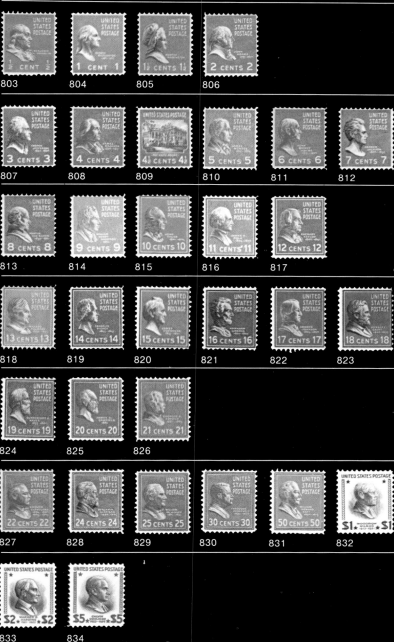

835

836

837

838

852

853

854

855

856

857

858

	Un	U	PB	#	FDC	Q
Issues of 1938, Perf. 11x10½						
835 3¢ Constitution Ratification, June 21	.23	.10	6.00		7.75	73,043,650
Perf. 11						
836 3¢ Swedish-Finnish 300th Anniv.,						
June 27	.23	.11	6.00	(6)	7.75	58,564,368
Perf. 11x10½						
837 3¢ Northwest Territory, July 15	.23	.11	16.50		7.75	65,939,500
838 3¢ Iowa Territory 100th Anniv.,						
Aug. 24	.23	.12	9.50		7.75	47,064,300
Issues of 1939, Coil Stamps, Perf. 10 Vertically						
839 1¢ green Washington (804)	.35	.08			9.00	
840 1½¢ bistre brown						
M. Washington (805)	.35	.09			9.00	
841 2¢ rose car. Adams (806)	.40	.08			9.50	
842 3¢ deep violet Jefferson (807)	.60	.08			10.00	
843 4¢ red violet Madison (808)	9.00	.40			11.00	
844 4½¢ dk. gray White House (809)	.70	.60			11.00	
845 5¢ bright blue Monroe (810)	7.50	.35			12.00	
846 6¢ red orange J.Q. Adams (811)	1.35	.16			12.50	
847 10¢ brown red Tyler (815)	17.00	.55			35.00	
Perf. 10 Horizontally						
848 1¢ green Washington (804)	.80	.12			9.00	
849 1½¢ bistre brown						
M. Washington (805)	1.35	.45			9.00	
850 2¢ rose car. Adams (806)	3.00	.45			10.00	
851 3¢ deep violet Jefferson (807)	2.50	.40			10.00	
Perf. 10½x11						
852 3¢ Golden Gate Exposition, Feb. 18	.13	.09	1.65		6.75	114,439,600
853 3¢ New York World's Fair, Apr. 1	.15	.09	2.00		7.00	101,699,550
Perf. 11						
854 3¢ Washington's Inauguration,						
Apr. 30	.32	.11	4.75	(6)	6.75	72,764,550
Perf. 11x10½						
855 3¢ Baseball Anniversary						
100th, June 12	.25	.10	3.50		14.00	81,269,600
Perf. 11						
856 3¢ Panama Canal, Aug. 15	.25	.10	6.00	(6)	6.75	67,813,350
Perf. 10½x11						
857 3¢ 300th Anniv. of Printing, Sept. 25	.13	.10	1.65		6.75	71,394,750
Perf. 11x10½						
858 3¢ 50th Anniv. of Statehood,						
Nov. 2	.13	.10	1.65		6.25	66,835,000

		Un	U	PB	#	FDC	Q
	Famous Americans Issue, 1940, Perf. 10½x11						
	Authors						
859	1¢ Washington Irving	.10	.10	1.25		1.65	56,348,320
860	2¢ James Fenimore Cooper	.11	.10	1.50		1.75	53,177,110
861	3¢ Ralph Waldo Emerson	.12	.09	2.25		2.00	53,260,270
862	5¢ Louisa May Alcott	.33	.30	14.00		5.00	22,104,950
863	10¢ Samuel L. Clemens						
	(Mark Twain)	2.25	2.25	65.00		8.25	13,201,270
	Poets						
864	1¢ Henry W. Longfellow	.12	.12	1.85		1.65	51,603,580
865	2¢ John Greenleaf Whitier	.11	.11	2.25		1.65	52,100,510
866	3¢ James Russell Lowell	.16	.09	4.00		1.75	51,666,580
867	5¢ Walt Whitman	.37	.33	.14.00		4.50	22,207,780
868	10¢ James Whitcomb Riley	3.15	2.65	65.00		8.25	11,835,530
	Educators						
869	1¢ Horace Mann	.10	.10	1.85		1.65	52,471,160
870	2¢ Mark Hopkins	.11	.09	1.65		1.65	52,366,440
871	3¢ Charles W. Eliot	.27	.09	3.75		1.75	51,636,270
872	5¢ Frances E. Willard	.55	.33	15.00		4.75	20,729,030
873	10¢ Booker T. Washington	2.35	2.00	40.00		8.25	14,125,580
	Scientists						
874	1¢ John James Audubon	.10	.09	1.50		1.65	59,409,000
875	2¢ Dr. Crawford W. Long	.11	.09	1.30		1.65	57,888,600
876	3¢ Luther Burbank	.12	.09	1.75		1.75	58,273,180
877	5¢ Dr. Walter Reed	.27	.25	12.00		4.50	23,779,000
878	10¢ Jane Addams	1.85	1.65	40.00		8.25	15,112,580

JANE ADDAMS

Jane Addams was convinced that the way to help the poor was to live among them. In 1889, at the age of 28, this social reformer rented a decaying mansion in the slums of Chicago and declared herself "at home" to neighbors.

Four years later, Hull House was the center of some 40 programs and activities, including a day nursery, gymnasium, dispensary and cooperative boarding house for working women. More than 2,000 people crossed its threshold every week.

But gradually Jane Addams realized that social services alone were not enough to meet the deep-seated problems of her neighborhood. She became a champion of the labor movement and entered the political fray.

Like many of the educators she gathered around her at Hull House, Jane Addams believed in learning by doing. On one occasion, to find out why the neighborhood garbage wasn't being picked up adequately, she got herself appointed garbage inspector. For some time she arose each morning at six to follow the annoyed collector on his rounds.

During many of her 46 years at Hull House, Jane Addams was attacked for her social reforms and for her opposition to World War I. But gradually the criticism turned to admiration, and then to honors when in 1931 she shared the Nobel Peace Prize. See Scott No. 878.

9   860   861   862   863

4   865   866   867   868

9   870   871   872   873

4   875   876   877   878

879

880

881

882

883

884

885

886

887

888

889

890

891

892

893

894

895

896

897

		Un	U	PB	#	FDC	Q
	1940 continued						
	Composers						
879	1¢ Stephen Collins Foster	.10	.10	1.50		1.65	57,322,790
880	2¢ John Philip Sousa	.15	.10	1.50		1.65	58,281,580
881	3¢ Victor Herbert	.15	.09	2.00		1.90	56,398,790
882	5¢ Edward MacDowell	.55	.30	15.00		4.50	21,147,000
883	10¢ Ethelbert Nevin	5.00	2.35	60.00		7.75	13,328,000
	Artists						
884	1¢ Gilbert Charles Stuart	.10	.09	1.10		1.65	54,389,510
885	2¢ James A. McNeill Whistler	.11	.10	1.10		1.65	53,636,580
886	3¢ Augustus Saint-Gaudens	.12	.09	1.25		1.75	55,313,230
887	5¢ Daniel Chester French	.40	.22	12.50		4.00	21,720,580
888	10¢ Frederic Remington	2.80	2.35	50.00		7.75	13,600,580
	Inventors						
889	1¢ Eli Whitney	.12	.11	3.00		1.65	47,599,580
890	2¢ Samuel F. B. Morse	.12	.10	1.75		1.65	53,766,510
891	3¢ Cyrus Hall McCormick	.20	.09	2.75		1.75	54,193,580
892	5¢ Elias Howe	1.35	.40	25.00		5.00	20,264,580
893	10¢ Alexander Graham Bell	16.00	3.35	145.00		13.50	13,726,580
	Issues of 1940, Perf. 11x10½						
894	3¢ Pony Express, Apr. 3	.45	.18	7.50		5.50	46,497,400
	Perf. 10½x11						
895	3¢ Pan American Union, Apr. 14	.38	.13	7.00		4.75	47,700,000
	Perf. 11x10½						
896	3¢ Idaho Statehood,						
	50th Anniversary, July 3	.20	.11	3.75		4.75	50,618,150
	Perf. 10½x11						
897	3¢ Wyoming Statehood,						
	50th Anniversary, July 10	.20	.11	3.25		4.75	50,034,400
	Perf. 11x10½						
898	3¢ Coronado Expedition, Sept. 7	.20	.11	3.25		4.75	60,943,700
	National Defense Issue, Oct. 16						
899	1¢ Statue of Liberty	.08	.08	.60		4.25	
900	2¢ Anti-aircraft Gun	.09	.08	.70		4.25	
901	3¢ Torch of Enlightenment	.12	.08	1.40		4.25	
	Perf. 10½x11						
902	3¢ Thirteenth Amendment,						
	Oct. 20	.25	.15	8.25		5.00	44,389,550

		Un	U	PB	#	FDC	Q
	Issue of 1941, Perf. 11x10½						
903	3¢ Vermont Statehood, Mar. 4	.20	.10	2.75		4.00	54,574,550
	Issues of 1942						
904	3¢ Kentucky Statehood, June 1	.18	.10	2.25		4.00	63,558,400
905	3¢ Win the War, July 4	.09	.05	.60		3.75	
906	5¢ Chinese Resistance, July 7	.35	.25	25.00		5.75	21,272,800
	Issues of 1943						
907	2¢ Allied Nations, Jan. 14	.07	.05	.50		3.25	1,671,564,200
908	1¢ Four Freedoms, Feb. 12	.06	.05	1.00		3.25	1,227,334,200
	Overrun Countries Issue, 1943-44, Perf. 12						
909	5¢ Poland, June 22	.25	.22	15.00		6.50	19,999,646
910	5¢ Czechoslovakia, July 12	.30	.18	6.00		5.00	19,999,646
911	5¢ Norway, July 27	.18	.15	3.50		4.50	19,999,646
912	5¢ Luxembourg, Aug. 10	.18	.15	3.50		4.50	19,999,646
913	5¢ Netherlands, Aug. 24	.18	.15	3.50		4.50	19,999,646
914	5¢ Belgium, Sept. 14	.18	.15	3.50		4.25	19,999,646
915	5¢ France, Sept. 28	.18	.15	3.50		4.25	19,999,646
916	5¢ Greece, Oct. 12	.85	.45	25.00		4.25	14,999,646
917	5¢ Yugoslavia, Oct. 26	.45	.30	14.00		4.25	14,999,646
918	5¢ Albania, Nov. 9	.45	.30	8.50		4.25	14,999,646
919	5¢ Austria, Nov. 23	.30	.30	8.50		4.25	14,999,646
920	5¢ Denmark, Dec. 7	.45	.40	10.00		4.25	14,999,646
921	5¢ Korea, Nov. 2, 1944	.25	.25	12.50		6.00	14,999,646

LUXEMBOURG

If you wanted to make a movie about kings and knights riding out from magnificent castles to do battle, you'd surely find the perfect location in Luxembourg, one of the smallest and proudest of the European states. Numerous castles dating from the 8th to the 16th centuries rise majestically from Luxembourg's rocky hills and pine forests. The castles are romantic, but they are built primarily as fortresses and are reminders of the many wars tiny Luxembourg has fought to remain independent and free.

Surrounded by European countries that would eventually become France, Germany and Belgium, Luxembourg was overrun and partitioned time and again.

Centuries of occupation did not dim the people's passion for independence. In World War I, Wilhelm II of Germany overran the country and in World War II, Adolph Hitler's Nazis invaded. Thousands of Luxembourgers escaped to enlist with Allied forces, and the country's rulers set up a government in exile. In 1945, the Battle of the Bulge, the last attempt to push the Allies back from German territory, was fought on Luxembourg soil. The devastation was monstrous.

But the proud Luxembourgers rebuilt their country. Today, in addition to the parapets and ramparts of ancient castles, you can see the stacks of mills and other industry in Luxembourg, which has taken its place as an economically strong member of the European Common Market. Only 999 square miles in size, tiny Luxembourg reminds us of the struggles of people to be free–from the times of knights and castles, to the present. See Scott No. 912.

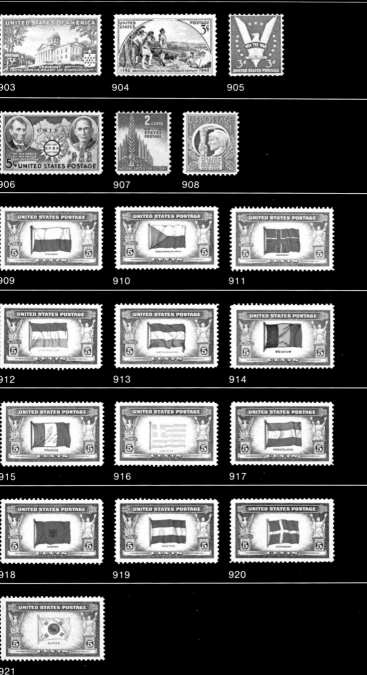

903

904

905

906

907

908

909

910

911

912

913

914

915

916

917

918

919

920

921

922 923 924

925 926 927

928 930

929

931 932 933

934 935 936 937

		Un	U	PB	#	FDC	Q
	Issues of 1944, Perf. 11x10½						
922	3¢ Transcontinental Railroad, May 10	.10	.10	2.00		5.50	61,303,000
923	3¢ Steamship, May 22	.10	.10	2.50		4.00	61,001,450
924	3¢ Telegraph, May 24	.10	.10	1.60		2.50	60,605,000
925	3¢ Philippines, Sept. 27	.10	.10	3.00		2.50	50,129,350
926	3¢ 50th Anniversary of						
	Motion Picture, Oct. 31	.10	.10	2.00		2.75	53,479,400
	Issues of 1945						
927	3¢ Florida Statehood, Mar. 3	.10	.09	1.00		2.50	61,617,350
928	5¢ United Nations Conference,						
	Apr. 25	.13	.07	.70		2.25	75,500,000
	Perf. 10½x11						
929	3¢ Iwo Jima (Marines), July 11	.10	.07	.60		3.00	137,321,000
	Issues of 1945-46, Perf. 11x10½						
	Franklin D. Roosevelt Issue						
930	1¢ F.D.R. and home at Hyde Park	.05	.05	.30		2.25	128,140,000
931	2¢ Roosevelt and "Little						
	White House", Ga.	.07	.07	.50		2.25	67,255,000
932	3¢ Roosevelt and White House	.10	.06	.55		2.25	133,870,000
933	5¢ F.D.R., Globe and						
	Four Freedoms, 1946	.13	.07	.75		2.25	76,455,400
934	3¢ U.S. Army in Paris, Sept. 28	.10	.06	.50		2.25	128,357,750
935	3¢ U.S. Navy, Oct. 27	.10	.06	.50		2.25	135,863,000
936	3¢ U.S. Coast Guard, Nov. 10	.10	.06	.50		2.25	111,616,700
937	3¢ Alfred E. Smith, Nov. 26	.10	.05	.50		2.25	308,587,700

ALFRED SMITH

Millions of Americans remember Al Smith as a symbol of the fabulous 20s—the years of good times, F. Scott Fitzgerald and the Dempsey fights. In fact, the philosophy of the four-time governor of New York was squarely at odds with the jazz era: he was a devoutly religious family man who never went to nightclubs.

But Al Smith had a gift for politics and people. He made friends with Tom Foley, a Tammany Hall leader, and at the age of 30 was elected to the New York legislature.

Spending his nights in a cheap boardinghouse trying to understand bills before the Assembly, he learned well and he learned fast. Smith became a shrewd and humorous campaigner, and in 1918 was elected to the first of four terms as New York's governor.

Smith's fame spread, and in 1924 Franklin Roosevelt put his name in nomination for President. It wasn't his year, but 1928 was. Democrats chose Smith on the first ballot, making him the first Catholic to run for President as a major party nominee.

Smith was badly defeated by Herbert Hoover, winning only eight states. Political analysts said he lost for three reasons: his association with Tammany, his opposition to prohibition, and, above all, his Roman Catholic faith.

The people of New York never forgot Smith. When he died in 1944, more than 200,000 people waited in the rain to pass his bronze casket. The next morning, 7,000 jammed St. Patrick's Cathedral, and 35,000 more clogged the streets—one of the greatest crowds ever assembled for a New York funeral. See Scott No. 937.

		Un	U	PB	#	FDC	Q
	1945-46 continued						
938	3¢ Texas Statehood, Dec. 29	.10	.06	.50		2.25	170,640,000
	Issues of 1946						
939	3¢ Merchant Marine, Feb. 26	.10	.05	.50		2.25	135,927,000
940	3¢ Veterans of World War II, May 9	.10	.05	.55		2.25	260,339,100
941	3¢ Tennessee Statehood, June 1	.10	.05	.50		2.25	132,274,500
942	3¢ Iowa Statehood, Aug. 3	.10	.05	.50		2.25	132,430,000
943	3¢ Smithsonian Institution, Aug. 10	.10	.05	.50		2.25	139,209,500
944	3¢ Kearny Expedition, Oct. 16	.10	.05	.50		2.25	114,684,450
	Issues of 1947, Perf. 10½x11						
945	3¢ Thomas A. Edison, Feb. 11	.10	.05	.50		2.25	156,540,510
	Perf. 11x10½						
946	3¢ Joseph Pulitzer, Apr. 10	.10	.05	.50		2.25	120,452,600
947	3¢ 100th Anniv. of the						
	Postage Stamp, May 17	.10	.05	.50		2.25	127,104,300
	Imperf.						
948	Souvenir sheet of two, May 19	1.60	1.10			3.00	10,299,600
948a	5¢ blue, single stamp (1)	.50	.30				
948b	10¢ brn. org., single stamp (2)	.70	.40				

Issued in sheets of two with marginal inscription commemorating the 100th anniversary of U.S. postage stamps and the Centenary International Philatelic Exhibition, held in New York in 1947.

		Un	U	PB	#	FDC	Q
	Perf. 11x10½						
949	3¢ Doctors, June 9	.10	.05	.50		1.25	132,902,000
950	3¢ Utah, July 24	.10	.05	.50		1.25	131,968,000
951	3¢ U.S. Frigate Constitution, Oct. 21	.10	.05	.50		2.00	131,488,000
	Perf. 10½x11						
952	3¢ Everglades Nat'l Park, Dec. 5	.10	.05	.50		1.25	122,362,000

EVERGLADES

"A man can't live in the Everglades," the Kingston Trio sang a few years back. Nevertheless, life abounds. Among the 4,000 square miles of marshland at Florida's southern tip live countless species of animals and plants—along with a small but determined number of Seminole Indians.

For the Everglades is not just a big swamp, but a dynamic ecology of land and water communities. In the changing balances of flood and fire, fresh and salt water, rainy seasons and drought, the glades have formed several different "life zones," or ecosystems.

The Everglades is best known for its abundance of birdlife, especially wading birds such as herons, egrets and roseate spoonbills (often mistaken for flamingos, which rarely visit south Florida). Many rare and endangered species of animals find refuge here—including the southern bald eagle, the Florida panther, the shy manatee and the Everglades mink.

The most illustrious citizen of the Everglades, however, is the alligator, "the keeper of the Everglades." Not long ago, the alligator was fighting a losing battle against poachers, who prized it for its valuable skin. But under nationwide protection, the alligator has staged a stunning comeback—amd most types have now been removed from the endangered species list. See Scott No. 952.

938

939

940

941

942

943

944

945

946

947

949

948

950

951

953

954

955

956

957

958

959

960

961

962

963

964

965

966

967

968

		Un	U	PB	#	FDC	Q
	Issues of 1948						
953	3¢ Dr. George Washington Carver,						
	Jan. 5	.10	.05	.50		1.25	121,548,000
	Perf. 11x10½						
954	3¢ Calif. Gold 100th Anniversary,						
	Jan. 24	.10	.05	.50		1.25	131,109,500
955	3¢ Mississippi Territory, Apr. 7	.10	.05	.50		1.25	122,650,500
956	3¢ Four Chaplains, May 28	.10	.05	.50		1.75	121,953,500
957	3¢ Wisconsin Statehood, May 29	.10	.05	.50		1.25	115,250,000
958	5¢ Swedish Pioneer, June 4	.13	.09	1.00		1.25	64,198,500
959	3¢ Progress of Women, July 19	.10	.05	.50		1.25	117,642,500
	Perf. 10½x11						
960	3¢ William Allen White, July 31	.10	.06	.60		1.25	77,649,600
	Perf. 11x10½						
961	3¢ U.S.-Canada Friendship, Aug. 2	.10	.05	.50		1.25	113,474,500
962	3¢ Francis Scott Key, Aug. 9	.10	.05	.50		1.25	120,868,500
963	3¢ Salute to Youth, Aug. 11	.10	.05	.50		1.25	77,800,500
964	3¢ Oregon Territory, Aug. 14	.10	.08	1.20		1.25	52,214,000
	Perf. 10½x11						
965	3¢ Harlan Fiske Stone, Aug. 25	.10	.08	2.75		1.25	53,958,100
966	3¢ Palomar Mt. Obs., Aug. 30	.12	.08	4.00		1.75	61,120,010
	Perf. 11x10½						
967	3¢ Clara Barton, Sept. 7	.10	.08	.60		1.25	57,823,000
968	3¢ Poultry Industry, Sept. 9	.10	.08	.80		1.25	52,975,000

WILLIAM ALLEN WHITE

Forty years ago, William Allen White was one of the most famous men in the country, a prize-winning journalist widely recognized as the leading spokesman for small-town, middle-class America. The son of an easygoing, freethinking Democrat and a stern, radical Republican mother, White learned early in life a tolerance for contrary views. In fact, for much of his life, White's public politics were at odds with his private beliefs.

For example, in 1936, White privately admitted that Franklin D. Roosevelt was better fit for the White House than Republican candidate Alf Landon, governor of White's home state of Kansas. Yet White, a Republican, not only endorsed Landon but used his considerable skills to develop campaign literature for the governor.

A few days before the election, a newspaper syndicate asked White to write a story for release if Landon won. White's ironic reply was characteristic:

"You have a quaint sense of humor," White wrote the syndicate. "If Landon is elected I'll write you a book about him, bind it in platinum, illustrate it with apples of gold and pictures of silver, and won't charge you a cent." See Scott No. 960.

		Un	U	PB	#	FDC	Q
	1948 continued						
	Perf. 10½ x 11						
969	3¢ Gold Star Mothers, Sept. 21	.10	.07	.65		1.25	77,149,000
970	3¢ Fort Kearny, Sept. 22	.10	.07	.65		1.25	58,332,000
971	3¢ Volunteer Firemen, Oct. 4	.10	.07	.75		· 1.25	56,228,000
972	3¢ Five Indian Tribes, Oct. 15	.10	.07	.75		1.25	57,832,000
973	3¢ Rough Riders, Oct. 27	.10	.08	1.20		1.25	53,875,000
974	3¢ Juliette Low, Oct. 29	.10	.07	.65		1.25	63,834,000
	Perf. 10½ x 11						
.975	3¢ Will Rogers, Nov. 4	.10	.07	1.00		1.25	67,162,200
976	3¢ Fort Bliss 100th Anniv., Nov. 5	.15	.08	5.25		1.25	64,561,000
	Perf. 11 x 10½						
977	3¢ Moina Michael, Nov. 9	.10	.07	.65		1.25	64,079,500
978	3¢ Gettysburg Address, Nov. 19	.10	.08	.70		1.25	63,388,000
	Perf. 10½ x 11						
979	3¢ American Turners, Nov. 20	.10	.08	.65		1.25	62,285,000
980	3¢ Joel Chandler Harris, Dec. 9	.10	.08	.75		1.25	57,492,610

ROUGH RIDERS

They came to Cuba in 1898–cowpunchers, ranchmen, hunters, professional gamblers and rascals of every sort. They joined with former football players, college boys and society men from fashionable eastern circles. They sweated in khaki pants and scratchy blue wool shirts, when they could get them. They ate tainted food when they had to and suffered from malaria, fever and fatigue. And they followed Theodore Roosevelt when he led them, fearlessly, up San Juan Hill.

The American press called them the Rough Riders, and they came to Cuba that sweltering summer to fight in the Spanish-American War to free Cuba from Spain. Teddy Roosevelt (who would become President of the U.S. in three years) had left his position as Secretary of the Navy and had been made a Colonel in the Army. He wanted to fight, and the Rough Riders wanted to fight with him.

On July 1 and 2, riding on horseback, Roosevelt led the Rough Riders as they scrambled up San Juan Hill, defying the Spanish soldiers spraying them with Gatling guns. More than 500 men stormed up the hill in waves, and 89 were killed and wounded in the effort. The American press hailed Teddy Roosevelt and his Rough Riders as heroes–but they were not the only heroes that day on San Juan Hill.

The 9th Cavalry and 10th Cavalry units, Black regiments (this was long before the U.S. forces were integrated), were also part of the 1st Brigade stationed near San Juan Hill. They were waiting for orders to take the hill when an impatient Teddy Roosevelt led his Rough Riders right through the 9th and on to San Juan Hill. The 9th and 10th were ordered to follow him and to lend support.

Later, a white soldier who had served under Roosevelt wrote to the Washington Post *that if it had not been for the Black cavalry, the Rough Riders would have been exterminated.*

To many, this joint effort, not so very long after the devastation of the U.S. Civil War, seemed an act of national and racial reconciliation.

Later, some of the Rough Riders petitioned the War Department to promote the Blacks of the 9th and 10th who served so bravely. During World War I, 62 of the noncommissioned officers of the 10th were commissioned, 20 of them as captains. See Scott No. 973.

969

970

971

972

973

974

975

976

977

978

979

980

981

982

983

984

985

986

987

988

989

990

991

992

993

994

995

996

997

998

999

1000

1001

1002

		Un	U	PB	#	FDC	Q
	Issues of 1949, Perf. 11x10½						
981	3¢ Minnesota Territory, Mar. 3	.10	.05	.50		1.25	99,190,000
982	3¢ Washington & Lee University,						
	Apr. 12	.10	.05	.50		1.25	104,790,000
983	3¢ Puerto Rico Election, Apr. 27	.10	.05	.50		1.50	108,805,000
984	3¢ Annapolis 300th Anniv., May 23	.10	.05	.50		1.25	107,340,000
985	3¢ Grand Army of the Republic,						
	Aug. 29	.10	.05	.50		1.25	117,020,000
	Perf. 10½x11						
986	3¢ Edgar Allan Poe, Oct. 7	.10	.05	.60		1.25	122,633,000
	Issues of 1950, Perf. 11x10½						
987	3¢ American Bankers Association,						
	Jan. 3	.10	.05	.50		1.25	130,960,00
	Perf. 10½x11						
988	3¢ Samuel Gompers, Jan. 27	.10	.05	.55		1.25	128,478,000
	National Capital 150th Anniv. Issue, Perf. 10½x11, 11x10½						
989	3¢ Statue of Freedom	.10	.05	.50		1.25	132,090,000
990	3¢ Executive Mansion	.10	.05	.50		1.25	130,050,000
991	3¢ Supreme Court Building	.10	.05	.50		1.25	131,350,000
992	3¢ U.S. Capitol Building	.10	.05	.50		1.25	129,980,000
	Perf. 11x10½						
993	3¢ Railroad Engineers, Apr. 29	.10	.05	.50		1.25	122,315,000
994	3¢ Kansas City, Mo., June 3	.10	.05	.50		1.25	122,170,000
995	3¢ Boy Scouts, June 30	.10	.06	.55		1.25	131,635,000
996	3¢ Indian Territory, July 4	.10	.05	.50		1.25	121,860,000
997	3¢ California Statehood, Sept. 9	.10	.05	.50		1.25	121,120,000
	Issues of 1951						
998	3¢ Confederate Veterans, May 30	.10	.05	.50		1.25	119,120,000
999	3¢ Nevada 100th Anniv., July 14	.10	.05	.50		1.25	112,125,000
1000	3¢ Landing of Cadillac, July 24	.10	.05	.50		1.25	114,140,000
1001	3¢ Colorado Statehood, Aug. 1	.10	.05	.50		1.25	114,490,000
1002	3¢ American Chem. Society,						
	Sept. 4	.10	.05	.50		1.25	117,200,000

		Un	U	PB	#	FDC	Q
	1951 continued						
1003	3¢ Battle of Brooklyn, Dec. 10	.10	.05	.50		1.25	116,130,000
	Issues of 1952						
1004	3¢ Betsy Ross, Jan. 2	.10	.05	.50		1.25	116,175,000
1005	3¢ 4-H Club, Jan. 15	.10	.05	.50		1.25	115,945,000
1006	3¢ B&O Railroad, Feb. 28	.11	.05	.50		2.00	112,540,000
1007	3¢ American Auto. Assn., Mar. 4	.10	.05	.50		.85	117,415,000
1008	3¢ NATO, Apr. 4	.10	.03	.55		.85	2,899,580,000
1009	3¢ Grand Coulee Dam, May 15	.10	.05	.50		.85	114,540,000
1010	3¢ General Lafayette, June 13	.10	.05	.50		.85	113,135,000
	Perf. 10½x11						
1011	3¢ Mt. Rushmore Mem., Aug. 11	.10	.05	.50		.85	116,255,000
	Perf. 11x10½						
1012	3¢ Engineering, Sept. 6	.10	.05	.50		.85	113,860,000
1013	3¢ Service Women, Sept. 11	.10	.05	.50		.85	124,260,000
1014	3¢ Gutenberg Bible, Sept. 30	.10	.05	.50		.85	115,735,000
1015	3¢ Newspaper Boys, Oct. 4	.10	.05	.50		.85	115,430,000
1016	3¢ Red Cross, Nov. 21	.10	.05	.50		.85	136,220,000
	Issues of 1953						
1017	3¢ National Guard, Feb. 23	.10	.05	.50		.85	114,894,600
1018	3¢ Ohio Statehood, Mar. 2	.10	.05	1.00		.85	118,706,000
1019	3¢ Washington Territory, Mar. 2	.10	.05	.55		.85	114,190,000
1020	3¢ Louisiana Purchase, Apr. 30	.10	.05	.50		.85	113,990,000
1021	5¢ Opening of Japan 100th Anniv.,						
	July 14	.13	.07	2.00		.85	89,289,600
1022	3¢ American Bar Assn., Aug. 24	.10	.05	.50		.85	114,865,000
1023	3¢ Sagamore Hill, Sep. 14	.10	.05	.50		1.00	115,780,000
1024	3¢ Future Farmers, Oct. 13	.10	.05	.50		.85	115,244,600

LAFAYETTE

The Marquis de Lafayette's love affair with America began when the Frenchman was nineteen years old; it lasted far into his old age.

Marie Joseph Paul Yves Roch Gilbert du Motier, Marquis de Lafayette, sailed his privately owned ship to America in the summer of 1777 to volunteer his services to General George Washington. Almost 50 years later, as a "National Guest" in 1824, Lafayette was accorded one of the most memorable parades in the history of Pennsylvania Avenue. The following spring, when Lafayette was about to return to Europe, huge crowds again turned out.

"In a sense," wrote historian Mary Cable, "it was more than a farewell to the great Frenchman; it was a farewell to the ties of the Revolution, the days of rule by gentlemen-born . . . that unique eighteenth-century American combination of court-liness and simplicity."

Lafayette wept, embraced President John Quincy Adams, and said goodbye to a nation he had cherished for a lifetime: "Adieu, adieu, grand et cher ami!" See Scott No. 1010.

1003

1004

1005

1006

1007

1008

1009

1010

1011

1012

1013

1014

1015

1016

1017

1018

1019

1020

1021

1022

1023

1024

1025

1026

1027

1028

1029

1030

1031

1031A

1032

1033

1034

1035

1036

1037

1038

1039

1040

1041

1042

1042A

1043

1044

1044A

1045

1046

1047

1048

1049

		Un	U	PB	#	FDC	Q
	1953 continued						
1025	3¢ Trucking Industry, Oct. 27	.10	.05	.50		.85	123,709,600
1026	3¢ General Patton, Nov. 11	.11	.05	.50		.85	114,798,600
1027	3¢ New York City						
	300th Anniversary, Nov. 20	.10	.05	.50		.85	115,759,600
1028	3¢ Gadsden Purchase, Dec. 30	.10	.05	.50		.85	116,134,600
	Issues of 1954						
1029	3¢ Columbia University 200th Anniv.,						
	Jan. 4	.10	.05	.50		.85	118,540,000
	Liberty Issue, 1954-68, Perf. 11x10½, 10½x11						
1030	½¢ Benjamin Franklin, 1955	.05	.05	.30		.85	Unlimited
1031	1¢ George Washington, 1954	.05	.05	.25		.85	
1031A	1¼¢ Palace of the Governors,						
	Santa Fe, 1960	.06	.05	1.75		.85	
1032	1½¢ Mount Vernon, 1956	.07	.07	7.50		.60	
1033	2¢ Thomas Jefferson, 1954	.06	.05	.25		.60	
1034	2½¢ Bunker Hill Monument						
	and Massachusetts flag, 1959	.08	.06	2.00		.60	
1035	3¢ Statue of Liberty, 1954	.08	.05	.40		.60	
1035a	Booklet pane of 6	3.75	—				
1036	4¢ Abraham Lincoln, 1954	.10	.05	.50		.60	
1036a	Booklet pane of 6	3.50	—				
1037	4½¢ The Hermitage, 1959	.12	.06	1.75		.60	
1038	5¢ James Monroe, 1954	.15	.05	.75		.60	
1039	6¢ Theodore Roosevelt, 1955	.45	.05	1.75		.65	
1040	7¢ Woodrow Wilson, 1956	.22	.05	1.50		.70	
	Perf. 11						
1041	8¢ Statue of Liberty, 1954	.22	.06	5.75		.80	
1042	8¢ Statue of Liberty, redrawn, 1958	.27	.05	1.75		.60	
	Perf. 11x10½, 10½x11						
1042A	8¢ John J. Pershing, 1961	.25	.05	1.50		.60	
1043	9¢ The Alamo, 1956	.27	.05	1.50		.90	
1044	10¢ Independence Hall, 1956	.28	.05	1.65		.90	
	Perf. 11						
1044A	11¢ Statue of Liberty, 1961	.30	.07	1.50		.90	
	Perf. 11x10½, 10½x11						
1045	12¢ Benjamin Harrison, 1959	.45	.05	2.50		.90	
1046	15¢ John Jay, 1958	.75	.05	2.75		1.00	
1047	20¢ Monticello, 1956	.70	.05	4.50		1.20	
1048	25¢ Paul Revere, 1958	2.75	.05	14.00		1.30	
1049	30¢ Robert E. Lee, 1955	1.60	.06	11.00		1.50	

	1954-68 Liberty Issue continued	Un	U	PB	#	FDC	Q
1050	40¢ John Marshall, 1955	3.75	.06	19.00		1.75	
1051	50¢ Susan B. Anthony, 1955	3.50	.05	20.00		6.00	
1052	$1 Patrick Henry, 1955	13.50	.07	75.00		11.00	
	Perf. 11						
1053	$5 Alexander Hamilton, 1956	125.00	6.00	725.00		75.00	
	Coil Stamps, Perf. 10 Vertically						
1054	1¢ dark green Washington						
	(1031), -54	.30	.06			.75	
	Perf. 10 Horizontally						
1054A	1¼¢ turquoise, Palace of the						
	Governors, Santa Fe (1031A), -1960	.30	.15			.90	
	Perf. 10 Vertically						
1055	2¢ rose carmine Jefferson (1033), -54	.06	.05			.75	
1056	2½¢ gray blue, Bunker Hill Monument						
	and Massachusetts flag (1034), -59	.35	.20			1.20	
1057	3¢ deep violet Statue of Liberty						
	(1035), 1954	.10	.05			.75	
1058	4¢ red violet Lincoln (1036), 1958	.15	.05			.75	
	Perf. 10 Horizontally						
1059	4½¢ blue green Hermitage						
	(1037), -59	2.25	.95			1.20	
	Perf. 10 Vertically						
1059A	25¢ green P. Revere (1048)	.65	.20			1.20	
	Issues of 1954, Perf. 11x10½						
1060	3¢ Nebraska Territory, May 7	.10	.05	.50		.75	115,810,000
1061	3¢ Kansas Territory, May 31	.10	.05	.50		.75	113,603,700
	Perf. 10½x11						
1062	3¢ George Eastman, July 12	.10	.05	.60		.75	128,002,000
	Perf. 11x10½						
1063	3¢ Lewis and Clark Expedition,						
	July 28	.10	.05	.50		.75	116,078,150
	Issues of 1955, Perf. 10½x11						
1064	3¢ Pennsylvania Academy of						
	Fine Arts, Jan. 15	.10	.05	.50		.75	116,139,800
	Perf. 11x10½						
1065	3¢ Land Grant Colleges, Feb. 12	.10	.05	.50		.75	120,484,800
1066	8¢ Rotary International, Feb. 23	.20	.08	1.75		.90	53,854,750
1067	3¢ Armed Forces Reserve, May 21	.10	.05	.50		.75	176,075,000
	Perf. 10½x11						
1068	3¢ New Hampshire, June 21	.10	.05	.50		.75	125,944,400
	Perf. 11x10½						
1069	3¢ Soo Locks, June 28	.10	.05	.50		.75	122,284,600
1070	3¢ Atoms for Peace, July 28	.11	.05	1.25		.75	133,638,850
1071	3¢ Fort Ticonderoga, Sept. 18	.10	.05	.50		.75	118,664,600

1050   1051   1052   1053

1060   1061   1062

1063   1064   1065

1066   1067   1068

1069   1070   1071

1072

1073

1074

1076

1077

1078

1079

080

1081

1082

1083

084

1085

1086

1087

088

1089

1090

1091

		Un	U	PB	#	FDC	Q
	1955 continued						
	Perf. 10½x11						
1072	3¢ Andrew W. Mellon, Dec. 20	.10	.05	.60		.75	112,434,000
	Issues of 1956						
1073	3¢ Benjamin Franklin, Jan. 17	.10	.05	.50		.75	129,384,550
	Perf. 11x10½						
1074	3¢ Booker T. Washington, Apr. 5	.10	.05	.50		.75	121,184,600
	Fifth International Philatelic Exhibition, Souvenir Sheet, Imperf.						
1075	Sheet of 2, Apr. 28	4.65	4.50			7.50	2,900,731
1075a	3¢ deep violet (1035)	2.00	1.75				
1075b	8¢ dk. vio. bl. & car. (1041)	2.25	2.00				
	Perf. 11x10½						
1076	3¢ New York Coliseum and						
	Columbus Monument, Apr. 30	.10	.05	.50		.75	119,784,200
	Wildlife Conservation Issue						
1077	3¢ Wild Turkey, May 5	.11	.05	.65		1.00	123,159,400
1078	3¢ Pronghorn Antelope, June 22	.11	.05	.65		1.00	123,138,800
1079	3¢ King Salmon, Nov. 9	.11	.05	.65		1.00	109,275,000
	Perf. 10½x11						
1080	3¢ Pure Food and Drug Laws,						
	June 27	.10	.05	.50		.80	112,932,200
	Perf. 11x10½						
1081	3¢ Wheatland, Aug. 5	.10	.05	.50		.80	125,475,000
	Perf. 10½x11						
1082	3¢ Labor Day, Sept. 3	.10	.05	.50		.80	117,855,000
	Perf. 11x10½						
1083	3¢ Nassau Hall, Sept. 22	.10	.05	.50		.80	122,100,000
	Perf. 10½x11						
1084	3¢ Devils Tower, Sept. 24	.10	.05	.50		.80	118,180,000
	Perf. 11x10½						
1085	3¢ Children's Issue, Dec. 15	.10	.05	.50		.80	100,975,000
	Issues of 1957						
1086	3¢ Alexander Hamilton, Jan. 11	.10	.05	.50		.80	115,299,450
	Perf. 10½x11						
1087	3¢ Polio, Jan. 15	.10	.05	.50		.80	186,949,627
	Perf. 11x10½						
1088	3¢ Coast and Geodetic Survey, Feb. 11	.10	.05	.50		.80	115,235,000
1089	3¢ Architects, Feb. 23	.10	.05	.50		.80	106,647,500
	Perf. 10½x11						
1090	3¢ Steel Industry, May 22	.10	.05	.50		.80	112,010,000
	Perf. 11x10½						
1091	3¢ Int'l. Naval Review, June 10	.10	.05	.50		.80	118,470,000

SUSAN B. ANTHONY

Susan B. Anthony was never one to duck a court fight—especially to test a law she opposed. She once declared she "would ignore all law to help the slave, and ignore it all to protect an enslaved woman."

Susan B. ignored the law in November 1872, when she and 15 other women voted in the city of Rochester. Their plan was to test whether woman suffrage was legal under the new Fourteenth Amendment, which guaranteed equal protection under the law to all citizens. Anthony was arrested and charged with voting illegally, but her trial was postponed. Naturally, she voted again in the next round of elections.

She and her colleagues used the months before the trial for intensive public education on women's rights. But their campaign came to nothing when the judge delivered an opinion, written before the trial began, directing the jury to find Susan B. Anthony guilty. He did not poll the jury or permit its members to consult together.

Anthony told the judge she would never pay a dollar of her $100 fine, and she never did. No moves were made to enforce her sentence. Consequently, she lost the chance to carry her fight to the Supreme Court. By persistently challenging the law, however, she was instrumental in changing it. By the time she died, in 1906, four states had granted women the right to vote. Fourteen years later, the Nineteenth Amendment extended the privilege to every woman in America. See Scott Nos. 784, 1051.

OVERLAND MAIL

In September, 1858, John Butterfield established the longest stagecoach route in the world to carry mail overland from St. Louis to San Francisco. The Oxbow Route actually began in Tipton, Missouri, and curved southwest, then north some 2,866 miles through Indian and rattlesnake country, desert sun, mountain passes and rivers.

Butterfield's government contract gave him only a year to organize the line. He ordered more than 200 coaches and wagons, plus accessories, and more than 800 horses and mules. The route was divided into nine sections, each with an experienced stageman as agent. Roads and stations had to be built and scores of workers hired in each section. Skeptics insisted it was an impossible task.

Nonetheless, the first stage from St. Louis rolled into San Francisco shortly after dawn on October 10, 1858, just 23½ days after it left Missouri. The coach was more than a day ahead of schedule, and when it pulled up in front of the post office that Sunday morning, no one was there to greet it. A New York reporter who made the historic trip wrote, "I though nobody was ever going to come to take the mail!" The Butterfield Overland Mail was an important step in the development of the West. It pioneered the route and solved many of the problems of the railroad that came after it, which eventually put the stagecoach out of business. See Scott No. 1120.

The Overland mail route ran from St. Louis to San Francisco.

1092

1093

1094

1095

1096

1097

1098

1099

		Un	U	PB	#	FDC	Q
	1957 continued						
1092	3¢ Oklahoma Statehood, June 14	.10	.05	.90		.80	102,230,000
1093	3¢ School Teachers, July 1	.10	.05	.50		.80	102,410,000
	Perf. 11						
1094	4¢ Flag Issue, July 4	.11	.06	.70		.80	84,054,400
	Perf. 10½x11						
1095	3¢ Shipbuilding, Aug. 15	.10	.05	.70		.80	126,266,000
	Perf. 11						
1096	8¢ Champion of Liberty, Aug. 31,						
	Ramon Magsaysay	.20	.10	1.90		.80	39,489,600
	Perf. 10½x11						
1097	3¢ Lafayette, Sept. 6	.10	.05	.50		.80	122,990,000
	Perf. 11						
1098	3¢ Wildlife Conservation, Nov. 22	.10	.05	.65		1.00	174,372,800
	Perf. 10½x11						
1099	3¢ Religious Freedom, Dec. 27	.10	.05	.50		.80	114,365,000

1100

1104

1105

1106

1107

1108

1109

1110

1111

1112

1113

1114

1115

1116

1117

1118

1119

1120

	Un	U	PB	#	FDC	Q
Issues of 1958						
1100 3¢ Gardening-Horticulture, Mar. 15	.10	.05	.50		.80	122,765,200
Perf. 11x10½						
1104 3¢ Brussels Fair, Apr. 17	.10	.05	.50		.80	113,660,200
1105 3¢ James Monroe, Apr. 28	.10	.05	.60		.80	120,196,580
1106 3¢ Minnesota Statehood, May 11	.10	.05	.50		.80	120,805,200
Perf. 11						
1107 3¢ Geophysical Year, May 31	.10	.05	1.50		.80	125,815,200
Perf. 11x10½						
1108 3¢ Gunston Hall, June 12	.10	.05	.50		.80	108,415,200
Perf. 10½x11						
1109 3¢ Mackinac Bridge, June 25	.10	.05	.50		.80	107,195,200
1110 4¢ Champion of Liberty, July 24,						
Simon Bolivar	.11	.05	.60		.80	115,745,280
Perf. 11						
1111 8¢ Champion of Liberty, July 24,						
Simon Bolivar	.20	.14	6.00		.80	39,743,640
Perf. 11x10½						
1112 4¢ Atlantic Cable 100th Anniversary,						
Aug. 15	.11	.05	.50		.80	114,570,200
Lincoln 150th Anniv. Issue, 1958-59, Perf. 10½x11, 11x10½						
1113 1¢ Portrait by George Healy,						
Feb. 12, '59	.05	.05	.40		.80	120,400,200
1114 3¢ Sculptured Head						
by Gutzon Borglum, Feb. 27, '59	.10	.06	.60		.80	91,160,200
1115 4¢ Lincoln and Stephen Douglas						
Debating, Aug. 27, 1958	.11	.05	.55		.80	114,860,200
1116 4¢ Statue in Lincoln Memorial						
by Daniel Chester French,						
May 30, '59	.11	.05	.65		.80	126,500,000
Issues of 1958, Perf. 10½x11						
1117 4¢ Champion of Liberty, Sept. 19,						
Lajos Kossuth	.11	.05	.60		.80	120,561,280
Perf. 11						
1118 8¢ Champion of Liberty, Sept. 19,						
Lajos Kossuth	.20	.10	4.25		.80	44,064,576
Perf. 10½x11						
1119 4¢ Freedom of Press, Sept. 22	.11	.05	.50		.80	118,390,200
Perf. 11x10½						
1120 4¢ Overland Mail, Oct. 10	.11	.05	.50		.80	125,770,200

		Un	U	PB	#	FDC	Q
	1958 continued						
	Perf. 10½x11						
1121	4¢ Noah Webster, Oct. 16	.11	.05	.50		.80	114,114,280
	Perf. 11						
1122	4¢ Forest Conservation, Oct. 27	.11	.05	.60		.80	156,600,200
	Perf. 11x10½						
1123	4¢ Fort Duquesne, Nov. 25	.11	.05	.50		.80	124,200,200
	Issues of 1959						
1124	4¢ Oregon Statehood, Feb. 14	.11	.05	.50		.80	120,740,200
	Perf. 10½x11						
1125	4¢ Champion of Liberty, Feb. 25, José de San Martin	.11	.05	.55		.80	133,623,280
	Perf. 11						
1126	8¢ Champion of Liberty, Feb. 25, José de San Martin	.20	.10	2.25		.80	45,569,088
	Perf. 10½x11						
1127	4¢ NATO, Apr. 1	.11	.05	.50		.80	122,493,280
	Perf. 11x10½						
1128	4¢ Arctic Explorations, Apr. 6	.11	.05	.85		.80	131,260,200
1129	8¢ World Peace through World Trade, Apr. 20	.20	.08	1.50		.80	47,125,200
1130	4¢ Nevada Silver, June 8	.11	.05	.50		.80	123,105,000
	Perf. 11						
1131	4¢ St. Lawrence Seaway, June 26	.11	.05	.50		.80	126,105,050
1132	4¢ 49-Star Flag, July 4	.11	.05	.50		.80	209,170,000
1133	4¢ Soil Conservation, Aug. 26	.11	.05	.65		.80	120,835,000
	Perf. 10½x11						
1134	4¢ Petroleum Industry, Aug. 27	.11	.05	.50		.80	115,715,000
	Perf. 11x10½						
1135	4¢ Dental Health, Sept. 14	.11	.05	.50		.80	118,445,000
	Perf. 10½x11						
1136	4¢ Champion of Liberty, Sept. 29, Ernst Reuter	.11	.05	.60		.80	111,685,000
	Perf. 11						
1137	8¢ Champion of Liberty, Sept. 29, Ernst Reuter	.20	.10	2.25		.80	43,099,200
	Perf. 10½x11						
1138	4¢ Dr. Ephraim McDowell, Dec. 3	.11	.05	.50		.80	115,444,000

1121

1122

1123

1124

1125

1126

1127

1128

1129

1130

1131

1132

1133

1134

1135

1136

1137

1138

1139

1140

1141

1142

1143

1144

1145

1146

1147

1148

1149

1150

1151

1152

		Un	U	PB	#	FDC	Q
	Issues of 1960-61, Perf. 11, American Credo						
1139	4¢ Quotation from Washington's						
	Farewell Address	.13	.05	1.00		.80	126,470,000
1140	4¢ B. Franklin Quotation	.11	.05	1.00		.80	124,560,000
1141	4¢ T. Jefferson Quotation	.14	.05	1.00		.80	115,455,000
1142	4¢ Francis Scott Key Quotation	.14	.05	1.00		.80	122,060,000
1143	4¢ Lincoln Quotation	.16	.05	1.00		.80	120,540,000
1144	4¢ Patrick Henry Quotation, 1961	.16	.05	1.00		.80	113,075,000
1145	4¢ Boy Scout Jubilee, Feb. 8	.11	.05	.50		.80	139,325,000
	Perf. 10½x11						
1146	4¢ Olympic Winter Games, Feb. 18	.11	.05	.50		.80	124,445,000
1147	4¢ Champion of Liberty, Mar. 7,						
	Masaryk	.11	.05	.60		.80	113,792,000
	Perf. 11						
1148	8¢ Champion of Liberty, Masaryk	.20	.10	2.50		.80	44,215,200
	Perf. 11x10½						
1149	4¢ World Refugee Year, Apr. 7	.11	.05	.50		.80	113,195,000
	Perf. 11						
1150	4¢ Water Conservation, Apr. 18	.11	.05	.65		.80	121,805,000
	Perf. 10½x11						
1151	4¢ SEATO, May 31	.11	.05	.50		.80	115,353,000
	Perf. 11x10½						
1152	4¢ American Woman, June 2	.11	.05	.50		.80	111,080,000

GIUSEPPE GARIBALDI

Giuseppe Garibaldi is remembered as a great guerilla leader and the man who united Italy. He might also have commanded Union forces in the War Between the States.

In 1861 rumors were flying on both sides of the Atlantic that the guerilla leader wanted to fight for the Union. A self-serving American consul in Antwerp named James W. Quiggle, acting without authority, wrote to Garibaldi asking if the rumors were true. Garibaldi indicated he was willing to go to America if President Lincoln felt he could be useful.

Useful, indeed! Lincoln and Secretary of State Seward were tantalized by the notion of obtaining Garibaldi's talents, especially after the Union defeat at Bull Run. But before they could muzzle the over-eager Quiggle, he had written to Garibaldi implying that command of the entire Union Army was at stake. This was not the case. The highest rank Lincoln was willing to confer was major general, and so the negotiations fell through. Diplomatic blunders and press leaks killed a second attempt to enlist Garibaldi's services. By the time the Union and Garibaldi were close to agreement, the conflict had shifted from guerrilla warfare to fixed battles along two fronts.

The incident does not seem to have affected Garibaldi's sentiments about the Union or its leader, however. He later gave to one of his grandsons the name of Lincoln. See Scott Nos. 1168-1169.

	1960-61 continued	Un	U	PB	#	FDC	Q
	Perf. 11						
1153	4¢ 50-Star Flag, July 4	.11	.05	.50		.80	153,025,000
	Perf. 11x10½						
1154	4¢ Pony Express 100th Anniv., July 19	.11	.05	.50		.80	119,665,000
	Perf. 10½x11						
1155	4¢ Employ the Handicapped, Aug. 28	.11	.05	.50		.80	117,855,000
1156	4¢ World Forestry Congress, Aug. 29	.11	.05	.50		.80	118,185,000
	Perf. 11						
1157	4¢ Mexican Independence, Sept. 16	.11	.05	.50		.80	112,260,000
1158	4¢ U.S.-Japan Treaty, Sept. 28	.11	.05	.50		.80	125,010,000
	Perf. 10½x11						
1159	4¢ Champion of Liberty, Oct. 8, I.J. Paderewski	.11	.05	.55		.80	119,798,000
	Perf. 11						
1160	8¢ Champion of Liberty, I.J. Paderewski	.20	.10	2.00		.80	42,696,000
	Perf. 10½x11						
1161	4¢ Sen. Taft Memorial, Oct. 10	.11	.05	.50		.80	106,610,000
	Perf. 11x10½						
1162	4¢ Wheels of Freedom, Oct. 15	.11	.05	.50		.80	109,695,000
	Perf. 11						
1163	4¢ Boy's Clubs of America, Oct. 18	.11	.05	.50		.80	123,690,000
1164	4¢ Automated P.O., Oct. 20	.11	.05	.50		.80	123,970,000
	Perf. 10½x11						
1165	4¢ Champion of Liberty, Oct. 26, Baron Gustaf Mannerheim	.11	.05	.55		.80	124,796,000
	Perf. 11						
1166	8¢ Champion of Liberty, Baron Gustaf Mannerheim	.20	.12	2.25		.80	42,076,800
1167	4¢ Camp Fire Girls, Nov. 4	.11	.05	.50		.80	116,210,000
	Perf. 10½x11						
1168	4¢ Champion of Liberty, Nov. 2, Giuseppe Garibaldi	.11	.05	.55		.80	126,252,000
	Perf. 11						
1169	8¢ Champion of Liberty, Giuseppe Garibaldi	.20	.12	2.25		.80	42,746,400
	Perf. 10½x11						
1170	4¢ Sen. George Memorial, Nov. 5	.11	.05	.50		.80	124,117,000
1171	4¢ Andrew Carnegie, Nov. 25	.11	.05	.50		.80	119,840,000
1172	4¢ John Foster Dulles Memorial, Dec. 6	.11	.05	.55		.80	117,187,000
	Perf. 11x10½						
1173	4¢ Echo I—Communications for Peace, Dec. 15	.35	.06	3.50		.80	124,390,000

153

1154

1155

1156

157

1158

1159

1160

1161

1162

1163

1164

165

1166

1167

1168

1169

1170

1171

1172

1173

1174

1175

1176

1177

1178

1179

1180

1181

1182

1183

1184

1185

1186

1187

1188

1189

1190

1191

		Un	U	PB	#	FDC	Q
	Issues of 1961, Perf. 10½x11						
1174	4¢ Champion of Liberty, Jan. 26,						
	Mahatma Gandhi	.11	.05	.55		.80	112,966,000
	Perf. 11						
1175	8¢ Champion of Liberty,						
	Mahatma Gandhi	.20	.10	2.25		.80	41,644,200
1176	4¢ Range Conservation, Feb. 2	.11	.05	.65		.80	110,850,000
	Perf. 10½x11						
1177	4¢ Horace Greeley, Feb. 3	.11	.05	.55		.80	98,616,000
	Civil War 100th Anniv. Issue, 1961-1965, Perf. 11x10½						
1178	4¢ Fort Sumter Centenary, 1961	.15	.05	1.25		1.25	101,125,000
1179	4¢ Shiloh Centenary, 1962	.11	.05	1.00		1.25	124,865,000
	Perf. 11						
1180	5¢ Gettysburg Centenary, 1963	.13	.05	1.00		1.25	79,905,000
1181	5¢ Wilderness Centenary, 1964	.13	.05	1.00		1.25	125,410,000
1182	5¢ Appomattox Centenary, 1965	.13	.05	1.10		1.25	112,845,000
	Issue dates: #1178, Apr. 12, 1961; #1179, Apr. 7, 1962; #1180, July 1, 1963; #1181, May 5, 1964; #1182, Apr. 9, 1965.						
	Issues of 1961						
1183	4¢ Kansas Statehood, May 10	.11	.05	.60		.75	106,210,000
	Perf. 11x10½						
1184	4¢ Sen. George W. Norris, July 11	.11	.05	.55		.75	110,810,000
1185	4¢ Naval Aviation, Aug. 20	.11	.05	.55		.90	116,995,000
	Perf. 10½x11						
1186	4¢ Workmen's Comp., Sept. 4	.11	.05	.55		.75	121,015,000
	Perf. 11						
1187	4¢ Frederic Remington, Oct. 4	.13	.05	1.20		.75	111,600,000
	Perf. 10½x11						
1188	4¢ Republic of China, Oct. 10	.11	.05	.55		.75	110,620,000
1189	4¢ Naismith-Basketball, Nov. 6	.11	.05	.55		.90	109,110,000
	Perf. 11						
1190	4¢ Nursing, Dec. 28	.11	.05	.70		.75	145,350,000
	Issues of 1962						
1191	4¢ New Mexico Statehood, Jan. 6	.11	.05	.55		.75	112,870,000

		Un	U	PB	#	FDC	Q
	1962 continued						
1192	4¢ Arizona Statehood, Feb. 14	.11	.05	1.00		.75	121,820,000
1193	4¢ Project Mercury, Feb. 20	.11	.05	1.50		1.50	289,240,000
1194	4¢ Malaria Eradication, Mar. 30	.11	.05	.55		.75	120,155,000
	Perf. 10½x11						
1195	4¢ Charles Evans Hughes, Apr. 11	.11	.05	.55		.75	124,595,000
	Perf. 11						
1196	4¢ Seattle World's Fair, Apr. 25	.11	.05	.70		.75	147,310,000
1197	4¢ Louisiana Statehood, Apr. 30	.11	.05	.55		.75	118,690,000
	Perf. 11x10½						
1198	4¢ Homestead Act, May 20	.11	.05	.55		.75	122,730,000
1199	4¢ Girl Scout Jubilee, July 24	.11	.05	.55		.75	126,515,000
1200	4¢ Sen. Brien McMahon, July 28	.11	.05	1.00		.75	130,960,000
1201	4¢ Apprenticeship, Aug. 31	.11	.05	.55		.75	120,055,000
	Perf. 11						
1202	4¢ Sam Rayburn, Sept. 16	.11	.05	.55		.75	120,715,000
1203	4¢ Dag Hammarskjöld, Oct. 23	.11	.05	.70		.75	121,440,000
1204	4¢ Hammarskjöld Special Printing:						
	black, brown and yellow						
	(yellow inverted)	.12	.11	5.00		6.00	40,270,000
1205	4¢ Christmas Issue, Nov. 1	.11	.05	.50		.75	861,970,000
1206	4¢ Higher Education, Nov. 14	.11	.05	.55		.75	120,035,000
1207	4¢ Winslow Homer, Dec. 15	.13	.05	1.50		.75	117,870,000

SAM RAYBURN

They called him "Mr. Sam." Irascible, powerful and intensely committed to his office, Samuel Taliaferro Rayburn was a politician in the grandest tradition. Elected 25 consecutive times to represent Texas in Congress, the Democrat served a record tenure in the House.

In 1940, Rayburn was elected Speaker of the House and set another record by holding that office for an unprecedented 17 years—twice as long as Henry Clay, the previous record-holder.

Rayburn was born in rural east Tennessee in 1882, and his family moved to Texas when Sam was five. At 18, he left the family farm to teach school and practice law, but politics intrigued him. He was elected to the Texas state legislature in 1907, and later served as Speaker of the House there.

In 1912, Rayburn went to Washington. The young Congressman earned a reputation as a proponent of progressive legislation, and his energy and political brilliance soon placed him among the most influential men on Capitol Hill.

What was Rayburn's secret for influencing a large group of often unruly Congressmen? "I am not a compromiser," he said. "I'd rather be known as a 'persuader'. I try to compromise by getting people to think my way." See Scott No. 202.

1192

1193

1194

1195

1196

1197

1198

1199

1200

1201

1203

1204

1202

1205

1206

1207

1208

1209

1213

1230

1231

1232

1233

1234

1235

1236

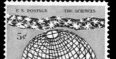
1237

1238

1239

1240

1241

1242

1243

1244

		Un	U	PB	#	FDC	Q
	Flag Issue of 1963						
1208	5¢ Flag over White House	.13	.05	.55		.75	
	Regular Issue of 1962-66, Perf. 11x10½						
1209	1¢ Andrew Jackson	.05	.05	.25		.75	
1213	5¢ George Washington	.13	.05	.65		.75	
1213a	Booklet pane of 5 (Your Mailman)	7.50	—				
	Coil Stamps, Perf. 10 Vertically						
1225	1¢ green Jackson (1209)	.09	.05			.75	
1229	5¢ dark blue gray Washington (1213)	1.10	.05			.75	
	Issues of 1963, Perf. 11						
1230	5¢ Carolina Charter, Apr. 6	.13	.05	.60		.75	129,945,000
1231	5¢ Food for Peace—Freedom from Hunger,						
	June 4	.13	.05	.60		.75	135,620,000
1232	5¢ W. Virginia Statehood, June 20	.13	.05	.60		.75	137,540,000
1233	5¢ Emancipation Proclamation,						
	Aug. 16	.13	.05	.60		.75	132,435,000
1234	5¢ Alliance for Progress, Aug. 17	.13	.05	.60		.75	135,520,000
	Perf. 10½x11						
1235	5¢ Cordell Hull, Oct. 5	.13	.05	.60		.75	131,420,000
	Perf. 11x10½						
1236	5¢ Eleanor Roosevelt, Oct. 11	.13	.05	.60		.75	133,170,000
	Perf. 11						
1237	5¢ Science, Oct. 14	.13	.05	1.35		.75	130,195,000
1238	5¢ City Mail Delivery, Oct. 26	.13	.05	.60		.75	128,450,000
1239	5¢ Red Cross 100th Anniv., Oct. 29	.13	.05	.60		.75	118,665,000
1240	5¢ Christmas Issue, Nov. 1	.13	.05	.60		.75	1,291,250,000
1241	5¢ John James Audubon, Dec. 7	.13	.05	1.25		.75	175,175,000
	Issues of 1964, Perf. 10½x11						
1242	5¢ Sam Houston, Jan. 10	.13	.05	.60		.75	125,995,000
	Perf. 11						
1243	5¢ Charles M. Russell, Mar. 19	.13	.05	1.20		.75	128,925,000
	Perf. 11x10½						
1244	5¢ New York World's Fair, Apr. 22	.13	.05	1.65		.75	145,700,000

		Un	U	PB	#	FDC	Q
	1964 continued						
	Perf. 11						
1245	5¢ John Muir, Apr. 29	.13	.05	.60		.75	120,310,000
	Perf. 11 x 10½						
1246	5¢ Kennedy Memorial, May 29	.13	.05	.60		.75	511,750,000
	Perf. 10½ x 11						
1247	5¢ New Jersey 300th Anniv., June 15	.13	.05	.60		.75	123,845,000
	Perf. 11						
1248	5¢ Nevada Statehood, July 22	.13	.05	.60		.75	122,825,000
1249	5¢ Register and Vote, Aug. 1	.13	.05	.60		.75	453,090,000
	Perf. 10½ x 11						
1250	5¢ Shakespeare, Aug. 14	.13	.05	.60		.75	123,245,000
1251	5¢ Doctors Mayo, Sept. 11	.13	.05	.60		.75	123,355,000
1252	5¢ American Music, Oct. 15, Perf. 11	.13	.05	.60		.75	126,970,000
1253	5¢ Homemakers, Oct. 26, Perf. 11	.13	.05	.60		.75	121,250,000
	Christmas Issue, Nov. 9						
1254	5¢ Holly, Perf. 11	.70	.05	7.50		.75	351,940,000
1255	5¢ Mistletoe, Perf. 11	.70	.05	7.50		.75	351,940,000
1256	5¢ Poinsettia, Perf. 11	.70	.05	7.50		.75	351,940,000
1257	5¢ Sprig of Conifer, Perf. 11	.70	.05	7.50		.75	351,940,000
1257b	Block of four, #1254-1257	—	—				
	Perf. 10½ x 11						
1258	5¢ Verrazano-Narrows Bridge, Nov. 21	.13	.05	.60		.75	120,005,000
	Perf. 11						
1259	5¢ Fine Arts, Dec. 2	.13	.05	.75		.75	125,800,000
	Perf. 10½ x 11						
1260	5¢ Amateur Radio, Dec. 15	.13	.05	.75		.75	122,230,000

ELEANOR ROOSEVELT

Reporters covering Eleanor Roosevelt during her husband's first presidential campaign were amazed at her calm in the midst of the election hysteria. Eleanor always maintained she had never wanted to be a president's wife. It was her firm intention not to allow her husband's activities to interfere with her own varied interests.

If she were selfish, Eleanor told a reporter, she could almost wish that Franklin had lost. She knew that life in Washington would be difficult and thought she would be severely criticized. The presidency, she continued, was "an extremely serious thing to undertake, you know."

Nonetheless, she was delighted by Franklin's victory. "You're always pleased to have someone you're very devoted to have what he wants," she said. "I couldn't have wanted it to go the other way. After all, I'm a Democrat, too." But Eleanor Roosevelt was much more than a Democrat. An effective public speaker, she toured the country endlessly, serving as her husband's eyes and ears. After the President's death, she was appointed a delegate to the United Nations where she was, quite appropriately, Chairman of the Commission on Human Rights. Eleanor Roosevelt will be the topic of a commemorative stamp to be issued in 1984, the 100th anniversary year of her birth. See Scott No. 1236.

1246

245

1247

248

1249

1250

1251

252

1253

254   1255
256   1257

1258

1259

1260

1261

1262

1263

1264

1265

1266

1267

1268

1269

1271

1270

1272

1273

1275

1276

1274

		Un	U	PB	#	FDC	Q
	Issues of 1965, Perf. 11						
1261	5¢ Battle of New Orleans, Jan. 8	.12	.05	.75		.75	115,695,000
1262	5¢ Physical Fitness-Sokol, Feb. 15	.12	.05	.75		.75	115,095,000
1263	5¢ Crusade Against Cancer, Apr. 1	.12	.05	.75		.75	119,560,000
	Perf. 10½ x 11						
1264	5¢ Churchill Memorial, May 13	.12	.05	.75		.75	125,180,000
	Perf. 11						
1265	5¢ Magna Carta, June 15	.12	.05	.75		.75	120,135,000
1266	5¢ Intl. Cooperation Year, June 26	.12	.05	.75		.75	115,405,000
1267	5¢ Salvation Army, July 2	.12	.05	.75		.75	115,855,000
	Perf. 10½ x 11						
1268	·5¢ Dante Alighieri, July 17	.12	.05	.75		.75	115,340,000
1269	5¢ Herbert Hoover, Aug. 10	.12	.05	.75		.75	114,840,000
	Perf. 11						
1270	5¢ Robert Fulton, Aug. 19	.12	.05	.75		.75	116,140,000
1271	5¢ Settlement of Florida, Aug. 28	.12	.05	1.00		.75	116,900,000
1272	5¢ Traffic Safety, Sept. 3	.12	.05	1.00		.75	114,085,000
1273	5¢ John Singleton Copley, Sept. 17	.13	.05	1.25		.75	114,880,000
1274	11¢ International Telecommunication Union,						
	Oct. 6	.45	.20	15.00		.75	26,995,000
1275	5¢ Adlai E. Stevenson, Oct. 23	.12	.05	.75		.75	128,495,000
1276	5¢ Christmas Issue, Nov. 2	.12	.05	.60		.75	1,139,930,000

LUNAR ROVER

From the beginning, the Lunar Rover won the hearts of the press and public. Though described as a "fourth astronaut," the Lunar Rover was anything but human in shape, and barely recognizable as a car. It did have a chassis, four wheels and two seats—but it lacked a windshield, body and doors. Quipped the editors of Newsweek *about the star of the 1971 Apollo 15 mission: "It's the sort of vehicle only a California teenager could love."*

Built by Boeing and General Motors to withstand the moon's extremes of temperature and terrain, the buggy measured a little more than ten feet long and six feet wide. A T-shaped handle between seats like camp chairs replaced the standard steering wheel. "It drives like a bumper car in an amusement park," said astronaut James B. Irwin.

Rubber tires could easily shatter like glass in the lunar cold, so the Moon Buggy's tires were made of open wire mesh. Two batteries powered one electric motor on each of the Rover's four wheels. The vehicle could race around the moon's surface at speeds of up to 10 miles per hour.

With the addition of a large radio transmitter, an antenna like a huge upside-down umbrella, a TV camera and geology tools, the Lunar Rover, according to The New Yorker, *looked like a "golf cart bristling with umbrellas, rakes, and a variety of long-handled tools."*

The rover, left on the moon, provided man's first view of a lunar lift-off through a battery-powered color camera mounted on the chassis, widening our view of lunar horizons. See Scott Nos. 1434-35.

		Un	U	PB	#	FDC		Q
Issues of 1965-78, Prominent Americans, Perf. 11x10½, 10½x11								
1278	1¢ Thomas Jefferson, 1968	.05	.05	.20		.35		
1278a	Booklet pane of 8, 1968	1.00	—					
1278b	Booklet pane of 4, 1971	.75	—					
1279	1¼¢ Albert Gallatin, 1967	.09	.09	22.50		.35		
1280	2¢ Frank Lloyd Wright, 1966	.05	.05	.30		.35		
1280a	Booklet pane of 5 + label, 1968	1.20	—					
1280c	Booklet pane of 6, 1971	1.00	—					
1281	3¢ Francis Parkman, 1967	.07	.05	.70		.35		
1282	4¢ Abraham Lincoln, 1965	.09	.05	.40		.35		
1283	5¢ George Washington, 1966	.15	.05	.50		.45		
1283B	5¢ Washington redrawn, 1967	.13	.05	1.00		.45		
1284	6¢ Franklin D. Roosevelt, 1966	.18	.05	.65		.45		
1284b	Booklet pane of 8, 1967	1.65	—					
1284c	Booklet pane of 5 + label, 1968	1.40	—					
1285	8¢ Albert Einstein, 1966	.20	.05	1.25		.50		
1286	10¢ Andrew Jackson, 1967	.24	.05	1.30		.60		
1286A	12¢ Henry Ford, 1968	.27	.05	1.75		.50		
1287	13¢ John F. Kennedy, 1967	.30	.05	1.65		.65		
1288	15¢ Oliver Wendell Holmes, 1968	.35	.05	1.50		.60		
1288B	15¢ dk. rose claret Holmes (1288),							
	Perf. 10, 1978	.40	.05			.75		
1288c	Booklet pane of 8, 1978	2.75	—					
1289	20¢ George C. Marshall, 1967	.33	.05	2.00		.80		
1290	25¢ Frederick Douglass, 1967	.42	.05	2.50		1.00		
1291	30¢ John Dewey, 1968	.65	.05	3.00		1.20		
1292	40¢ Thomas Paine, 1968	.70	.06	4.00		1.60		
1293	50¢ Lucy Stone, 1968	1.00	.05	5.00		2.50		
1294	$1 Eugene O'Neill, 1967	2.00	.07	10.00		6.25		
1295	$5 John Bassett Moore, 1966	10.00	2.85	50.00		55.00		
	No. 1288B issued only in booklets.							
Coil Stamps, Issues of 1966-78, Perf. 10 Horizontally								
1297	3¢ violet Parman (1281), 1975	.07	.05			.75		
1298	6¢ gray brown F.D.R. (1284), 1967	.18	.05			.75		
	Perf. 10 Vertically							
1299	1¢ green Jefferson (1278), 1968	.05	.05			.75		
1303	4¢ black Lincoln (1282), 1966	.11	.08			.75		
1304	5¢ blue Washington (1283), 1966	.13	.05			.75		
1305	6¢ Franklin D. Roosevelt, 1968	.20	.05			.75		
1305E	15¢ rose claret Holmes (1288), 1978	.40	.07			.75		
1305C	$1 dull purple Eugene O'Neill							
	(1294), 1973	2.00	.80			3.00		

278

1279

1280

1281

283

1283B

1284

1285

1286

286A

1287

1288

1289

290

1291

1292

1293

1294

295

1305

1306

1307

1308

1309

1310

1312

1313

1314

1311

1315

1316

1317

1318

1319

		Un	U	PB	#	FDC	Q
	Issues of 1966, Perf. 11						
1306	5¢ Migratory Bird Treaty, Mar. 16	.12	.05	1.00		.75	116,835,000
1307	5¢ Humane Treatment of Animals,						
	Apr. 9	.12	.05	.90		.75	117,470,000
1308	5¢ Indiana Statehood, Apr. 16	.12	.05	.75		.75	123,770,000
1309	5¢ American Circus, May 2	.12	.05	.90		.75	131,270,000
	Sixth International Philatelic Exhibition Issues						
1310	5¢ Stamped Cover, May 21	.12	.05	.90		.75	122,285,000
	Imperf.						
1311	5¢ Souvenir Sheet, May 23	.20	.20			.75	14,680,000
	Issued in sheets of one stamp with marginal inscription commemorating the Sixth International Philatelic Exhibition (SIPEX), held in Washington, D.C. from May 21-30.						
	Perf. 11						
1312	5¢ Bill of Rights, July 1	.12	.05	.75		.75	114,160,000
	Perf. 10½ x 11						
1313	5¢ Polish Millennium, July 30	.12	.05	.90		.75	128,475,000
	Perf. 11						
1314	5¢ National Park Service, Aug. 25	.12	.05	.75		.75	119,535,000
1315	5¢ Marine Corps Reserve, Aug. 29	.12	.05	1.00		.75	125,110,000
1316	5¢ General Federation of Women's						
	Clubs, Sept. 12	.12	.05	1.00		.75	114,853,200
1317	5¢ Johnny Appleseed, Sept. 24	.12	.05	1.00		.75	124,290,000
1318	5¢ Beautification of America, Oct. 5	.12	.05	1.75		.75	128,460,000
1319	5¢ Great River Road, Oct. 21	.12	.05	1.00		.75	127,585,000

SAN ANTONIO HEMISFAIR

By world's fair standards, the San Antonio HemisFair was small—only 92 acres. But the 1968 celebration of the Texas city's 250th anniversary made its mark in other ways. Unlike most international exhibitions, it was located downtown, only six blocks from the Alamo. Its planners paid as much attention to the old as the new, creating a tasteful blend of modern buildings and lovely 18th century houses restored for the occasion.

The fair did have some "firsts" and "biggests." It was the first world's fair to be held in the southern part of the United States. And it boasted the tallest observation tower in the Western Hemisphere—the 622-foot Tower of the Americas, which featured a revolving restaurant and observation decks.

Like other international expositions, the HemisFair left some buildings behind that have become part of the San Antonio scene. Besides the Tower of the Americas, these include the State of Texas pavilion, which tells the state's story through 26 cultural groups, the Museum of Transportation, and a convention center, theater and amusement park. See Scott No. 1340.

The Military Plaza in old San Antonio.

		Un	U	PB	#	FDC	Q
	1966 continued						
1320	5¢ Savings Bond—Servicemen, Oct. 26	.12	.05	1.00		.75	115,875,000
1321	5¢ Christmas Issue, Nov. 1	.12	.05	.75		.75	1,173,547,420
1322	5¢ Mary Cassatt, Nov. 17	.17	.05	2.75		.75	114,015,000
	Issues of 1967						
1323	5¢ National Grange, Apr. 17	.12	.05	.90		.75	121,105,000
1324	5¢ Canada 100th Anniv., May 25	.12	.05	.90		.75	132,045,000
1325	5¢ Erie Canal, July 4	.12	.05	.90		.75	118,780,000
1326	5¢ "Peace"—Lions, July 5	.12	.05	.90		.75	121,985,000
1327	5¢ Henry David Thoreau, July 12	.12	.05	.90		.75	111,850,000
1328	5¢ Nebraska Statehood, July 29	.12	.05	.90		.75	117,225,000
1329	5¢ Voice of America, Aug. 1	.12	.05	1.20		.75	111,515,000
1330	5¢ Davy Crockett, Aug. 17	.12	.05	1.00		.75	114,270,000
	Space Accomplishments Issue, Sep. 29						
1331	5¢ Space-Walking Astronaut	1.00	.20				60,432,500
1331a	Pair, #1331-1332	3.50	2.00	17.50	8.00		
1332	5¢ Gemini 4 Capsule and Earth	1.00	.20	17.50			60,432,500
1333	5¢ Urban Planning, Oct. 2	.15	.05	3.00		.75	110,675,000
1334	5¢ Finnish Independence, Oct. 6	.15	.05	3.50		.75	110,670,000
	Perf. 12						
1335	5¢ Thomas Eakins, Nov. 2	.15	.05	3.00		.75	113,825,000
	Perf. 11						
1336	5¢ Christmas Issue, Nov. 6	.12	.05	.60		.75	1,208,700,000
1337	5¢ Mississippi Statehood, Dec. 11	.15	.05	2.50		.75	113,330,000
	Issues of 1968-71						
1338	6¢ Flag and White House	.12	.03	.60		.75	

MARY CASSATT

Mary Cassatt's contributions to American art as a painter and printmaker are well known. In fact, she is generally regarded as America's foremost woman artist. But she also had considerable influence over several wealthy American art collectors.

At Mary Cassatt's suggestion, Mrs. Potter Palmer, Chicago's leading art patron, bought Edgar Degas' On the Stage, *the painting that laid the foundation for the outstanding French Impressionist collection now owned by Chicago's Art Institute.*

But Cassatt's greatest accomplishment was to help her extremely rich friends Louisine and Henry Havenmeyer adorn the mansion that Louis Tiffany designed for them on New York's Fifth Avenue. Cassatt led the Havenmeyers from city to village in Italy, Spain and France, acting as guide and teacher in their search for great works of art. She convinced them to buy works by El Greco and Goya, then unknown in the United States, as well as masterpieces by her Impressionist friends in Paris. Mrs. Havenmeyer later recalled that Mary Cassatt "had the flair of an old hunter" when tracking down pictures. Cassatt's acquisitions became the basis for the famous Havenmeyer Collection in New York's Metropolitan Museum of Art. See Scott No. 1322.

1320

1321

1322

1323

1324

1325

1326

1327

1328

1329

1330

1331   1332

1333

1334

1335

1336

1337

1338

1341

1342

1339   1340

1345

1346

1343   1344

1347

1348

1349

1350

1351

1352

1353

1354

	Un	U	PB	#	FDC	Q
1968-71 continued						
Perf. 11x10½						
1338D 6¢ dark blue, red & green (1338), 1970	.15	.05	3.25	(20)	.75	
1338F 8¢ multicolored (1338), 1971	.20	.05	3.50	(20)	.75	
Coil Stamps of 1969-71, Perf. 10 Vertically						
1338A 6¢ dark blue, red & green (1338), 1969	.17	.05			.75	
1338G 8¢ multicolored (1338), 1971	.23	.05			.75	
Issues of 1968, Perf. 11						
1339 6¢ Illinois Statehood, Feb. 12	.18	.05	1.00		.75	141,350,000
1340 6¢ HemisFair '68, Mar. 30	.18	.05	1.00		.75	144,345,000
1341 $1 Airlift, Apr. 4	6.00	2.50	32.50		6.50	
1342 6¢ "Youth"—Elks, May 1	.18	.05	1.00		.75	147,120,000
1343 6¢ Law and Order, May 17	.18	.05	1.00		.75	130,125,000
1344 6¢ Register and Vote, June 27	.18	.05	1.00		.75	158,700,000
Historic Flag Series, July 4						
1345 6¢ Ft. Moultrie Flag (1776)	1.10	.35			4.00	23,153,000
1346 6¢ Ft. McHenry Flag (1795-1818)	1.10	.35			4.00	23,153,000
1347 6¢ Washington's Cruisers Flag (1775)	.50	.35			4.00	23,153,000
1348 6¢ Bennington Flag (1777)	.50	.35			4.00	23,153,000
1349 6¢ Rhode Island Flag (1775)	.50	.35			4.00	23,153,000
1350 6¢ First Stars and Stripes Flag (1777)	.50	.35			4.00	23,153,000
1351 6¢ Bunker Hill Flag (1775)	.50	.35			4.00	23,153,000
1352 6¢ Grand Union Flag (1776)	.50	.35			4.00	23,153,000
1353 6¢ Phila. Light Horse Flag (1775)	.75	.35			4.00	23,153,000
1354 6¢ First Navy Jack (1775)	.75	.35			4.00	23,153,000
1345/1346 Plate Block of 4	—	—	5.50			
1354a Strip of ten, #1345-1354	10.00	6.50	22.50	(20)	12.00	

THE ERIE CANAL

The grand old Erie Canal was completed in 1825, after seven years of mosquito-plagued construction and at a cost of some $8 million. The 363-mile ditch, the country's first major highway to the West, proved a great commercial success.

The first boat to enter the canal was the Chief Engineer of Rome. *In 1818, it carried canal commissioners and the governor of New York from Rome to Utica, with appropriate fanfare.*

Today most of the canal is all but deserted, absorbed by the New York State Barge System. The only passenger ship to ply these quiet waters is the Emita II, *a retired Maine ferry. From early June into October, the* Emita II *cruises from Syracuse west to Lockport or east to Albany. During the three-day trip, the captain gives periodic talks on canal history as the ship passes under low bridges and through locks. At night, passengers stay in canalside motels.*

Though canal traffic is considerable lighter than it was during the Erie's peak years, life aboard the Emita II *is otherwise much the same as it was in the 19th century. Children still come out to greet the gaily colored ship, and passengers continue to doze comfortably in the main salon. See Scott No. 1352.*

		Un	U	PB	#	FDC	Q
	1968 continued						
	Perf. 12						
1355	6¢ Walt Disney, Sept. 11	.20	.05	1.75		1.00	153,015,000
	Perf. 11						
1356	6¢ Father Marquette, Sept. 20	.17	.05	1.10		.75	132,560,000
1357	6¢ Daniel Boone, Sept. 26	.17	.05	1.10		.75	130,385,000
1358	6¢ Arkansas River, Oct. 1	.17	.05	1.10		.75	132,265,000
1359	6¢ Leif Erikson, Oct. 9	.17	.05	1.20		.75	128,710,000
	Perf. 11x10½						
1360	6¢ Cherokee Strip, Oct. 15	.20	.05	1.65		.75	124,775,000
	Perf. 11						
1361	6¢ John Trumbull, Oct. 18	.25	.05	2.75		.75	128,295,000
1362	6¢ Waterfowl Conservation, Oct. 24	.25	.05	3.50		.75	142,245,000
1363	6¢ Christmas Issue, Nov. 1	.15	.05	2.75	(10)	.75	1,410,580,000
1364	6¢ American Indian, Nov. 4	.35	.05	3.50		.75	125,100,000
	Issues of 1969, Beautification of America, Jan. 16						
1365	6¢ Capitol, Azaleas and Tulips	1.00	.08	13.50		2.00	48,142,500
1366	6¢ Washington Monument,						
	Potomac River and Daffodils	1.00	.08	13.50		2.00	48,142,500
1367	6¢ Poppies and Lupines						
	along Highway	1.00	.08	13.50		2.00	48,142,500
1368	6¢ Blooming Crabapples						
	along Street	1.00	.08	13.50		2.00	48,142,500
1368a	Block of four, #1365-1368	8.50	3.50	8.50		5.00	
1369	6¢ American Legion, Mar. 15	.17	.05	1.10		.75	148,770,000
1370	6¢ Grandma Moses, May 1	.17	.05	1.35		.75	139,475,000

WASHINGTON MONUMENT

"Less is more." Contemporary architects may argue endlessly over the truth of that catchphrase. But in the case of the Washington Monument, it is indisputable: less money meant a more *suitable and infinitely more impressive memorial.*

The original design for the monument was created by Robert Mills, winner of a competition held by the National Monument Society in 1833. Though the competition called for a "harmonious blend . . . of durability, simplicity and grandeur," Mill's entry was more like an elaborately iced birthday cake with a single candle. It called for a decorated 600-foot pillar surrounded by a ring of 100-foot pillars supporting a roof. Within this colonnade would be the tombs of George Washington and other Revolutionary heroes; at its entrance would stand a group of statues featuring Washington driving a four-horse chariot.

Fortunately, the public and government were unable—or unwilling—to pay for construction of this elaborate monstrosity. Congressman Robert C. Winthrop convinced the building committee to omit the cake and icing, leaving only the towering obelisk, a four-sided pillar that gradually tapers and ends in a steep pyramid at its apex.

Today the monument stands, some 555 feet in height, as a majestic focal point for the city of Washington. It is one of the country's most familiar—and perhaps its most beautiful—piece of architecture. In its simplicity, it endures. See Scott No. 1366.

1356

1357

1355

1358

1359

1360

1361

1362

1363

1364

1365
1367

1366
1368

1369

1370

1371

1372

1373

1374

1375

1376
1378

1377
1379

1380

1381

1382

1383

1385

1384

1384a

1386

		Un	U	PB	#	FDC	Q
	1969 continued						
1371	6¢ Apollo 8, May 5	.25	.05	3.50		2.00	187,165,000
1372	6¢ W. C. Handy, May 17	.17	.05	1.00		.75	125,555,000
1373	6¢ California Settlement, July 16	.17	.05	1.00		.75	144,425,000
1374	6¢ John Wesley Powell, Aug. 1	.17	.05	1.00		.75	135,875,000
1375	6¢ Alabama Statehood, Aug. 2	.17	.05	1.00		.75	151,110,000
	Botanical Congress Issue						
1376	6¢ Douglas Fir (Northwest)	1.65	.09	15.00		2.00	39,798,750
1377	6¢ Lady's Slipper (Northeast)	1.65	.09	15.00		2.00	39,798,750
1378	6¢ Ocotillo (Southwest)	1.65	.09	15.00		2.00	39,798,750
1379	6¢ Franklinia (Southeast)	1.65	.09	15.00		2.00	39,798,750
	Block of four, #1376-1379	12.00	3.50	12.00		5.00	
	Perf. 10½x11						
1380	6¢ Dartmouth College Case, Sept. 22	.18	.05	1.35		.75	129,540,000
	Perf. 11						
1381	6¢ Professional Baseball, Sept. 24	.20	.05	1.75		.75	130,925,000
1382	6¢ Intercollegiate Football, Sept. 26	.20	.05	1.85		.75	139,055,000
1383	6¢ Dwight D. Eisenhower, Oct. 14	.15	.05	1.00		.75	150,611,200
	Perf. 11x10½						
1384	6¢ Christmas Issue, Nov. 3	.15	.05	2.25	(10)	.75	1,709,795,000
1384a	Precanceled	.75	.06				
1385	6¢ Hope for Crippled, Nov. 20	.15	.05	1.00		.75	127,545,000
1386	6¢ William M. Harnett, Dec. 3	.15	.05	1.20		.75	145,788,800

INTERCOLLEGIATE FOOTBALL

"Outlined against the blue-gray October sky, the Four Horsemen rode again. In dramatic lore they were known as famine, pestilence, destruction and death. These are only aliases. Their real names are Stuhldreher, Miller, Crowley and Layden."

When sportswriter Grantland Rice wrote those unforgettable words in 1924, Knute Rockne and the Four Horsemen ruled football at Notre Dame, Notre Dame ruled collegiate football, and collegiate football ruled the country.

Though college teams had been playing modern football since before the turn of the century, not until the 1920s did the sport become a national mania and a large-scale business enterprise. Along with the popularity, of course, came accusations: football was undermining the morale of the nation's youth, not to mention our institutions of higher education, with distractions from the true role of a university.

Those charges have been leveled against college football over the years. But the popularity of the game has overcome these criticisms. In 1948, when the National Collegiate Athletic Association began keeping statistics, attendance at college football games was about 19 million. In 1981, nearly 36 million people attended college football games. See Scott No. 1382.

Knute Rockne, Notre Dame's famed coach.

		Un	U	PB	#	FDC	Q
	Issues of 1970, Natural History, May 6						
1387	6¢ American Bald Eagle	.17	.08	3.75		2.00	50,448,550
1388	6¢ African Elephant Herd	.17	.08	3.75		2.00	50,448,550
1389	6¢ Tlingit Chief in Haida Ceremonial						
	Canoe	.17	.08	3.75		2.00	50,448,550
1390	6¢ Brontosaurus, Stegosaurus and						
	Allosaurus from Jurassic Period	.17	.08	3.75		2.00	50,448,550
1390a	Block of four, #1387-1390	1.35	.75	1.35		3.00	
1391	6¢ Maine Statehood, July 9	.18	.05	1.10		.75	171,850,000
	Perf. 10½x11						
1392	6¢ Wildlife Conservation, July 20	.18	.05	1.10		.75	142,205,000
	Issues of 1970-74, Perf. 11x10½, 10½x11, 11						
1393	6¢ Dwight D. Eisenhower, 1970	.12	.05	.60		.75	
1393a	Booklet pane of 8	1.50	—				
1393b	Booklet pane of 5 + label	1.25	—				
1393D	7¢ Benjamin Franklin, 1972	.16	.05	1.35		.75	
1394	8¢ Eisenhower, 1971	.18	.05	1.00		.75	
1395	8¢ Eisenhower, 1971	.30	.05			.75	
1395a	Booklet pane of 8, 1971	2.00	—				
1395b	Booklet pane of 6, 1971	1.75	—				
1395c	Booklet pane of 4 + 2 labels, -72	1.35	—				
1395d	Booklet pane of 7 + label, 1972	2.50	—				
1396	8¢ U.S. Postal Service, 1971	.18	.05	7.50	(12)	.75	
1397	14¢ Fiorello H. LaGuardia, 1972	.25	.10	2.35		.85	
1398	16¢ Ernie Pyle, 1971	.35	.05	2.35		.75	
1399	18¢ Dr. Elizabeth Blackwell, 1974	.40	.06	1.80		1.25	
1400	21¢ Amadeo P. Giannini, 1973	.45	.18	2.10		1.00	
	Coil Stamps, Perf. 10 Vertically						
1401	6¢ dark blue gray Eisenhower						
	(1393), 1970	.12	.05			.75	
1402	8¢ deep claret Eisenhower (1395), -71	.20	.05			.75	
	Issues of 1970, Perf. 11						
1405	6¢ Edgar Lee Masters, Aug. 22	.17	.05	1.00		.75	137,660,000
1406	6¢ Woman Suffrage, Aug. 26	.17	.05	1.00		.75	135,125,000
1407	6¢ South Carolina, Sept. 12	.17	.05	1.00		.75	135,895,000
1408	6¢ Stone Mountain Mem., Sep. 19	.17	.05	1.00		.75	132,675,000
1409	6¢ Fort Snelling, Oct. 17	.17	.05	1.00		.75	134,795,000

AMERICAN BALD EAGLE

AFRICAN ELEPHANT HERD

1391

HAIDA CEREMONIAL CANOE

THE AGE OF REPTILES

1387
1389

1388
1390

1392

393

1393D

1394

1396

1397

398

1399

1400

1405

1406

407

1408

1409

1410
1412

1411
1413

1414

1414a

1415
1417

1416
1418

1419

1420

1421

1422

1423

1424

1425

1426

1427
1429

1428
1430

		Un	U	PB	#	FDC	Q
	Perf. 11x10½, Anti-Pollution Issue, Oct. 28						
1410	6¢ Save Our Soil	.40	.09			2.00	40,400,000
1411	6¢ Save Our Cities	.40	.09			2.00	40,400,000
1412	6¢ Save Our Water	.40	.09			2.00	40,400,000
1413	6¢ Save Our Air	.40	.09			2.00	40,400,000
1413a	Block of four, #1410-1413	2.35	2.25			3.00	
	Plate Block of 10			9.50			
	Christmas Issue, Nov. 5, Perf. 10½x11						
1414	6¢ Nativity, by Lorenzo Lotto	.17	.05	3.00	(8)	1.40	638,730,000
1414a	Precanceled	.25	.06				358,245,000
	Perf. 11x10½						
1415	6¢ Tin and Cast-Iron Locomotive	.60	.08			1.40	122,313,750
1415a	Precanceled	1.50	.10				109,912,500
1416	6¢ Toy Horse on Wheels	.60	.08			1.40	122,313,750
1416a	Precanceled	1.50	.10				109,912,500
1417	6¢ Mechanical Tricycle	.60	.08			1.40	122,313,750
1417a	Precanceled	1.50	.10				109,912,500
1418	6¢ Doll Carriage	.60	.08			1.40	122,313,750
1418a	Precanceled	1.50	.10				109,912,500
1418b	Block of four, #1415-1418	3.75	2.75	4.75		3.00	
1418c	Block of four, precanceled	10.00	6.50	8.00		3.00	
	Plate Block of 8			12.00			
	Perf. 11						
1419	6¢ United Nations, Nov. 20	.17	.05	1.25		.75	127,610,000
1420	6¢ Landing of the Pilgrims, Nov. 21	.17	.05	1.25		.75	129,785,000
	Disabled Veterans and Servicemen Issue, Nov. 24						
1421	6¢ Disabled American Veterans						
	Emblem	.17	.06			.75	67,190,000
1422	6¢ U.S. Servicemen	.17	.06	7.00		.75	67,190,000
1421/1422	Pair	.35	.35	7.00		1.20	
	Issues of 1971						
1423	6¢ American Wool Industry, Jan. 19	.17	.05	1.00		.75	135,305,000
1424	6¢ Gen. Douglas MacArthur, Jan. 26	.17	.05	1.00		.75	134,840,000
1425	6¢ Blood Donor, Mar. 12	.17	.05	1.00		.75	130,975,000
	Perf. 11x10½						
1426	8¢ Missouri 150th Anniv., May 8	.20	.05	3.50	(12)	.75	161,235,000
	Perf. 11, Wildlife Conservation Issue, June 12						
1427	8¢ Trout	.18	.08	2.25		1.75	43,920,000
1428	8¢ Alligator	.18	.08	2.25		1.75	43,920,000
1429	8¢ Polar Bear and Cubs	.18	.08	2.25		1.75	43,920,000
1430	8¢ California Condor	.18	.08	2.25		1.75	43,920,000
1430a	Block of four, #1427-1430	.90	.70	1.30		3.00	

		Un	U	PB	#	FDC	Q
	1971 continued						
1431	8¢ Antarctic Treaty, June 23	.18	.05	1.65		.75	138,700,000
1432	8¢ American Revolution						
	200th Anniversary, July 4	.40	.05	7.50		.75	138,165,000
1433	8¢ John Sloan, Aug. 2	.18	.05	1.65		.75	152,125,000
	Decade of Space Achievements Issue, Aug. 2						
1434	8¢ Earth, Sun, Landing Craft						
	on Moon Pair	.18	.05	2.25		.75	88,147,500
1435	8¢ Lunar Rover and Astronauts	.18	.05	2.25		.75	88,147,500
1434/1435 Pair		.40	.35	2.25		1.75	
1436	8¢ Emily Dickinson, Aug. 28	.18	.05	1.25		.75	142,845,000
1437	8¢ San Juan, Sept. 12	.18	.05	1.25		.75	148,755,000
	Perf. 10½x11						
1438	8¢ Prevent Drug Abuse, Oct. 5	.18	.05	1.85	(6)	.75	139,080,000
1439	8¢ CARE, Oct. 27	.18	.05	2.10	(8)	.75	130,755,000
	Perf. 11, Historic Preservation Issue, Oct. 29						
1440	8¢ Decatur House, Washington, D.C.	.22	.08	2.25		1.20	42,552,000
1441	8¢ Whaling Ship *Charles W. Morgan*	.22	.08				42,552,000
1442	8¢ Cable Car, San Francisco, Calif.	.22	.08				42,552,000
1443	8¢ San Xavier del Bac Mission, Ariz.	.22	.08				42,552,000
1443a	Block of four, #1440-1443	1.00	.75	1.30		3.00	
	Perf. 10½x11, Christmas Issue, Nov. 10						
1444	8¢ Adoration of the Shepherds,						
	by Giorgione	.18	.05	2.50	(12)	.75	1,074,350,000
1445	8¢ Partridge in a Pear Tree,						
	by Jamie Wyeth	.18	.05	2.50	(12)	.75	979,540,000
	Issues of 1972, Perf. 11						
1446	8¢ Sidney Lanier, Feb. 3	.18	.05	1.00		.75	137,355,000
	Perf. 10½x11						
1447	8¢ Peace Corps, Feb. 11	.18	.05	1.50	(6)	.75	150,400,000

1431

1432

1433

434   1435

1436

1437

438   1439

1440   1441
1442   1443

1452

1448 1449
1450 1451

1453

1454

1455

1460

1456 1457
1458 1459

1461 1462

	Un	U	PB	#	FDC	Q
1972 continued						
National Parks 100th Anniversary Issue, Perf. 11						
1448 2¢ Hulk of Ship, Apr. 5	.05	.05	2.50		1.25	172,730,000
1449 2¢ Cape Hatteras Lighthouse, Apr. 5	.05	.05			1.25	172,730,000
1450 2¢ Laughing Gulls on Driftwood,						
Apr. 5	.05	.05			1.25	172,730,000
1451 2¢ Laughing Gulls and Dune, Apr. 5	.05	.05			1.25	172,730,000
1451a Block of four, Cape Hatteras,						
#1448-1451	.20	.20	.25		1.25	
Plate Block of 4			2.50			
1452 6¢ Wolf Trap Farm, June 26	.15	.08	1.25		.75	104,090,000
1453 8¢ Yellowstone, Mar. 1	.18	.05	1.00		.75	164,096,000
1454 15¢ Mt. McKinley, July 28	.35	.25	2.50		.75	53,920,000

Note: Beginning with this issue, the U.S.P.S. began to offer stamp collectors first day cancellations affixed to 8x10½ inch souvenir pages. The pages are similar to the stamp announcements that have appeared on post office bulletin boards since Scott No. 1132.

	Un	U	PB	#	FDC	Q
1455 8¢ Family Planning, Mar. 18	.18	.05	1.00		.75	153,025,000
Perf. 11x10½, American Revolution Bicentennial Issue, Jul. 4,						
Craftsmen in Colonial America						
1456 8¢ Glassmaker	.20	.07	3.00		1.00	50,472,500
1457 8¢ Silversmith	.20	.07			1.00	50,472,500
1458 8¢ Wigmaker	.20	.07			1.00	50,472,500
1459 8¢ Hatter	.20	.07			1.00	50,472,500
1459a Block of four, #1456-1459	.95	.70	1.35		2.50	
Plate Block of 4			3.00			
Olympic Games Issue, Aug. 17						
1460 6¢ Bicycling and Olympic Rings	.15	.12	2.00	(10)	.75	67,335,000
1461 8¢ Bobsledding	.18	.05	2.25	(10)	.85	179,675,000
1462 15¢ Running	.35	.35	4.00	(10)	1.00	46,340,000

POLAR BEARS

At the Legion Hall in Churchill, Manitoba, a polar bear ambled in at midday and started toward a crowd of dart throwers. The club steward, an old British army major, shouted, "You're no member. Get out!" The bear left.

For a number of years now, the village of Churchill has been overrun with polar bears, perhaps the most dangerous carnivore in North America. For several months each fall, the bears walk the streets, often followed by crowds of children, dogs and photographers. The problem: Churchill is located on the bear's migration path.

But despite the dangers, Churchill is determined that man and beast coexist peacefully. Phone directories list bear-alert numbers. A bear patrol of pupils checks for the presence of bears before school dismisses. And Halloween volunteers with short-wave radios ring the town to protect trick-or-treaters.

Nonetheless, the residents of this Canadian village bristle at any suggestion to rid themselves of the magnificent beast (which is threatened with extinction). As one resident said: "Nothing unites the people of the town as much as polar bears. We love them." See Scott Nos. 1429 & 1885.

		Un	U	PB	#	FDC	Q
	1972 continued						
1463	8¢ P.T.A. 75th Anniv., Sept. 15	.18	.05	1.00		.75	180,155,000
	Perf. 11, Wildlife Conservation Issue, Sep. 20						
1464	8¢ Fur Seals	.20	.07	1.40		2.00	49,591,200
1465	8¢ Cardinal	.20	.07			2.00	49,591,200
1466	8¢ Brown Pelican	.20	.07			2.00	49,591,200
1467	8¢ Bighorn Sheep	.20	.07			2.00	49,591,200
1467a	Block of 4, #1464-1467	.95	.70	1.10		3.00	
	Plate Block of 4			1.40			

Note: With this issue the U.S.P.S. introduced the "American Commemorative Series" Stamp Panels. Each panel contains a block of four mint stamps, mounted with text, and background illustrations.

		Un	U	PB	#	FDC	Q
	Perf. 11x10½						
1468	8¢ Mail Order 100th Anniv., Sept. 27	.18	.05	2.75	(12)	.75	185,490,000
	Perf. 10½x11						
1469	8¢ Osteopathic Medicine, Oct. 9	.18	.05	1.35	(6)	.75	162,335,000
	Perf. 11						
1470	8¢ American Folklore Issue, Oct. 13	.18	.05	1.00		.75	162,789,950
	Perf. 10½x11, Christmas Issue, Nov. 9						
1471	8¢ Angel from "Mary,						
	Queen of Heaven"	.18	.05	2.75	(12)	.75	1,003,475,000
1472	8¢ Santa Claus	.18	.05	2.75	(12)	.75	1,017,025,000
	Perf. 11						
1473	8¢ Pharmacy, Nov. 11	.18	.05	1.00		.75	165,895,000
1474	8¢ Stamp Collecting, Nov. 17	.18	.05	1.00		.75	166,508,000

WILLA CATHER

When the Cather family moved from Virginia to Red Cloud, Nebraska, in 1883, the effect on nine-year-old Willa was devastating. Nothing in her early years in genteel Virginia had prepared her for life on the prairie. Her new home was an utterly different world—isolated, overwhelmingly flat, filled with strange-speaking immigrants from Scandinavia and Eastern Europe. Willa later wrote that the move was like experiencing, "an erasure of personality."

She soon realized that she shared a great deal with these new Americans. Like her, they had been uprooted and were struggling as pioneers, and this feeling of solidarity helped her overcome her misgivings.

On horseback, she visited the settlers in their sod houses and they introduced her to the great music and literature of Europe. And Willa grew to love the beauty of the prairie as she had the woods of Virginia.

The pioneering spirit is the focus of Willa Cather's work. Her most famous books— O Pioneers! *(1913),* My Antonia *(1918), the Pulitzer-Prize-winning* One of Ours *(1922) and* A Lost Lady *(1923)—celebrate the unflagging heroism of the settlers and mourn the passing of the prairie way of life.*

Miss Cather's ability to evoke the prairie through her vivid descriptions made her both a popular and critical success. See Scott No. 1487.

463

1464
1466

1465
1467

468

1469

1470

1471

1472

1473

1474

475

1476

1477

478

1479

1480
1482

1481
1483

1484

1485

1486

1487

1488

		Un	U	PB	#	FDC	Q
	Issues of 1973, Perf. 11x10½						
1475	8¢ Love, Jan. 26	.18	.05	1.35	(6)	.75	330,055,000
	This "special stamp for someone special" depicts "Love" by contemporary artist Robert Indiana.						
	Perf. 11						
	American Revolution Bicentennial Issues, Communications in Colonial America						
1476	8¢ Printer and Patriots Examining						
	Pamphlet, Feb. 16	.18	.05	1.35		.75	166,005,000
1477	8¢ Posting a Broadside, Apr. 13	.18	.05	1.35		.75	163,050,000
1478	8¢ Postrider, June 22	.18	.05	1.35		.75	159,005,000
1479	8¢ Drummer, Sept. 28	.18	.05	1.35		.75	147,295,000
	Boston Tea Party, July 4						
1480	8¢ British Merchantman	.18	.08			1.75	49,068,750
1481	8¢ British Three-master	.18	.08			1.75	49,068,750
1482	8¢ Boats and Ship's Hull	.18	.08			1.75	49,068,750
1483	8¢ Boat and Dock	.18	.08			1.75	49,068,750
1483a	Block of four, Boston Tea Party,						
	#1480-1483	.75	.60	.95		3.75	
	Plate Block of 4			1.35			
	American Arts Issue						
1484	8¢ George Gershwin, Feb. 28	.18	.05	2.75	(12)	.75	139,152,000
1485	8¢ Robinson Jeffers, Aug. 13	.18	.05	2.75	(12)	.75	128,048,000
1486	8¢ Henry Ossawa Tanner, Sept. 10	.18	.05	2.75	(12)	.75	146,008,000
1487	8¢ Willa Cather, Sept. 20	.18	.05	2.75	(12)	.75	139,608,000
1488	8¢ Nicolaus Copernicus, Apr. 23	.18	.05	.80		.75	159,475,000

FLIGHT COVERS

The first air mail message was sent from Ben Franklin's son in Dover, England, to his grandson in Calais, France, by balloon in 1764. "I daresay," wrote the elder member of the enterprising Franklin family, "you will like to be one of the first who gets a Letter across the British Channel by this kind of aerial Conveyance."

Today, flight covers—envelopes carried on flights that contributed to the development of aviation—are a fascinating philatelic specialty. Historical covers are rarely official, since most were carried on experimental, pathfinder flights. Souvenir "first flight" covers receive a special cachet to commemorate the inauguration of a new air mail route. Technically, a "pure" first flight cover bears a postmark with the initial date on which the stamp can be used to prepay postage.

Covers illustrate the methods used by postal systems to deliver mail. The American Air Mail Catalogue contains entries ranging from a cover carried by one of the first seaplanes in 1912 to sections on Jet and Aerospace flight covers. Future collectors may well seek first flight covers that will be launched via missile and travel coast to coast in 30 minutes.

Old air mail symbols.

		Un	U	PB	#	FDC	Q
Perf. 10½x11, Postal Service Employees Issue, Apr. 30							
1489	8¢ Stamp Counter	.18	.09			1.10	48,602,000
1490	8¢ Mail Collection	.18	.09			1.10	48,602,000
1491	8¢ Letter Facing Conveyor	.18	.09			1.10	48,602,000
1492	8¢ Parcel Post Sorting	.18	.09			1.10	48,602,000
1493	8¢ Mail Cancelling	.18	.09			1.10	48,602,000
1494	8¢ Manual Letter Routing	.18	.09			1.10	48,602,000
1495	8¢ Electronic Letter Routing	.18	.09			1.10	48,602,000
1496	8¢ Loading Mail on Truck	.18	.09			1.10	48,602,000
1497	8¢ Mailman	.18	.09			1.10	48,602,000
1498	8¢ Rural Mail Delivery	.18	.09			1.10	48,602,000
1498a	Strip of ten, #1489-1498	2.25	1.75	2.25 (20)		6.00	
	Plate Block of 10			2.25 (10)			
	Margin Block of 20						
	(5P#/10 tabs)			4.50			

POSTAL INSPECTION SERVICE

They don't always get their man. But the Postal Inspection Service, the nation's oldest law enforcement agency, has a 98 percent conviction rate of those it does apprehend.

The service is not widely known among the general public. But among the nation's criminal population, the agency is famous—and feared—for the thoroughness of its methods and the lengths to which inspectors will go to solve a crime.

Agents like to tell the story of a burglary that happened years ago to a company that shared a building with a post office. The burglars chalked a line on the floor between their victim's offices and the post office. Next to it they scrawled, "Inspectors, we did not cross the line."

From the beginning the Postal Inspection Service has employed an elite group of agents and the most modern available crime-fighting methods. In the days before fingerprinting was developed in the early 1900s, inspectors used the Bertillon system of identifying criminals according to their physical features—then the most precise method then known. In the 1960s, inspectors solved a murder case by using neutron activation analysis of particles from a bomb transported through the mails.

The service is responsible for enforcing some 85 statutes covering all types of postal crime. Its more than 1,800 investigators work a minimum of 48 hours a week, and frequently more—"the best deal the American taxpayer has," according to one writer.

The service has the respect even of those it apprehends. In the words of a mailbox thief on the morning of his arrest, "I don't know what kind of law you are, but you are some kind of law!"

Variations on the Post Office Department symbol.

U.S. POSTAL SERVICE 8¢   **U.S. POSTAL SERVICE** 8¢   **U.S. POSTAL SERVICE** 8¢   **U.S. POSTAL SERVICE** 8¢

| Mail is picked up from nearly a third of a million local collection boxes, as well as your mailbox. | More than 87 billion letters and packages are handled yearly—almost 300 million every delivery day. | The People in your Postal Service handle and deliver more than 500 million packages yearly. | Thousands of machines, buildings, and vehicles must be operated and maintained to keep your mail moving. |

People Serving You   People Serving You   People Serving You   People Serving You

1490   1491   1492   1493

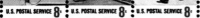

U.S. POSTAL SERVICE 8¢   **U.S. POSTAL SERVICE** 8¢   **U.S. POSTAL SERVICE** 8¢   **U.S. POSTAL SERVICE** 8¢

| Employees use modern, high-speed equipment to sort and process huge volumes of mail in central locations. | Thirteen billion pounds of mail are handled yearly by postal employees as they speed your letters and packages. | Our customers include 54 million urban and 12 million rural families, plus 9 million businesses. | Employees cover 4 million miles each delivery day to bring mail to your home or business. |

People Serving You   People Serving You   People Serving You   People Serving You

Harry S. Truman

U.S. Postage 8 cents

499

Progress in Electronics

1500

Progress in Electronics

1501

Progress in Electronics

502

RURAL AMERICA

504

RURAL AMERICA

1505

RURAL AMERICA

1506

Lyndon B. Johnson

United States
8 cents

1503

Christmas

Raphael
National Gallery
of Art

8 U.S.

507

US 8¢

CHRISTMAS

1508

UNITED STATES 10¢

1509

We hold these Truths...

UNITED STATES 10¢

1510

IT ALL DEPENDS ON

ZIP CODE

1511

	Un	U	PB	#	FDC	Q
Perf. 11						
1499 8¢ Harry S. Truman, May 8	.18	.05	1.00		.75	157,052,800
Electronics Progress Issue, July 10						
1500 6¢ Marconi's Spark Coil and Gap	.15	.10	1.25		.75	53,005,000
1501 8¢ Transistor and						
Printed Circuit Board	.18	.05	1.00		.75	159,775,000
1502 15¢ Microphone, Speaker,						
Vacuum Tube, TV Camera	.35	.25	2.25		.80	39,005,000
1503 8¢ Lyndon B. Johnson, Aug. 27	.18	.05	2.50	(12)	.75	152,624,000
Issues of 1973-74, Rural America Issue						
1504 8¢ Angus and Longhorn Cattle,						
by F.C. Murphy, Oct. 5, 1973	.18	.05	1.00		.75	145,840,000
1505 10¢ Chautauqua centenary,						
Aug. 6, 1974	.20	.05	1.00		.75	151,335,000
1506 10¢ Kansas hard winter wheat						
centenary, Aug. 16, 1974	.20	.05	1.00		.75	141,085,000
Perf. 10½x11, Christmas Issue, Nov. 7, 1973						
1507 8¢ Madonna and Child by Raphael	.18	.05	2.10	(12)	.75	885,160,000
1508 8¢ Christmas Tree in Needlepoint	.18	.05	2.10	(12)	.75	939,835,000
Issue of 1973-74, Perf. 11x10½						
1509 10¢ 50-Star and 13-Star Flags, 1973	.20	.05	4.50	(20)	.75	
1510 10¢ Jefferson Memorial						
and Signature, 1973	.20	.05	1.00		.75	
1510b Booklet pane of 5 + label, 1973	1.50	—				
1510c Booklet pane of 8, 1973	2.00	—				
1510d Booklet pane of 6, 1974	2.50	—				
1511 10¢ Mail Transport; "ZIP", 1974	.20	.05	1.80	(8)	.75	

EARLY TELEVISION

Once upon a time there was no television. Today, well over 100 million TV sets are in use in the United States, and the medium has become such a major force in our lives that we tend to forget that in 1949 there were only about 1 million sets.

Yet what is even more surprising is that it took TV so long to take off—given that the first true television broadcast took place in England in 1926.

There are two reasons why it took another 25-35 years after that first broadcast for TV to arrive. The first one was, of course, World War II, which played havoc with the whole world's timetables. The other reason is that TV is not a single invention; it is the product of many individual advances by many people. Before TV could become a true household medium, many more advances in the areas of sending and receiving images were needed.

Today there are television experts who argue that TV is still in its infancy. They point to recent advances—video tape, satellite transmission, cable TV, the VHF bands, the miniaturization of broadcasting and receiving components, and the arrival of two-way TV communication—as evidence that what we have now is just the beginning. See Scott No. 1502.

		Un	U	PB	#	FDC	Q
	1973-74 continued						
	Coil Stamps, Perf. 10 Vertically						
1518	6.3¢ Bells, Oct. 1, 1974	.15	.12			.75	
1519	10¢ red & blue Flags (1509), 1973	.22	.05			.75	
1520	10¢ blue Jefferson Memorial (1510),-73	.22	.05			.75	
	Issues of 1974, Perf. 11						
1525	10¢ V.F.W. Emblem, Mar. 11	.20	.05	1.25		.75	143,930,000
	Perf. 10½ x 11						
1526	10¢ Robert Frost, Mar. 26	.20	.05	1.00		.75	145,235,000
	Perf. 11						
1527	10¢ Cosmic Jumper and Smiling Sage,						
	by Peter Max, Apr. 18	.20	.05	2.60	(12)	.75	135,052,000
	Perf. 11x10½						
1528	10¢ Horses Rounding Turn, May 4	.20	.05	2.60	(12)	.75	156,750,000
	Perf. 11						
1529	10¢ Skylab II, May 14	.20	.05	1.00		.75	164,670,000
	Centenary of UPU Issue, June 6						
1530	10¢ Michelangelo, by Raphael	.20	.15			1.10	23,769,600
1531	10¢ "Five Feminine Virtues,"						
	by Hokusai	.20	.15			1.10	23,769,600
1532	10¢ Old Scraps,						
	by John Frederick Peto	.20	.15			1.10	23,769,600
1533	10¢ The Lovely Reader,						
	by Jean Liotard	.20	.15			1.10	23,769,600
1534	10¢ Lady Writing Letter, by Terborch	.20	.15			1.10	23,769,600
1535	10¢ Inkwell and Quill,						
	by Jean Chardin	.20	.15			1.10	23,769,600
1536	10¢ Mrs. John Douglas,						
	by Thomas Gainsborough	.20	.15			1.10	23,769,600
1537	10¢ Don Antonio Noriega, by Goya	.20	.15			1.10	23,769,600
1537a	Block or strip of 8, #1530-37	1.60	—	1.60		4.25	
	Plate Block of 16			3.40			

1518

1519

1520

1525

1526

1527

1528

1529

1530   1531   1532   1533

1538

1539

1540

1541

1542

1543
1544

1545
1546

1547

1548

1549

1550

1551

1552

		Un	U	PB	#	FDC	Q
	1974 continued						
	Mineral Heritage Issue, June 13						
1538	10¢ Petrified Wood	.20	.08	—		1.50	41,803,200
1539	10¢ Tourmaline	.20	.08			1.50	41,803,200
1540	10¢ Amethyst	.20	.08			1.50	41,803,200
1541	10¢ Rhodochrosite	.20	.08			1.50	41,803,200
1541a	Block of 4, #1538-1541	.80	.65	.80		3.00	
	Plate Block of 4			1.25			
	Nos. 1538-1541 printed in blocks of four in panes of 48.						
1542	10¢ Fort Harrod, June 15	.20	.05	1.00		.75	156,265,000
	American Revolution Bicentennial, First Continental Congress, July 4						
1543	10¢ Carpenter's Hall	.22	.07	1.20		1.10	48,896,250
1544	10¢ "We ask but for Peace,						
	Liberty and Safety"	.22	.07			1.10	48,896,250
1545	10¢ "Deriving their Just Powers"	.22	.07			1.10	48,896,250
1546	10¢ Independence Hall	.22	.07			1.10	48,896,250
1546a	Block of four, #1543-1546	.90	.70	.80		3.00	
	Nos. 1543-1546 printed in blocks of four in panes of 50.						
	Plate Block of 4			1.20			
1547	10¢ Molecules and Drops of Gasoline						
	and Oil, Sept. 22	.20	.05	1.00		.75	148,850,000
1548	10¢ The Headless Horseman, Oct. 10	.20	.05	1.00		.75	157,270,000
1549	10¢ Little Girl, Oct. 12	.20	.05	1.00		.75	150,245,000
	Christmas Issues, 1974						
1550	10¢ Angel, Oct. 23	.20	.05	2.20 (10)		.75	835,180,000
1551	10¢ Sleigh Ride, by Currier and Ives,						
	Oct. 23	.20	.05	2.60 (12)		.75	882,520,000
1552	10¢ Weather Vane; precanceled,						
	Nov. 15, Imperf. Self-adhesive	.22	.07	5.50 (20)		.75	213,155,000

TOURMALINE

Electric gems? Some gems do, in fact, have the ability to generate electricity. One of them is tourmaline, a complex mineral that is found mainly in California, Maine and Brazil.

Tourmaline came to the attention of the Western world when some Dutch children found that the stone, when heated by the sun, would attract and repel ashes and paper. This phenomenon is known as pyroelectricity: the development of positive and negative electricity at opposite ends of the crystal. The same property causes tourmalines to collect far more dust in a heated shop window than other gems.

Tourmaline demonstrates another electrical property known as piezoelectricity— the ability to generate an electric charge under pressure (instead of heat). This property makes tourmaline useful in instrumentation for submarines because the crystals are able to register the depth electrically. See Scott No. 1539.

Tourmaline is used for submarine instrumentation.

		Un	U	PB	#	FDC	Q
	Issues of 1975						
	American Art Issue, Perf. 10½x11, 11						
1553	10¢ Benjamin West, Self-portrait,						
	Feb. 10	.20	.05	2.20	(10)	.75	156,995,000
1554	10¢ Paul Laurence Dunbar, May 1	.20	.05	2.20	(10)	.75	146,365,000
1555	10¢ D. W. Griffith, May 27	.20	.05	1.00		.75	148,805,000
	Space Issue, Perf. 11						
1556	10¢ Pioneer 10, Feb. 28	.20	.05	1.00		1.10	173,685,000
1557	10¢ Mariner 10, Apr. 4	.20	.05	1.00		1.10	158,600,000
1558	10¢ "Labor and Management", Mar. 13	.20	.05	1.80	(8)	.75	153,355,000
	American Bicentennial Issues, Contributors to the Cause, Mar. 25, Perf. 11x10½						
1559	8¢ Sybil Ludington	.18	.11	1.75	(10)	.75	63,205,000
1560	10¢ Salem Poor	.20	.05	2.20	(10)	.75	157,865,000
1561	10¢ Haym Salomon	.20	.05	2.20	(10)	.75	166,810,000
1562	18¢ Peter Francisco	.40	.35	4.00	(10)	.75	44,825,000
	Perf. 11						
1563	10¢ "Birth of Liberty",						
	by Henry Sandham, April 19	.20	.05	2.60	(12)	.75	144,028,000
	Perf. 11x10½						
1564	10¢ Battle of Bunker Hill,						
	by John Trumbull, June 17	.20	.05	2.60	(12)	.75	139,928,000

PAUL LAURENCE DUNBAR

When Stephen Foster was America's favorite composer and Currier and Ives the most admired artists, Paul Laurence Dunbar was the ranking popular poet. Hailed in his twenties as America's foremost black writer, Dunbar wrote six books of poems, four novels, four books of stories and more before his death in 1906 at age 34.

Unfortunately, much of Dunbar's work seems sentimental and melodramatic to today's readers since it reflects the taste of the times for "plantation poetry" and nostalgia for the "good old days" before the Civil War. Dunbar's distinctive use of dialect fits right in with American turn-of-the-century sentimentality, and he enjoyed immense popular appeal among both blacks and whites.

Dunbar, a son and grandson of slaves, was not blind to the evils of his day. His novels painted realistic pictures of the problems faced by freed blacks, both North and South. "A major poet, maybe he was not," writes critic Gossie Harold Hudson, "but the history of American literature would be incomplete without him." See Scott No. 1554.

Paul Laurence Dunbar, one of America's foremost black writers, died at age 34 in 1906.

553

1554

1555

1556

557

1558

YOUTHFUL HEROINE
On the dark night of April 26, 1777, 16-year-old Sybil Ludington rode her horse "Star" alone through the Connecticut countryside rallying her father's militia to repel a raid by the British on Danbury.

1559

GALLANT SOLDIER
The conspicuously courageous actions of black foot soldier Salem Poor at the Battle of Bunker Hill on June 17, 1775, earned him citations for his bravery and leadership ability.

560

FINANCIAL HERO
Businessman and broker Haym Salomon was responsible for raising most of the money needed to finance the American Revolution and later to save the new nation from collapse.

1561

FIGHTER EXTRAORDINARY
Peter Francisco's strength and bravery made him a legend around campfires. He fought with distinction at Brandywine, Yorktown and Guilford Court House.

1562

563

1564

1569
1570

1565   1566
1567   1568

1571

1572   1574
1573   1575

1576

1577   1578

		Un	U	PB	#	FDC	Q
	Military Uniforms, July 4, Perf. 11						
1565	10¢ Soldier with Flintlock Musket,						
	Uniform Button	.22	.07	—	(12)	.90	44,963,750
1566	10¢ Sailor with Grappling Hook,						
	First Navy Jack, 1775	.22	.07			.90	44,963,750
1567	10¢ Marine with Musket,						
	Full-rigged Ship	.22	.07			.90	44,963,750
1568	10¢ Militiaman with Musket,						
	Powder Horn	.22	.07			.90	44,963,750
1568a	Block of 4, #1565-1568	.90	.75	.80	(12)	2.40	
	Plate Block of 12			2.60			
	Apollo-Soyuz Space Issue, July 15, Perf. 11x10½						
1569	10¢ Apollo and Soyuz after Docking,						
	and Earth	.20	.09			1.00	80,931,600
1569a	Pair, #1569-1570	.40	.40	2.60	(12)	2.75	
1570	10¢ Spacecraft before Docking,						
	Earth and Project Emblem	.20	.09				80,931,600
1571	10¢ Worldwide Equality for Women,						
	Aug. 26	.20	.05	1.40	(6)	.75	145,640,000
	Postal Service Bicentennial Issue, Sep. 3						
1572	10¢ Stagecoach and Trailer Truck	.22	.07	2.60	(12)	.75	42,163,750
1573	10¢ Old and New Locomotives	.22	.07			.75	42,163,750
1574	10¢ Early Mail Plane and Jet	.22	.07			.75	42,163,750
1575	10¢ Satellite for Transmission						
	of Mailgrams	.22	.07			.75	42,163,750
1575a	Block of 4, #1572-1575	.90	.75	.80		2.40	
	Plate Block of 12			2.60			
	Perf. 11						
1576	10¢ World Peace, Sept. 29	.20	.05	1.00		.75	146,615,000
	Banking and Commerce Issue, Oct. 6						
1577	10¢ Engine Turning, Indian Head Penny						
	and Morgan Silver Dollar	.20	.06			.75	73,098,000
1577a	Pair, #1577-1578	.40	.35	1.00		1.00	
1578	10¢ Seated Liberty, Quarter, $20 Gold						
	(Double Eagle), Engine Turning	.20	.06	1.00		.75	73,098,000

		Un	U	PB	#	FDC	Q
Christmas Issue, Oct. 14, Perf. 11							
1579	(10¢) Madonna by Domenico						
	Ghirlandaio	.20	.05	2.60	(12)	.75	739,430,000
1580	(10¢) Christmas Card,						
	by Louis Prang, 1878	.20	.05	2.60	(12)	.75	878,690,000
1580b	Perf. 10½x11	—	—				
Issues of 1975-79, Americana, Perf. 11x10½							
1581	1¢ Inkwell & Quill, 1977	.05	.05	.15		.40	
1582	2¢ Speaker's Stand, 1977	.05	.05	.20		.40	
1582b	2¢ Speaker's Stand, Reissue 1982						
1584	3¢ Early Ballot Box, 1977	.06	.05	.30		.40	
1585	4¢ Books, Bookmark, Eyeglasses,	.07	.05	.40		.40	
	Size: 17½x20½mm., 1977						
1590	9¢ Capitol Dome (1591), 1977	.75	.30			1.00	
1590a	Perf. 10	27.50	.10				
	Size: 18½x22½mm.						
1591	9¢ Capitol Dome, 1975	.16	.05	.90		.60	
1592	10¢ Contemplation of Justice, 1977	.17	.05	1.00		.60	
1593	11¢ Printing Press, 1975	.18	.05	1.10		.60	
1594	12¢ Torch	.20	.05				
1595	13¢ Liberty Bell, 1975	.30	.05			.60	
1595a	Booklet pane of 6	1.85	—				
1595b	Booklet pane of 7 + label	2.15	—				
1595c	Booklet pane of 8	2.00	—				
1595d	Booklet pane of 5 + label, 1976	1.75	—				
1596	13¢ Eagle and Shield, 1975	.25	.05	3.38	(12)	.60	
Perf. 11							
1597	15¢ Fort McHenry Flag, 1978	.30	.05	2.10	(6)	.65	
Perf. 11x10½							
1598	15¢ Fort McHenry Flag (1597), 1978	.35	.06			.65	
1598a	Booklet pane of 8	2.50	—				
1599	16¢ Head of Liberty, 1978	.32	.08	1.60		.65	
1603	24¢ Old North Church, 1975	.50	.06	2.40		.75	
1604	28¢ Fort Nisqually, 1978	.60	.06	2.80		1.10	
1605	29¢ Sandy Hook Lighthouse, 1978	.60	.10	2.90		1.10	
1606	30¢ One-room Schoolhouse	.50	.08	3.00		1.10	

No. 1590 is on white paper. No. 1591 on gray paper. Nos. 1590 and 1590a, 1595, 1598 issued only in booklets. Additional American Series, see No. 1813.

1582b

579

1580

1581
1584

1582
1585

591
593

1592
1594

1595d

596
598

1618
1599

1603
1605

1604
1606

1613

1614

1615

1608
1611

1610
1612

1615c

1622

1629   1630   1631

1616

1623a

1632

	1975-79 continued	Un	U	PB	#	FDC	Q
1608	50¢ Whale Oil Lamp	.85	.10	5.00		1.25	
1610	$1 Candle and Rushlight Holder	1.65	.12	10.00		3.00	
1611	$2 Kerosene Table Lamp	3.35	.50	20.00		4.75	
1612	$5 Railroad Lantern	8.50	2.75	50.00		10.00	
	Coil Stamps, Perf. 10 Vertically						
1613	3.1¢ Guitar	.09	.08			.40	
1614	7.7¢ Saxhorns, 1976	.22	.15			.60	
1615	7.9¢ Drum, 1976	.23	.15			.60	
1615C	8.4¢ Piano, 1978	.18	.09			.60	
1616	9¢ Capitol Dome (1591), 1976	.20	.06			.60	
1617	10¢ Contemplation of Justice						
	(1592), 1977	.20	.06			.60	
1618	13¢ Liberty Bell (1595), 1975	.25	.05			.65	
1618C	15¢ Fort McHenry Flag (1597), 1978	.30	.05			.65	
1619	16¢ Head of Liberty (1599), 1978	.35	.10			.60	
	Perf. 11x10½						
1622	13¢ Flag over Independence Hall,-75	.25	.05	5.50 (20)		.65	
1623	13¢ Flag over Capitol, 1977	.30	.06			1.00	
1623a	Booklet pane of 8	2.25	—				
1623b	Perf. 10	1.00	.50				
1623c	Booklet pane of 8, Perf. 10	32.50	—				
	Nos. 1623, 1623b issued only in booklets						
	Coil Stamp, Perf. 10 Vertically						
1625	13¢ Flag over Independence Hall						
	(1622), 1975	.30	.05			.65	
	Issues of 1976						
1629	13¢ Drummer Boy	.25	.07			.65	73,151,666
1630	13¢ Old Drummer	.25	.07			.65	73,151,666
1631	13¢ Fifer	.25	.07			.65	73,151,666
1631a	Spirit of 76, #1629-1631	.75	.60	3.40 (12)		1.75	
	Strip of 3			.78			
1632	Interphil	.25	.05	1.30		.65	157,825,000

INDEPENDENCE HALL

Both the Declaration of Independence and the Constitution were created in the same chamber of the Pennsylvania State House, now known as Independence Hall.

Today the building is a noble American shrine. But it once came dangerously close to destruction by the great events that took place within and around it.

Throughout the colonial period, the Assembly doorkeeper and his family lodged in the building. During the Revolution, it was occupied by the British and later served as a hospital for American soldiers. According to one Congressman, these uses had left it "filthy and sordid," with "the inside torn much to pieces."

Lafayette's 1824 American visit revived interest in restoring the building, which by that time was known as Independence Hall. The City of Philadelphia purchased the hall and square for $70,000—a rescue that one historian deemed "a financial and spiritual investment unequaled in the history of American cities." See Scott No. 1622.

		Un	U	PB	#	FDC	Q
American Bicentennial, State Flags Issue, Feb. 23, 1976							
1633	13¢ Delaware	.50	.40			1.75 ea.	8,720,100
1634	13¢ Pennsylvania	.50	.40				8,720,100
1635	13¢ New Jersey	.50	.40				8,720,100
1636	13¢ Georgia	.50	.40				8,720,100
1637	13¢ Connecticut	.50	.40				8,720,100
1638	13¢ Massachusetts	.50	.40				8,720,100
1639	13¢ Maryland	.50	.40				8,720,100
1640	13¢ South Carolina	.50	.40				8,720,100
1641	13¢ New Hampshire	.50	.40				8,720,100
1642	13¢ Virginia	.50	.40				8,720,100
1643	13¢ New York	.50	.40				8,720,100
1644	13¢ North Carolina	.50	.40				8,720,100
1645	13¢ Rhode Island	.50	.40				8,720,100
1646	13¢ Vermont	.50	.40				8,720,100
1647	13¢ Kentucky	.50	.40				8,720,100
1648	13¢ Tennessee	.50	.40				8,720,100
1649	13¢ Ohio	.50	.40				8,720,100
1650	13¢ Louisiana	.50	.40				8,720,100
1651	13¢ Indiana	.50	.40				8,720,100
1652	13¢ Mississippi	.50	.40				8,720,100
1653	13¢ Illinois	.50	.40				8,720,100
1654	13¢ Alabama	.50	.40			1.75 ea.	8,720,100
1655	13¢ Maine	.50	.40				8,720,100
1656	13¢ Missouri	.50	.40				8,720,100
1657	13¢ Arkansas	.50	.40				8,720,100
1658	13¢ Michigan	.50	.40				8,720,100
1659	13¢ Florida	.50	.40				8,720,100
1660	13¢ Texas	.50	.40				8,720,100
1661	13¢ Iowa	.50	.40				8,720,100
1662	13¢ Wisconsin	.50	.40				8,720,100
1663	13¢ California	.50	.40				8,720,100
1664	13¢ Minnesota	.50	.40				8,720,100
1665	13¢ Oregon	.50	.40				8,720,100
1666	13¢ Kansas	.50	.40				8,720,100
1667	13¢ West Virginia	.50	.40				8,720,100
1668	13¢ Nevada	.50	.40				8,720,100
1669	13¢ Nebraska	.50	.40				8,720,100
1670	13¢ Colorado	.50	.40				8,720,100
1671	13¢ North Dakota	.50	.40				8,720,100
1672	13¢ South Dakota	.50	.40				8,720,100
1673	13¢ Montana	.50	.40				8,720,100
1674	13¢ Washington	.50	.40				8,720,100
1675	13¢ Idaho	.50	.40				8,720,100

633

1634

1635

1636

1637

1638

1639

1640

1641

1642

1643

1644

1645

1646

1647

1648

1649

1650

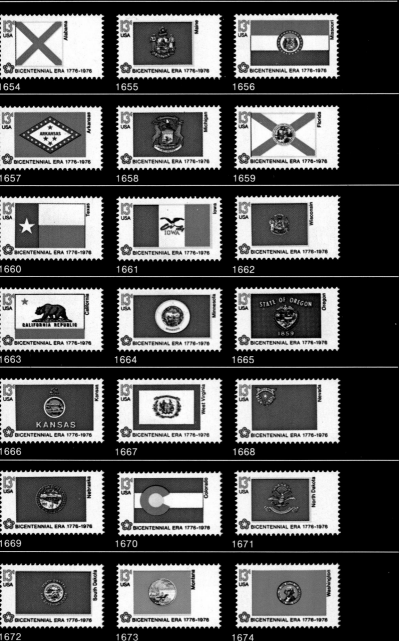

1654   1655   1656

1657   1658   1659

1660   1661   1662

1663   1664   1665

1666   1667   1668

1669   1670   1671

1672   1673   1674

1675

1676

1677

1678

1679

1680

1681

1682

STATE FLAG ISSUE, 1976

*One of the most unusual issues in the history of American stamps was
February 3, 1976. It consisted of a sheet of 50 13-cent stamps, each pic
ferent state flag, arranged in chronological order of the states' entry in*

*In 1876, the year of the national Centennial, only 9 of the 38 states ...
had true state flags: Florida, Georgia, Louisiana, New York, South Ca
Vermont, Virginia and Wisconsin. As individual states began to partic
and exhibitions and develop their state capitals, the number of state f
By 1914, 35 out of 48 states had adopted flags; a dozen years later, eve
Union had a flag to fly for the sesquicentennial.*

*To look at the state flag stamps is to journey through American hist
tral star in the state flag of Arkansas, for example, stands for the Conf
stars on that flag represent the three successive countries to which Ar
belonged—Spain, France and the United States.*

*Several state flags feature an animal or plant for which the state is
California's flag shows a grizzly bear, and Wyoming's displays a buffa
flags pay homage to indigenous Americans. The flag of New Mexico fe
ancient Zuni sun symbol, while Oklahoma's flag displays an Indian w
with eagle feathers. See Scott Nos. 1633-1682.*

The grizzly bear, symbol on
California's state flag.

1683

1684

1685

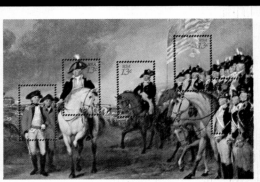

The Surrender of Lord Cornwallis at Yorktown
From a Painting by John Trumbull

1686

The Declaration of Independence, 4 July 1776 at Philadelphia
From a Painting by John Trumbull

1687

	1976 continued	Un	U	PB	#	FDC	Q
1676	13¢ Wyoming	.50	.40				8,720,100
1677	13¢ Utah	.50	.40				8,720,100
1678	13¢ Oklahoma	.50	.40				8,720,100
1679	13¢ New Mexico	.50	.40				8,720,100
1680	13¢ Arizona	.50	.40				8,720,100
1681	13¢ Alaska	.50	.40				8,720,100
1682	13¢ Hawaii	.50	.40				8,720,100
1682a	Sheet of 50, #1633-1682	18.50	—			32.50	
1683	13¢ Bell's Telephone Patent						
	Application, Mar. 10	.25	.05	1.30		.65	159,915,000
1684	13¢ Ford-Pullman Monoplane						
	and Laird Swallow Biplane, Mar. 19	.25	.05	2.90	(10)	.65	156,960,000
1685	13¢ Various Flasks, Separatory Funnel,						
	Computer Tape, Apr. 6	.25	.05	3.40	(12)	.65	158,470,000
	American Bicentennial Issues, Souvenir Sheets, May 29						
	Sheets of 5 Stamps Each						
1686	13¢ Surrender of Cornwallis at Yorktown,						
	by John Trumbull	4.25	4.25			6.00	1,990,000
1687	18¢ Declaration of Independence,						
	by John Trumbull	5.75	5.75			7.50	1,983,000

EARLY CHEMISTRY

What is air? Today we know it's a tasteless, colorless, mostly odorless gas whose major life sustaining element is oxygen. But until the 18th century, the exact nature and composition of air was a deep mystery.

One of the first to probe this question successfully was the Englishman Joseph Priestly (1733-1804). Priestly was a scientist as well as a Unitarian minister, and when he moved in next to a brewery in 1767, he became intrigued by the bubbling gas that rose from the brewing vats.

After learning to produce this gas at home, Priestly tried dissolving it in water. He drank his experiment and found that it yielded "a glass of exceedingly pleasant sparkling water." He didn't know it, but by mixing the gas we know today as carbon dioxide with water, Priestly was paving the way for our soda pop industry.

Priestly's most famous discovery occurred on August 1, 1774, when he heated red mercuric oxide powder, and generated a "new species of air." When he found that mice could live on this gas, Priestly became convinced that our air was not composed—as was previously believed—of just one element.

Yet neither Priestly nor the Swede Carl Wilhelm Scheele (1742-1786), who had isolated the same gas a few years earlier, fully understood the significance of their discovery. It was the great French scientist, Antoine Lavoisier (1743-1794) who made the mental leap. Lavoisier found that the process of burning is the union of the burning substance and this new species of air, which Lavoisier named oxygen.

Together Priestly, Scheele and Lavoisier launched a revolution in the way people viewed their world. They and others made it possible for the modern science of chemistry to develop. Among the details this science has revealed is that our air is composed of nitrogen, oxygen and traces of argon, carbon dioxide, helium, krypton, neon and xenon. See Scott No. 1685.

		Un	U	PB	#	FDC	Q
	1976 continued						
1688	24¢ Washington Crossing the Delaware,						
	by Emanuel Leutze/						
	Eastman Johnson	7.75	7.75			8.50	1,953,000
1689	31¢ Washington Reviewing Army						
	at Valley Forge, by William T. Trego	10.00	10.00			9.50	1,903,000

HARRIET TUBMAN

Harriet Tubman did not make a "good slave." At the age of seven she was beaten because she reached for a lump of sugar from her mistress' table. Five years later, an overseer threw a two-pound weight at her, nearly killing her. She was driven by one passion: freedom for herself and her family.

In 1849, at the age of 29, Harriet escaped from her Maryland master and made her way to Philadelphia. But freedom for herself was not enough. She returned to Baltimore the next year to guide her sister and two children to freedom. In 1851, she spirited out her brother and his family, and five years later she brought out her aged parents. In all, she led more than 300 slaves to freedom in the decade before the Civil War.

Although she could neither write nor read, Harriet Tubman was courageous and shrewd. Once, suspecting pursuers on her trail, she deliberately boarded a south-bound train, certain that no one would think she would head in that direction. On another occasion, she kept 25 runaways hidden all day in a swamp. When one man refused to go on, she put a revolver to his head and told him, "Move or die." A few days later he was safe in Canada.

Harriet Tubman's exploits earned her the title, "the Moses of her people." But in her own eyes, she had no choice. "There was one of two things I had a right to, liberty or death," she said. "If I could not have one, I would have the other . . ." See Scott No. 1744.

Harriet Tubman, far left, with a group of slaves she helped to escape.

Washington Crossing the Delaware
From a Painting by Emanuel Leutze / Eastman Johnson

Washington Reviewing His Ragged Army at Valley Forge
From a Painting by William T. Trego

690

1691   1692   1693   1694

1699

1700

695   1696
697   1698

		Un	U	PB	#	FDC	Q
	1976 continued						
1690	13¢ Franklin and Map						
	of North America, 1776, June 1	.25	.05	1.30		.65	164,890,000
	American Bicentennial Issue, Declaration of Independence, by Trumbull, July 4						
1691	13¢	.25	.07				51,008,750
1692	13¢	.25	.07				51,008,750
1693	13¢	.25	.07				51,008,750
1694	13¢	.25	.07			.65	51,008,750
1694a	Strip of 4, #1691-1694	1.00	.70	5.50	(20)	2.00	
	Plate Block of 20			5.50			
	Olympic Games Issue, July 16						
1695	13¢ Diving	.35	.07			.70	46,428,750
1696	13¢ Skiing	.35	.07			.70	46,428,750
1697	13¢ Running	.35	.07			.70	46,428,750
1698	13¢ Skating	.35	.07			.70	46,428,750
1698a	Block of 4, #1695-1698	1.50	.85			2.00	
1699	13¢ Clara Maass, Aug. 18	.25	.05	3.40	(12)	.65	130,592,000
1700	13¢ Adolph S. Ochs, Sept. 18	.25	.05	1.30		.65	158,332,800
	Christmas Issue, Oct. 27						
1701	13¢ Nativity,						
	by John Singleton Copley	.25	.05	3.40	(12)	.65	809,955,000
	Christmas Issue, Oct. 27, 1976 continued						
1702	13¢ "Winter Pastime,"						
	by Nathaniel Currier	.25	.05	2.86	(10)	.65	481,685,000
1703	13¢ as 1702	.25	.05	5.70	(20)	.65	481,685,000

No. 1702 has overall tagging. Lettering at base is black and usually ½mm. below design. As a rule, no "snowflaking" in sky or pond. Pane of 50 has margins on 4 sides with slogans. No. 1703 has block tagging the size of the printed area. Lettering at base is gray black and usually ¾mm. below design. "Snowflaking" generally in sky and pond. Pane of 50 has margin only at right or left, and no slogans.

CLARA MAASS

One of the most heroic stories to emerge from the Spanish-American War concerns the battle against yellow fever—a disease that conquered more soldiers than the number who fell to bullets.

Clara Maass was in her early twenties when she was assigned as a volunteer nurse to a Cuban inoculation station. There volunteers exposed themselves to infected mosquitos in a grim effort to prove conclusively that the insects carried the disease; they also hoped that a relatively mild attack would render them immune to further infection. Clara Maass volunteered and in June contracted a mild case of yellow fever. It was not severe enough to prove she was immunized, however, and in August she submitted to another bite. This one took her life.

The experiments were instrumental in the victory over yellow fever. Much has been written about the role of the generals in that medical war—Dr. Walter Reed and his associates. In 1976 a simple, thirteen-cent stamp was issued to commemorate the heroic sacrifice of a private: Nurse Clara Maass. See Scott No. 1699.

		Un	U	PB	#	FDC	Q
	Issues of 1977 American Bicentennial, Perf. 11						
1704	13¢ Washington,						
	by Charles Wilson Peale, Jan. 3	.25	.05	2.90	(10)	.65	150,328,000
1705	13¢ Tin Foil Phonograph, Mar. 23	.25	.05	1.30		.65	176,830,000
	Pueblo Indian Art Issue, Apr. 13						
1706	13¢ Zia Pot	.25	.07	3.00	(10)	.65	48,994,000
1707	13¢ San Ildefonso Pot	.25	.07				48,994,000
1708	13¢ Hopi Pot	.25	.07				48,994,000
1709	13¢ Acoma Pot	.25	.07				48,994,000
1709a	Block of 4, #1706-1709	1.10	.90			2.00	
	Plate Block of 10			3.00			
1710	13¢ Spirit of St. Louis, May 20	.25	.05	3.65	(12)	.65	208,820,000
1711	13¢ Columbine and Rocky Mountains,						
	May 21	.25	.05	3.65	(12)	.65	192,250,000
	Butterfly Issue, June 6						
1712	13¢ Swallowtail	.28	.07	3.65	(12)	.65	54,957,500
1713	13¢ Checkerspot	.28	.07				54,957,500
1714	13¢ Dogface	.28	.07				54,957,500
1715	13¢ Orange Tip	.28	.07				54,957,500
1715a	Block of 4, #1712-1715	1.15	.85	3.65	(12)	2.00	
	Plate Block of 12			5.65			
	American Bicentennial Issues						
1716	13¢ Marquis de Lafayette, June 13	.25	.05	1.30		.65	159,852,000
	Skilled Hands for Independence, July 4						
1717	13¢ Seamstress	.30	.07	3.65	(12)	.65	47,077,500
1718	13¢ Blacksmith	.30	.07				47,077,500
1719	13¢ Wheelwright	.30	.07				47,077,500
1720	13¢ Leatherworker	.30	.07				47,077,500
1720a	Block of 4, #1717-1720	1.25	.85	3.65	(12)	2.00	
	Plate Block of 12			5.65			

EARLY PHONOGRAPHS

Of all his many inventions, the phonograph was Thomas Alva Edison's favorite, perhaps because its discovery was so serendipitous.

In July 1877, the man who brought us electric light and power typewriters and motion picture cameras was working on a device to record Morse code messages on waxed paper.

By chance one day, he pulled the embossed waxed paper out from under a spring which rested on it. To his astonishment, the paper produced a musical note.

By the end of November, Edison had developed a working drawing for a device that would record and reproduce the human voice. He instructed an assistant to build a model, and on December 6 the inventor tested it. He recorded his recitation of "Mary had a little lamb," and the words played back clearly.

"I was never so taken aback in my life," he said later. "I was always afraid of things that worked for the first time."

Washington at Princeton 1777 by Peale
US Bicentennial 13c

1704

CENTENNIAL OF SOUND RECORDING

1705

Zia Museum of New Mexico
Pueblo Art USA 13c

San Ildefonso Denver Art Museum
Pueblo Art USA 13c

Hopi Heard Museum Phoenix
Pueblo Art USA 13c

Acoma School of American Research
Pueblo Art USA 13c

1706   1707
1708   1709

50th Anniversary Solo Transatlantic Flight
USA·13c

1710

COLORADO

13c
USA
THE CENTENNIAL STATE

1711

Swallowtail
USA13c *Papilio oregonius*

Checkerspot
USA13c *Euphydryas phaeton*

Dogface
USA13c *Colias eurydice*

Orange-Tip
USA13c *Anthocaris midea*

1712   1713
1714   1715

Lafayette

US Bicentennial 13c

1716

the SEAMSTRESS
for INDEPENDENCE USA 13c

the BLACKSMITH
for INDEPENDENCE USA 13c

the WHEELWRIGHT
for INDEPENDENCE USA 13c

the LEATHERWORKER
for INDEPENDENCE USA 13c

1717   1718
1719   1720

721

1722

1723
1724

725

1726

1727

1729

1730

1731

1734

1735

1737

Surrender at Saratoga 1777 by Trumbull
US Bicentennial 13 cents
1728

1732
1733

	Un	U	PB	#	FDC	Q
1977 continued						
Perf. 11x10½						
1721 13¢ Peace Bridge and Dove, Aug. 4	.25	.05	1.30		.65	163,625,000
American Bicentennial Issue, Perf. 11						
1722 13¢ Herkimer at Oriskany,						
by Yohn Frederick, Aug. 6	.25	.05	3.10	(10)	.65	156,296,000
Energy Issue, Oct. 20						
1723 13¢ Energy Conservation	.25	.06			.65	79,338,000
1723a Pair, #1723-1724	.50	.40	3.65	(12)	1.20	
1724 13¢ Energy Development	.25	.06			.65	79,338,000
American Bicentennial Issues						
1725 13¢ Farm House, Sept. 9	.25	.05	1.30		.65	154,495,000
First civil settlement in Alta, California, 200th anniversary.						
1726 13¢ Articles of Confederation, Sept. 30	.25	.05	1.30		.65	168,050,000
200th anniversary of the Drafting of the Articles of Confederation, York Town, Pa.						
1727 13¢ Movie Projector and						
Phonograph, Oct. 6	.25	.05	1.30		.65	156,810,000
American Bicentennial Issue						
1728 13¢ Surrender of Saratoga,						
by John Trumbull, Oct. 7	.25	.05	3.10	(10)	.65	153,736,000
Christmas Issue, Oct. 21						
1729 13¢ Washington at Valley Forge	.25	.05	5.70	(20)	.65	882,260,000
1730 13¢ Rural Mailbox	.25	.05	3.10	(10)	.65	921,530,000
Issues of 1978, Perf. 11						
1731 13¢ Carl Sandburg, Jan. 6	.25	.05	1.30		.65	156,580,000
Capt. Cook Issue, Jan. 20						
1732 13¢ Capt. Cook	.25	.06	1.30		.70	101,095,000
1732a Pair, #1732-1733	.50	.40			1.50	
1733 13¢ "Resolution" and "Discovery"	.25	.06	1.30		.70	101,095,000
1734 13¢ Indian Head Penny, 1877, Jan. 11	.25	.08	1.30		.90	
1735 (15¢) Eagle (A), May 22	.30	.05	1.50		.65	
Perf. 11x10½						
1736 (15¢) orange Eagle (1735), May 22	.35	.05			.65	
1736a Booklet pane of 8	2.50	—				
1737 15¢ Roses, July 11	.40	.05				
1737a Booklet pane of 8	2.75	—				
Nos. 1736 and 1737 issued only in booklets.						

		Un	U	PB	#	FDC	Q
1977 & 1980 Issues Windmills, Feb. 7, Perf. 11							
1738	15¢ Virginia, 1720	.40	.05			.65	
1739	15¢ Rhode Island, 1790	.40	.05			.65	
1740	15¢ Massachusetts, 1793	.40	.05			.65	
1741	15¢ Illinois, 1860	.40	.05			.65	
1742	15¢ Texas, 1890	.40	.05			.65	
1742a	Booklet pane of 10	3.50	—			6.50	
Coil Stamp, Perf. 10 Vertically							
1743	(15¢) orange Eagle (1735), May 22	.35	.05			.65	
Perf. 11							
1744	13¢ Harriet Tubman, Feb. 1	.25	.05	3.65	(12)	.65	156,555,000
American Folk Art Issue, American Quilts, Mar. 8, 1978							
1745	13¢ Basket design, red & orange	.30	.06			.65	41,295,600
1746	13¢ Basket design, red	.30	.06				41,295,600
1747	13¢ Basket design, orange	.30	.06				41,295,600
1748	13¢ Basket design, black	.30	.06				41,295,600
1748a	Block of 4, #1745-1748	1.20	.75			2.00	
	Plate Block of 12			3.65			
American Dance Issue, Apr. 26							
1749	13¢ Ballet	.30	.06			.65	39,399,600
1750	13¢ Theater	.30	.06				39,399,600
1751	13¢ Folk Dance	.30	.06				39,399,600
1752	13¢ Modern Dance	.30	.06				39,399,600
1752a	Block of 4, #1749-1752	1.20	.75			2.00	
	Plate Block of 12			3.65			
1753	13¢ French Alliance, May 4	.25	.05	1.30		.65	102,920,000
Perf. 10½ x 11							
1754	13¢ Dr. Papanicolaou with Microscope,						
	May 13	.25	.05	1.30		.65	152,355,000
Performing Arts Issue, Perf. 11							
1755	13¢ Jimmie Rodgers, May 24	.25	.06	3.65	(12)	.65	94,625,000
1756	15¢ George M. Cohan, July 3	.28	.05	4.20	(12)	.65	151,570,000

1738   1739   1740   1741   1742

1744

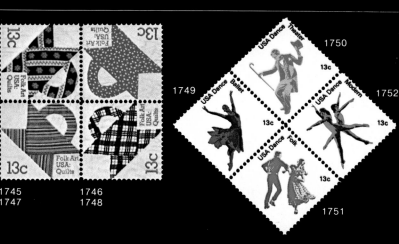

1745
1747

1746
1748

1749

1750

1752

1751

1753

1754

1755

1756

1757

Photography USA 15c

1758

1759

| 1760 | 1761 |
| 1762 | 1763 |

1768   1769

| 1764 | 1765 |
| 1766 | 1767 |

		Un	U	PB	#	FDC	Q
	1978 continued						
1757	13¢ Souvenir sheet of 8, June 10	2.10	2.10			3.50	15,170,400
1758	15¢ Photographic Equipment, June 26	.28	.05	4.20	(12)	.65	163,200,000
1759	15¢ Viking I Landing on Mars, July 20	.28	.05	1.50		.80	158,880,000
	American Owls, Aug. 26						
1760	15¢ Great Gray Owl		.30	.06	1.50	.65	46,637,500
1761	15¢ Saw-whet Owl		.30	.06			46,637,500
1762	15¢ Barred Owl		.30	.06			46,637,500
1763	15¢ Great Horned Owl		.30	.06			46,637,500
1763a	Block of 4, #1760-1763		1.15	.90		2.00	
	American Trees, Oct. 9						
1764	15¢ Giant Sequoia		.30	.06		.65	42,034,000
1765	15¢ White pine		.30	.06			42,034,000
1766	15¢ White Oak		.30	.06			42,034,000
1767	15¢ Gray Birch		.30	.06			42,034,000
1767a	Block of 4, #1764-1767		1.15	.90	4.20	(12)	2.00	
	Plate Block of 12				4.20			
	Christmas Issue, Oct. 18						
1768	15¢ Madonna and Child		.28	.05	4.20	(12)	.65	963,370,000
1769	15¢ Hobby Horse		.28	.05	4.20	(12)	.65	916,800,000

VIKING MARS MISSION

On July 20, 1976, the day America's Viking 1 spacecraft successfully touched down on Mars, the distance between Earth and Mars was approximately 211,750,000 miles. The trip had taken 11 months.

Though no life forms—or even the complex organic compounds that are thought to be the building blocks of life—were found, the Viking twins did relay an incredible wealth of information back to eager scientists.

For example, the Vikings showed that there are indeed some basic similarities between Mars' evolution and Earth's. Yet the Vikings also demonstrated that the differences between Earth and Mars are even more remarkable. Mars' atmosphere is not only oxygen poor, but it is only about one-hundredth as dense as Earth's. And the abundance of water in the Martian atmosphere is now so low that rain is not possible. And if those conditions aren't harsh enough to discourage life, the temperature is. At the height of summer on Mars' northern hemisphere, the temperature rarely climbs above —68° Celsius. See Scott No. 1759.

Relief map of the Mare Australe region of Mars.

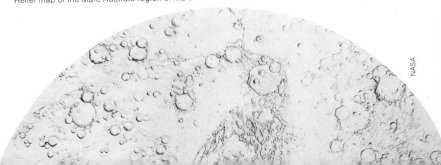

NASA

		Un	U	PB	#	FDC	Q
	Issues of 1979, Perf. 11						
1770	15¢ Robert F. Kennedy, Jan. 12	.28	.05	1.50		.65	159,297,600
1771	15¢ Martin Luther King, Jr., Jan. 13	.28	.05	4.20	(12)	.65	166,435,000
1772	15¢ Internt'l Year of the Child, Feb. 15	.28	.05	1.50		.65	162,535,000
	Perf. 10½ x 11						
1773	15¢ John Steinbeck, Feb. 27	.28	.05	1.50		.65	155,000,000
1774	15¢ Albert Einstein, Mar. 4	.28	.05	1.50		.65	157,310,000
	American Folk Art Issue, Apr. 19, Pennsylvania Toleware						
1775	15¢ Coffeepot	.30	.06			.65	43,524,000
1776	15¢ Tea Caddy	.30	.06				43,524,000
1777	15¢ Sugar Bowl	.30	.06				43,524,000
1778	15¢ Coffeepot	.30	.06				43,524,000
1778a	Block of 4, #1775-1778	1.15	.85			2.00	174,096,000
	Plate Block of 10			3.50			
	American Architecture Issue, June 4						
1779	15¢ Virginia Rotunda	.30	.06	1.50		.65	41,198,400
1780	15¢ Baltimore Cathedral	.30	.06	1.50		.65	41,198,400
1781	15¢ Boston State House	.30	.06	1.50		.65	41,198,400
1782	15¢ Philadelphia Exchange	.30	.06	1.50		.65	41,198,400
1782a	Block of 4, #1779-1782	1.15	.85			2.00	164,793,600
	Endangered Flora Issue, June 7						
1783	15¢ Persistent Trillium	.30	.06			.65	40,763,750
1784	15¢ Hawaiian Wild Broadbean	.30	.06			.65	40,763,750
1785	15¢ Contra Costa Wallflower	.30	.06			.65	40,763,750
1786	15¢ Antioch Evening Primrose	.30	.06			.65	40,763,750
1786a	Block of 4, #1783-1786	1.15	.80			2.00	163,055,000
	Plate Block of 12			4.20			
1787	15¢ Seeing Eye Dogs, June 15	.28	.05	6.50	(20)	.65	161,860,000

JOHN STEINBECK

Americans ravaged by the Depression and the Dust Bowl found an eloquent voice in the fiction of John Steinbeck. With powerfully graphic writing, Steinbeck cried out against social injustice and lauded the dignity and courage of the nation's down-trodden.

From his travels with a group of "Okies"—the nickname given the plains families who left their ruined farms and migrated west—Steinbeck created his finest achievement, The Grapes of Wrath (1939).

Most of his major work, which also includes Of Mice and Men and East of Eden, was written during the thirties and forties. But in 1962 he produced another best-seller when he recounted his cross-country adventures with his pet poodle in Travels with Charley.

A winner of both the Nobel Prize and Pulitzer Prize, Steinbeck saw his fiction translated into 34 languages and successfully adapted for the stage and screen. "Our Land," he wrote in 1966, "wide open, fruitful and incredibly dear and beautiful." Throughout his life, John Steinbeck's faith remained as steadfast as that of his characters. He died in 1968 at age 66 and is buried in his native Salinas, California. See Scott No. 1773.

1770

1771

1772

1773

1774

1775
1777

1776
1778

1787

1779
1781

1780
1782

1783
1785

1784
1786

1788

1789

1790

1791
1793

1792
1794

1799

1800

1795
1797

1796
1798

1801

1802

1803

1804

		Un	U	PB	#	FDC	Q
	1979 continued						
1788	15¢ Special Olympics, Aug. 9	.28	.05	3.50	(10)	.65	165,775,000
1789	15¢ John Paul Jones,						
	by Charles Willson Peale, Sept. 23	.30	.05	3.50	(10)	.65	160,000,000
	Olympic Games Issue, Sept.						
1790	10¢ Javelin	.25	.18	2.75	(12)	.60	67,195,000
1791	15¢ Running	.45	.07	4.25	(12)	.65	46,726,250
1792	15¢ Swimming	.45	.07	4.25	(12)	.65	46,726,250
1793	15¢ Canoeing	.45	.07			.65	46,726,250
1794	15¢ Equestrian	.45	.07			.65	46,726,250
1794a	Block of 4, #1791-1974	1.75	.90			2.00	187,650,000
	Issues of 1980						
	Winter Olympic Games Issue, Feb. 1						
1795	15¢ Speed Skating	.30	.06	4.25	(12)	.65	
1796	15¢ Downhill Skiing	.30	.06	4.25	(12)	.65	
1797	15¢ Ski Jump	.30	.06			.65	
1798	15¢ Hockey Goaltender	.30	.06			.65	
1798a	Block of 4, #1795-1798	1.15	.85			2.00	208,295,000
	Christmas Issue, Oct. 18, 1979						
1799	15¢ Virgin and Child, by Gerard David	.28	.05	4.25	(12)	.65	873,710,000
1800	15¢ Santa Claus	.28	.05	4.25	(12)	.65	931,880,000
1801	15¢ Will Rogers, Nov. 4	.28	.05	4.25	(12)	.65	161,290,000
1802	15¢ Vietnam Veterans, Nov. 11	.28	.05	3.50	(10)	.65	172,740,000
	Perf. 11½ x 11½						
1803	15¢ W.C. Fields, Jan. 29	.28	.05	4.25	(12)	.65	168,995,000
	Perf. 11						
1804	15¢ Benjamin Banneker, Feb. 15	.28	.05	4.25	(12)	.65	160,000,000

BOBBY JONES

Robert Tyre Jones, Jr., the champion amateur golfer who scored the legendary grand slam, lived a life of startling contrasts.

At age 14 Jones played in the 1916 U.S. Amateur, a contest that began his "seven lean years" of brilliant golf without major victories. These years were marred by a violent temper, and he often pitched clubs in disappointment and defeat.

In 1923 Jones ended the seven lean years by winning the U.S. Open, and his "eight fat years" began. Meanwhile, he had graduated from Georgia Tech, Harvard and Emory, was admitted to the bar and had conquered his temper.

The height of Jones' career, of course, was winning the grand slam in 1930: the U.S. Open, British Open, U.S. Amateur and British Amateur. (Lloyd's of London quoted 50 to 1 odds that he wouldn't do it.) When he retired at 28 (an age when many champions are just getting started), he had developed a reputation for the fine sportsmanship that was as famous as his game. See Scott No. 1933.

		Un	U	PB	#	FDC	Q
	1980 continued						
	Letter Writing Issue, Feb. 25						
1805	15¢ Letter Preserve Memories	.32	.07	11.00	(36)	.65	
1806	15¢ P.S. Write Soon	.32	.07	11.00	(36)	.65	
1807	15¢ Letters Lift Spirits	.32	.07	11.00	(36)	.65	
1808	15¢ P.S. Write Soon	.32	.07	11.00	(36)	.65	
1809	15¢ Letters Shape Opinions	.32	.07	11.00	(36)	.65	
1810	15¢ P.S. Write Soon	.32	.07	11.00	(36)	.65	
1810a	15¢ Strip of 6, #1805-1810	1.85	1.35			3.00	233,598,000
	Plate Block of 36			11.00			
	Perf. 10						
1811	1¢ Americana Type Coil, March 6	.05	.05			.65	
1813	3.5¢ Coil, June 23	.10	.08			.65	
1816	12¢ Freedom of Conscience,						
	Apr. 8	.20	.07				
1818	(18¢) "B" Mar. 15	.35	.05				
1819	(18¢) "B" Booklet	.45	.05				
1820	(18¢) "B" Coil	.35	.05				
	Perf. 10½x11						
1821	15¢ Frances Perkins, April 10	.28	.05	1.50		.65	163,510,000
	Perf. 11						
1822	15¢ Dolley Madison, May 20	.28	.05	1.50		.65	256,620,000
1823	15¢ Emily Bissell, May 31	.28	.05	1.50		.65	95,695,000
1824	15¢ Helen Keller/Anne Sullivan,						
	June 27	.28	.05	1.50		.65	153,975,000
1825	15¢ Veterans Administration, July 21	.28	.05	1.50		.65	160,000,000
1826	15¢ General Bernardo de Galvez,						
	July 23	.28	.05	1.50		.65	103,855,000

FRANKLIN DELANO ROOSEVELT

Franklin Delano Roosevelt was never a man to be satisfied with a single activity—even if that activity was the enormously complex one of being President of the United States. His hobbies, interests and "projects" were legion.

Roosevelt's favorite and best known hobby, however, was stamp collecting. He started the hobby as a young boy of ten, under the guidance of his mother, who had collected the Penny Black of 1840 and the first issue of the United States of 1847.

The President's passion for stamps did not stop with collecting. During his presidency he approved 225 new stamp designs, and frequently sketched designs or corrections of his own. One of these was for a six-cent airmail stamp, for which he drew an eagle in flight.

One of Roosevelt's final decisions regarding stamps was a commemorative stamp to mark the opening of the United Nations Conference on International Organization. When he died, just two weeks before the stamp was to appear, the Post Office ordered a revision. The final stamp included the words "Franklin D. Roosevelt," the date, and a laurel branch, in memory of one of the world's best known stamp collectors. See 1982 issues, page 36.

1805   1807   1809
1806   1808   1810

1811   1813   1816   1818

1821

1822

1823   1824   1825   1826

Coral Reefs USA 15c
Brain Coral: U.S. Virgin Islands

Coral Reefs USA 15c
Elkhorn Coral: Florida

Coral Reefs USA 15c
Chalice Coral: American Samoa

Coral Reefs USA 15c
Finger Coral: Hawaii

Organized Labor
Proud and Free
USA 15c

Edith Wharton

USA 15c

Glow by Josef Albers USA 15c
Learning
never ends

1831

1832

1833

1827
1829

1828
1830

Heiltsuk, Bella Bella
Indian Art USA 15c

Chilkat Tlingit
Indian Art USA 15c

Tlingit
Indian Art USA 15c

Bella Coola
Indian Art USA 15c

1834
1836

1835
1837

		Un	U	PB	#	FDC	Q
1980 continued							
Coral Reefs Issue, Aug. 26							
1827	15¢ Brain Coral	.30	.06	4.50	(12)		
1828	15¢ Elkhorn Coral	.30	.06				
1829	15¢ Chalice Coral	.30	.06	4.50	(12)		
1830	15¢ Finger Coral	.30	.06			.65	
1830a	Block of 4, #1827-1830	1.15	.80			2.00	205,165,000
	Plate Block of 12			4.50			
1831	15¢ Organized Labor, Sept. 1	.28	.05	4.50	(12)	.65	166,590,000
1832	15¢ Edith Wharton, Sept. 5	.28	.05	1.50		.65	163,275,000
1833	15¢ American Education, Sept. 12	.28	.05			.65	160,000,000
Indian Art—Masks Issue, Sept. 25							
1834	15¢ Bella Bella	.30	.06			.65	
1835	15¢ Chilkat	.30	.06			.65	
1836	15¢ Tlingit	.30	.06			.65	
1837	15¢ Bella Coola	.30	.06			.65	
1837a	Block of 4, #1834-1837	1.15	.80			2.00	152,404,000
	Plate Block of 10			3.50			

EVERETT DIRKSEN

Most politicians seek distinction by cultivating a neat, tailored appearance. Not Everett Dirksen. During his 35 years in the U.S. Congress, Dirksen sought to stand out by cultivating a rumpled appearance. His baggy pants and deliberately mussed hair made him a cartoonist's delight. In 1967, Newsweek *magazine described him as a "rather noble old ruin—a Victorian relic with misty blue eyes, a tiara of gray-gold ringlets run amok, and the melancholy mien of a homeless bassett hound."*

Perhaps the most distinctive aspect of the Illinois Congressman was his oratory. His voice became one of the most readily identifiable in the country, his style rambling and full of irrelevancies. Dirksen joked about his meanderings: "I have a surprise for you," he told his fellow Senators one day. "I shall depart from my usual custom and talk about the bill that is up for discussion today."

But behind the "just plain folks" image lurked a professional legislator who, during his long years of minority party status, was responsible for some of the most important laws of our time, including the civil rights acts of the 1960s.

When he died in 1969, Dirksen was honored as only three Senators had been before him. He lay in state under the great Capitol dome—the same spot that had once borne the body of Abraham Lincoln. See Scott No. 1874.

		Un	U	PB	#	FDC	Q
	1980 continued						
	American Architecture Issue, Oct. 9						
1838	15¢ Smithsonian	.30	.06				
1839	15¢ Trinity Church	.30	.06				
1840	15¢ Pennsylvania Academy of						
	Fine Arts	.30	.06				
1841	15¢ Lyndhurst	.30	.06				
1841a	Block of 4, #1838-1841	1.15	.80				155,024,000
	Plate Block of 4			1.50			
1842	15¢ Christmas Stained Glass Windows,						
	Oct. 16	.28	.05			.65	693,250,000
1843	15¢ Christmas Antique Toys,						
	Oct. 16	.28	.05			.65	718,715,000
	Issues of 1980-1981 continued						
	Great Americans Issue						
1849	17¢ Rachel Carson, May 28, '81	.28	.06	1.75		.75	
1850	18¢ George Mason, May 7, '81	.30	.05	1.75		.75	
1851	18¢ Sequoyah, Dec. 27, '80	.32	.07	2.00		.80	
1859	35¢ Dr. Charles Drew, June 3, '81	.55	.07	3.50		1.00	
	Issues of 1981						
1874	15¢ Everett Dirksen, Jan. 4	.28	.05	1.50		.65	160,155,000
1875	15¢ Whitney Moore Young, Jr.,						
	Jan. 30	.28	.05	1.50		.65	159,505,000
	Flower Issue, April 23						
1876	18¢ Rose	.35	.06			.75	52,658,250
1877	18¢ Camellia	.35	.06			.75	52,658,250
1878	18¢ Dahlia	.35	.06			.75	52,658,250
1879	18¢ Lily	.35	.06			.75	52,658,250
1879a	Block of 4, #1876-1879	1.35	.85	1.75		2.50	

CRAZY HORSE MONUMENT

When it's finished some time in the future, Korczak Ziolkowski's monument to the legendary Oglala Sioux chief Crazy Horse will be the world's largest sculpture: 513 feet high by 641 feet long.

It will be so big that 4,000 men would be able to stand on Crazy Horse's outstretched arm. A five-room house would fit comfortably inside one flaring nostril of the stallion he rides. And all four of the majestic presidential heads that make up neighboring Mt. Rushmore (22 miles east) would fit inside Crazy Horse's head.

The idea for this monumental work came from Henry Running Bear, a Sioux Chief and nephew of Crazy Horse—who in his short life also proved a cunning and able warrior. He regularly out-fought the U.S. Cavalry, and played a major role in the defeat of Col. George A. Custer in the famous battle of the Little Big Horn.

Chief Running Bear asked Ziolkowski to carve the statue because of Ziolkowski's experience working under Gutzon Borglum on Mt. Rushmore, and because, he said, "My fellow chiefs and I would like the white man to know that the red man had great heroes, too." See 1982 issues, page 35.

1842   1843

1838   1839
1840   1841

1849   1850   1851   1859

1874   1875

1876   1877
1878   1879

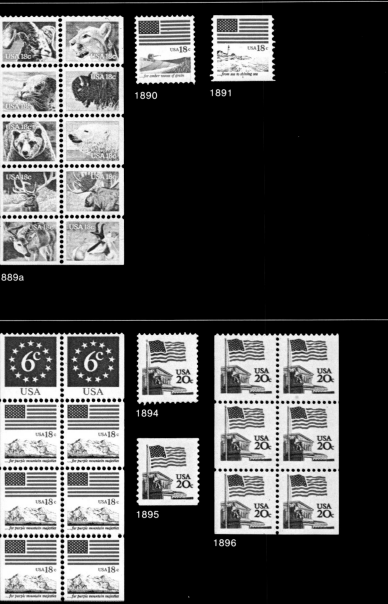

889a

1890

1891

1894

1895

1896

		Un	U	PB	#	FDC	Q
	1981 continued						
	Wildlife Issue, May 14						
1880	18¢ Bighorned Sheep	.38	.06			.75	
1881	18¢ Puma	.38	.06			.75	
1882	18¢ Harbor Seal	.38	.06			.75	
1883	18¢ Bison	.38	.06			.75	
1884	18¢ Brown Bear	.38	.06			.75	
1885	18¢ Polar Bear	.38	.06			.75	
1886	18¢ Elk (wapiti)	.38	.06			.75	
1887	18¢ Moose	.38	.06			.75	
1888	18¢ White Tailed Deer	.38	.06			.75	
1889	18¢ Prong Horned Antelope	.38	.06			.75	
1889a	Booklet Pane of 10, #1880-1889	3.50				7.00	
	Flag Issue, April 24						
1890	18¢ Flag and Anthem, for amber						
	waves of grain	.30	.05	7.50 (20)		.75	
1891	18¢ Flag and Anthem, from sea						
	to shining sea, coil	.35	.05			.75	
1892	6¢ USA Circle of Stars	.25	.10			.75	
1893	18¢ Flag and Anthem, for purple						
	mountains majesties, booklet	.35	.06			.75	
1893a	Booklet Pane of 8,						
	2 #1892, 6 #1893	2.35	—				
1894	20¢ Flag over Supreme Court	.33	.05				
1895	20¢ Flag over Supreme Court,						
	coil	.33	.05				
1896	20¢ Flag over Supreme Court,						
	booklet	.35	.05				

JACKIE ROBINSON

In the spring of 1947, a young baseball player stepped up to the plate in his first game as a Brooklyn Dodger, swung the bat and sent a wall crashing to the ground. That barrier was the "color wall," and Jackie Robinson, 28, had become the first black player to break into the all-white major leagues.

Just 35 years ago, baseball was still one of the last segregated sports in America. Black players, many with records equalling or surpassing white stars of the era, were restricted to the Negro National League. Robinson was a superlative athlete, but when he signed with Dodger President Branch Rickey, the ballplayer knew that the major leagues would be a test of both his skill and courage.

Robinson led the league in stolen bases, and was named Rookie of the Year. A legendary career was launched.

Jackie Robinson retired in 1957, knowing that his dream of being baseball's first black manager would not be fulfilled. But at the time of his death in 1972, a door that had been previously closed to young black athletes was now open, and Jackie Robinson helped make baseball a truly all-American sport. See 1982 issues, page 47.

		Un	U	PB	#	FDC	Q
	1981 continued						
	Transportation Issues						
1900	9.3¢ Mail Wagon	.15	.06				
1905	17¢ Electric Auto, June 25	.30	.05			.75	
1906	18¢ Surrey, May 18	.30	.05			.75	
1907	20¢ Fire Pumper	.33	.05				
1910	18¢ American Red Cross, May 1	.33	.05	1.75		.75	165,175,000
1911	18¢ Savings and Loan, May 8	.33	.05	1.75		.75	107,240,000
	Space Achievement Issue, May 21						
1912	18¢ Exploring the Moon	.35	.10			.75	42,227,375
1913	18¢ Benefitting Mankind	.35	.10			.75	42,227,375
1914	18¢ Benefitting Mankind	.35	.10			.75	42,227,375
1915	18¢ Understanding the Sun	.35	.10			.75	42,227,375
1916	18¢ Probing the Planets	.35	.10			.75	42,227,375
1917	18¢ Benefitting Mankind	.35	.10			.75	42,227,375
1918	18¢ Benefitting Mankind	.37	.10			.75	42,227,375
1919	18¢ Comprehending the						
	Universe	.35	.10			.75	42,227,375
1919a	Block of 8, #1912-1919	2.65	1.75	3.50	(8)	5.00	
1920	18¢ Professional Management,						
	June 18	.33	.05	1.75		.75	99,420,000

EMILY BISSELL

In 1907 Dr. Joseph P. Wales asked Emily Bissell to help him raise money for a small tuberculosis hospital in Delaware. She started out in December with a goal of $300 and in three weeks raised ten times that amount. In the process she started the nation's first Christmas Seal campaign.

Bissell got the idea from a magazine article about a Christmas stamp program in Denmark. She sketched a design for a red cross surrounded by holly and inscribed, "Merry Christmas." A printer agreed to put out 50,000 stamps and wait for his pay until after they were sold. The stamps went on sale December 7, 1907, in the Wilmington, Delaware, post office. The first day's results were hardly encouraging: less than $25 sold.

Four days later Emily Bissel went to Philadelphia and won the backing of the city's leading newspaper, the North American. Within three weeks almost 400,000 stamps were sold. Since then the Christmas Seal campaign has become an annual nationwide event to raise money to fight tuberculosis and other lung diseases.

In 1942 Emily Bissell won the Trudeau Medal of the National Tuberculosis Association, the first person outside the medical profession to receive it. Her work in social welfare also led to Delaware's first child labor law, first children's playground, first free gym for boys, first Boys' Brigade (a forerunner of the Boy Scouts) and first free kindergarten. See Scott No. 1823.

Symbol of the Christmas Seal.

1900   1905   1906   1907

1910   1911

 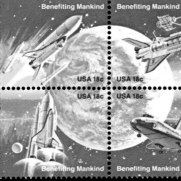  

1912   1913   1914   1915
1916   1917   1918   1919

1920

1925

1926

1921
1923

1922
1924

1927

1928
1930

1929
1931

1934

1932

1933

		Un	U	PB	#	FDC	Q
	1981 continued						
	Wildlife Habitat Issue, June 26						
1921	18¢ Wetland Habitats	.35	.06			.75	46,732,500
1922	18¢ Grassland Habitats	.35	.06			.75	46,732,500
1923	18¢ Mountain Habitats	.35	.06			.75	46,732,500
1924	18¢ Woodland Habitats	.35	.06			.75	46,732,500
1924a	Block of 4, #1921-1924	1.35	.80	1.75		2.50	
1925	18¢ International Year of the						
	Disabled, June 29	.33	.05	1.75		.75	100,265,000
1926	18¢ Edna St. Vincent Millay,						
	July 10	.30	.05	1.75		.75	99,615,000
1927	18¢ Alcoholism, Aug. 19	.33	.05	8.00	(20)	.75	97,535,000
	American Architecture Issue, Aug. 28						
1928	18¢ NYU Library	.35	.06			.75	41,827,000
1929	18¢ Biltmore House	.35	.06			.75	41,827,000
1930	18¢ Palace of the Arts	.35	.06			.75	41,827,000
1931	18¢ National Farmer's Bank	.35	.06			.75	41,827,000
1931a	Block of 4, #1928-1931	1.35	.80	1.75		2.50	
1932	18¢ Babe Zaharias, Sept. 22	.30	.05	1.75		.75	101,625,000
1933	18¢ Bobby Jones, Sept. 22	.30	.05	1.75		.75	99,170,000
1934	18¢ Remington Sculpture, Oct. 9	.30	.05			.75	101,155,000
1935	18¢ James Hoban, Oct. 13	.30	.05			.75	101,200,000
1936	20¢ James Hoban, Oct. 13	.33	.05			.75	167,360,000

IGOR STRAVINSKY

Igor Stravinsky's The Rite of Spring *is widely regarded as the single most important piece of symphonic music composed in the first half of our century. Yet like many works of genius, it scandalized its first audiences.*

The first two people to hear the piece were Pierre Monteux, conductor of the Ballets Russes, and producer Sergei Diaghilev. Stravinsky played the entire score for them on a piano in a tiny rehearsal room of a Monte Carlo Theater.

"I was convinced he was raving mad," Monteux recalled. "The very walls resounded as Stravinsky pounded away, occasionally stamping his feet and jumping up and down to accentuate the force of the music. Not that it needed such emphasis."

Still, Monteux recognized that Stravinsky was far ahead of his time. The Rite of Spring *made its debut in Paris on May 29, 1913. At first the audience just squirmed. Then low murmurs escalated to hoots and catcalls, and finally there was a mass stampede to the exit. The score was better received in America. After the first Boston performance, in January 1924, the critic H.T. Parker called Stravinsky's work a "masterpiece" that would become a "beacon and goal to a whole generation of composers up and down the European and American earth." Indeed, it has. See 1982 issues, page 34.*

		Un	U	PB	#	FDC	Q
	Issues of 1981 continued						
1937	20¢ Yorktown 1781, Oct. 16	.35	.06			.75	81,210,000
1938	20¢ Virginia Capes 1781, Oct. 16	.35	.06			.75	81,210,000
1938a	Pair, #1937-1938	.65	.40			1.00	
1939	(20¢) Christmas Madonna,						
	Oct. 28	.37	.05			.75	597,720,000
1940	(20¢) Christmas Child Art, Oct. 28	.37	.05			.75	792,600,000
1941	20¢ John Hanson, Nov. 5	.33	.05			.75	167,130,000
	U.S. Desert Plants Issue, December						
1942	20¢ Barrel Cactus	.35	.06			.75	47,890,000
1943	20¢ Agave	.35	.06			.75	47,890,000
1944	20¢ Beavertail Cactus	.35	.06			.75	47,890,000
1945	20¢ Saguaro	.35	.06			.75	47,890,000
1945a	Block of 4, #1942-1945	1.35	.80			1.50	
1946	(20¢) "C" Eagle	.33	.05				
1947	(20¢) "C" Eagle, coil	.33	.05				
1948	(20¢) "C" Eagle, booklet	.35	.05				

HORATIO ALGER

If you were a boy during the 1800s and wanted something to read, chances are you'd reach for a book by Horatio Alger. You'd have a wide selection—Alger wrote over 100 novels for children, almost all of them tales of young people who became rich beyond their dreams by a combination of "luck and pluck" (an actual Alger title). Horatio Alger books like Ragged Dick, Tattered Tom *and* Dan The Newsboy *are seldom read today, but his influence on a generation was so great that his name entered our language. We still call rags-to-riches success "a real Horatio Alger story."*

From Alger's birth in 1834, it was decided that he should become a Unitarian clergyman like his father. Nicknamed "Holy Horatio" by his friends, young Alger dutifully, if somewhat circuitously, embarked on the required training. At Harvard Divinity School, Alger won an essay contest and realized his real calling was writing. But he hesitated to disappoint his parents, and it was not until six years later that he resigned his pulpit and moved to New York to write.

He soon found his inspiration. On an evening walk he discovered the Newsboy's Lodging House, and quickly became a frequent visitor, winning the confidences of the boys who lived there. From his observations came Alger's first success, Ragged Dick, *or* Street Life in New York With The Boot-Blacks. *Many more volumes followed, based on these boys' experiences.*

Victorian parents approved of Alger's fiction because virtue and hard work were always lavishly rewarded, but children loved him simply because he knew how to tell a good story. His heroes and situations were highly idealized, but they always rang true through his sentimental prose. He vividly captured the "exotic" world of big city streets and packed his fast-paced novels with plenty of incredible adventures.

Despite his enormous success—his works sold over 30 million copies—Alger yearned to write a serious novel for adults. But children's books proved too lucrative a temptation, and he never succeeded in pursuing his dream. He died in 1899 a frustrated man, but gained some consolation in knowing that he had entertained millions of children. See 1982 issues, page 45.

1935

1936

1937

1938

1939

1940

1941

1942

1943
1944

1945

1946

AIR MAIL STAMPS
SPECIAL DELIVERY STAMPS

		Un	U	PB	#	FDC	Q
	Air Post Stamps						
	For prepayment of postage on all mailable matter sent by airmail. All unwatermarked.						
	Issue of 1918, Perf. 11						
C1	6¢ Curtiss Jenny	150.00	47.50	2,250.00	(6)	18,000.00	3,395,854
C2	16¢ Curtiss Jenny	210.00	67.50	4,850.00	(6)	18,000.00	3,793,887
C3	24¢ Curtiss Jenny	225.00	71.50	1,250.00		21,000.00	2,134,888
C3a	Center Inverted		145,000.00				
	Issue of 1923						
C4	8¢ Wooden Propeller and						
	Engine Nose	60.00	26.50	1,200.00	(6)	750.00	6,414,576
C5	16¢ Air Service Emblem	200.00	60.00	6,250.00	(6)	1,250.00	5,309,275
C6	24¢ De Havilland Biplane	240.00	50.00	7,000.00	(6)	1,400.00	5,285,775
	Issue of 1926-27						
C7	10¢ Map of U.S.						
	and Two Mail Planes	9.00	.55	125.00	(6)	110.00	42,092,800
C8	15¢ olive brown (C7)	10.50	3.35	150.00	(6)	125.00	15,597,307
C9	20¢ yellow green (C7)	30.00	3.00	325.00	(6)	150.00	17,616,350
	Issue of 1927						
C10	10¢ Lindbergh's "Spirit of						
	St. Louis," June 18	21.00	3.75	325.00	(6)	40.00	20,379,179
C10a	Booklet pane of 3	165.00	—				
	Nos. C1-C10 inclusive were also available for ordinary postage.						
	Issue of 1928						
C11	5¢ Beacon on Rocky Mountains,						
	July 25	11.50	.75	100.00	(6)	50.00	106,887,675
C12	5¢ Winged Globe, Feb. 10	26.50	.55	400.00	(6)	20.00	97,641,200
	Graf Zeppelin Issue, Apr. 19						
C13	65¢ Zeppelin over Atlantic Ocean	535.00	500.00	7,250.00	(6)	3,500.00	93,536
C14	$1.30 Zeppelin between						
	Continents	1,100.00	850.00	16,500.00	(6)	2,600.00	72,428
C15	$2.60 Zeppelin Passing Globe	1,800.00	1,300.00	24,500.00	(6)	3,750.00	61,296
	Issued for use on mail carried on the first Europe-Pan-American round-trip flight of Graf Zeppelin, May 1930.						
	Issues of 1931-32, Perf. 10½x11						
C16	5¢ violet (C12)	12.00	.55	250.00		350.00	57,340,050
C17	8¢ olive bistre (C12)	5.00	.30	90.00		20.00	76,648,803

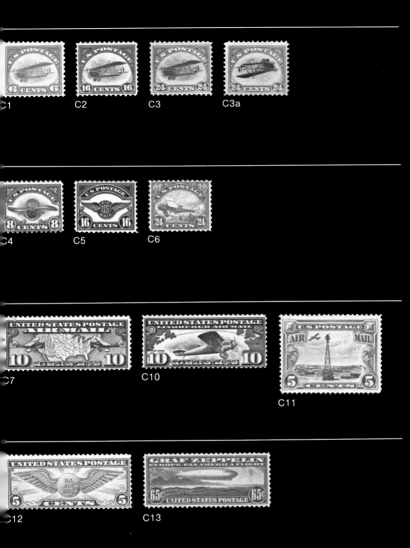

C1   C2   C3   C3a

C4   C5   C6

C7   C10   C11

C12   C13

C14   C15

C18

C20

C21

C23

C24

C25

C32

C33

C34

		Un	U	PB	#	FDC	Q
	Issue of 1933, Perf. 11						
C18	50¢ Century of Progress, Oct. 2	200.00	175.00	2,250.00	(6)	400.00	324,070
	Issue of 1934, Perf. 10½x11						
C19	6¢ dull orange (C12), July 1	6.50	.11	45.00		200.00	302,205,100
	Issue of 1935, Perf. 11						
C20	25¢ Transpacific, Nov. 22	4.00	1.70	75.00	(6)	50.00	10,205,400
	Issue of 1937						
C21	20¢ The "China Clipper" over the						
	Pacific, Feb. 15	26.50	2.35	350.00	(6)	50.00	12,794,600
C22	50¢ carmine (C21)	26.50	6.75	325.00	(6)	50.00	9,285,300
	Issue of 1938						
C23	6¢ Eagle Holding Shield,						
	Olive Branch, and Arrows, May 14	.70	.09	12.50		20.00	349,946,500
	Issue of 1939						
C24	30¢ Transatlantic, May 16	25.00	1.75	375.00	(6)	40.00	19,768,150
	Issues of 1941-44, Perf. 11x10½						
C25	6¢ Twin-motor Transport Plane, 1941	.18	.05	1.00		1.50	4,476,527,700
C25a	Booklet pane of 3	6.00	—				
	Singles No. C25a are imperf. at sides or imperf. at sides and bottom.						
C26	8¢ olive green (C25), 1944	.23	.05	1.50		3.00	1,744,876,650
C27	10¢ violet (C25), 1941	2.25	.15	20.00		5.00	67,117,400
C28	15¢ brown carmine (C25), 1941	5.75	.28	24.00		7.50	78,434,800
C29	20¢ bright green (C25), 1941	3.75	.30	22.50		7.50	42,359,850
C30	30¢ blue (C25), 1941	4.75	.28	25.00		12.50	59,880,850
C31	50¢ orange (C25), 1941	30.00	4.00	200.00		32.50	11,160,600
	Issue of 1946						
C32	5¢ DC-4 Skymaster, Sept. 25	.12	.05	.75		1.50	864,753,100
	Issues of 1947, Perf. 10½x11						
C33	5¢ DC-4 Skymaster, Mar. 26	.12	.05	.75		1.00	971,903,700
	Perf. 11x10½						
C34	10¢ Pan American Union Building,						
	Washington, D.C., Aug. 30	.35	.06	2.50		2.00	207,976,550
C35	15¢ Statue of Liberty						
	and New York Skyline, Aug. 20	.40	.06	2.85		2.75	756,186,350
C36	25¢ Plane over San Francisco-						
	Oakland Bay Bridge, July 30	1.50	.08	7.50		3.50	132,956,100
	Issues of 1948						
	Coil Stamp, Perf. 10 Horizontally						
C37	5¢ carmine (C33), Jan. 15	1.40	1.25			1.75	Unlimited
	Perf. 11x10½						
C38	5¢ New York City, July 31	.13	.12	25.00		1.35	38,449,100

	Issues of 1949	Un	U	PB	#	FDC	Q
	Perf. 10½x11						
C39	6¢ carmine (C33), Jan. 18	.15	.05	.85		1.00	5,070,095,200
C39a	Booklet pane of 6	17.50	—				
	Perf. 11x10½						
C40	6¢ Alexandria 200th Anniv., May 11	.15	.10	.95		1.00	75,085,000
	Coil Stamp, Perf. 10 Horizontally						
C41	6¢ carmine (C33), Aug. 25	4.50	.06			1.10	Unlimited
	Universal Postal Union Issue, Perf. 11x10½						
C42	10¢ Post Office Dept. Bldg., Nov. 18	.35	.35	4.75		1.50	21,061,300
C43	15¢ Globe and Doves Carrying						
	Messages, Oct. 7	.40	.40	3.75		1.75	36,613,100
C44	25¢ Boeing Stratocruiser						
	and Globe, Nov. 30	.75	.70	15.00		2.25	16,217,100
C45	6¢ Wright Brothers, Dec. 17	.20	.10	1.00		3.00	80,405,000
	Issue of 1952						
C46	80¢ Diamond Head, Honolulu,						
	Hawaii, Mar. 26	15.00	1.25	100.00		15.00	18,876,800
	Issue of 1953						
C47	6¢ Powered Flight, May 29	.15	.12	.85		1.50	78,415,000
	Issue of 1954						
C48	4¢ Eagle in Flight, Sept. 3	.10	.09	6.00		.75	50,483,600
	Issue of 1957						
C49	6¢ Air Force, Aug. 1	.15	.10	1.50		1.75	63,185,000
	Issues of 1958						
C50	5¢ rose red (C48), July 31	.20	.15	5.00		.80	72,480,000
	Perf. 10½x11						
C51	7¢ Silhouette of Jet Liner, July 31	.20	.05	1.30		.75	532,410,300
C51a	Booklet pane of 6	16.50	—				1,326,960,000
	Coil Stamp, Perf. 10 Horizontally						
C52	7¢ blue (C51)	4.50	.10			.90	157,035,000
	Issues of 1959, Perf. 11x10½						
C53	7¢ Alaska Statehood, Jan. 3	.20	.09	1.75		.65	90,055,200
	Perf. 11						
C54	7¢ Balloon Jupiter, Aug. 17	.20	.09	1.75		1.10	79,290,000
	Issued for the 100th anniversary of the carrying of mail by the balloon Jupiter from Lafayette to Crawfordsville, Indiana.						
	Perf. 11x10½						
C55	7¢ Hawaii Statehood, Aug. 21	.20	.09	1.75		1.00	84,815,000
	Perf. 11						
C56	10¢ Pan-American Games, Aug. 27	.35	.30	8.00		.90	38,770,000
	Issue of 1959-66						
C57	10¢ Liberty Bell, June 10,1960	3.00	.80	15.00		1.50	39,960,000
C58	15¢ Statue of Liberty, Jan. 13, 1961	.60	.08	5.00		1.10	Unlimited
C59	25¢ Abraham Lincoln, Apr. 22, 1960	.60	.06	4.00		1.50	Unlimited

C40

C42

C43

C44

C45

C46

C47

C48

C49

C51

C53

C54

C55

C56

C57

C58

C59

C60

C62

C63

C64

C66

C67

C68

C69

C70

C71

C72

C74

C75

C76

C77

C78

C79

	Issue of 1960, Perf. 10½x11	Un	U	PB	#	FDC	Q
C60	7¢ Jet Airliner (C51), Aug. 12	.20	.05	1.50		.70	289,460,000
C60a	Booklet pane of 6	21.50	—				
	Coil Stamp, Perf. 10 Horizontally						
C61	7¢ carmine (C60), Oct. 22	7.75	.25			1.00	87,140,000
	Issue of 1961, Perf. 11						
C62	13¢ Liberty Bell, June 28,1961	.65	.10	7.00		.80	Unlimited
C63	15¢ Statue of Liberty, Jan. 13, 1961	.35	.06	2.25		1.00	Unlimited
	No. C63 has a gutter between the two parts of the design; No. C58 does not.						
	Issue of 1962, Perf. 10½x11						
C64	8¢ Jetliner over Capitol, Dec. 5	.20	.05	1.10		.60	Unlimited
C64c	Booklet pane of 5 + label	2.25	—				
	Coil Stamp, Perf. 10 Horizontally						
C65	8¢ carmine (C64), Dec. 5	.40	.06			.80	Unlimited
	Issue of 1963, Perf. 11						
C66	15¢ Montgomery Blair, May 3	1.30	.70	14.00		1.35	42,245,000
	Issues of 1963, Perf. 11x10½						
C67	6¢ Bald Eagle, July 12	.18	.14	5.00		.50	Unlimited
	Perf. 11						
C68	8¢ Amelia Earhart, July 24	.35	.12	5.25		2.10	63,890,000
	Issue of 1964						
C69	8¢ Robert H. Goddard, Oct. 5	1.00	.12	7.50		2.75	65,170,000
	Issues of 1967						
C70	8¢ Alaska Purchase, Mar. 30	.45	.18	10.00		.70	64,710,000
C71	20¢ "Columbia Jays" by Audubon,						
	Apr. 26	1.65	.09	10.00		2.00	165,430,000
	Issues of 1968, Perf. 11x10½						
C72	10¢ 50-Star Runway, Jan. 5	.30	.05	2.25		.60	Unlimited
C72b	Booklet pane of 8	3.25	—				
C72c	Booklet pane of 5 + label	4.75	—				
	Coil Stamp, Perf. 10 Vertically						
C73	10¢ carmine (C72)	.45	.05			.60	Unlimited
	Air Mail Service Issue, Perf. 11						
C74	10¢ Curtiss Jenny, May 15	.45	.14	13.50		1.50	74,180,000
C75	20¢ U.S.A. and Jet, Nov. 22	1.00	.08	6.50		1.10	Unlimited
	Issue of 1969						
C76	10¢ Moon Landing, Sept. 9	.25	.15	3.50		1.75	152,364,800
	Issues of 1971-73, Perf. 10½x11, 11x10½						
C77	9¢ Plane, May 15, 1971	.20	.15	3.00		.50	Unlimited
C78	11¢ Silhouette of Jet, May 7, 1971	.25	.05	1.35		.50	Unlimited
C78a	Booklet pane of 4 + 2 labels	1.25	—				
C79	13¢ Winged Airmail Envelope,						
	Nov. 16, 1973	.28	.05	1.65		.55	Unlimited
C79a	Booklet pane of 5 + label,						
	Dec. 27, 1973	1.60	—				

		Un	U	PB	#	FDC	Q
	1971-73 continued						
	Perf. 11						
C80	17¢ Statue of Liberty, July 13, 1971	.45	.10	2.75		.60	Unlimited
	Perf. 11x10½						
C81	21¢ red, blue and black (C75)						
	May 21, 1971	.45	.08	2.75		.75	Unlimited
	Coil Stamps, Perf. 10 Vertically						
C82	11¢ Silhouette of Jet, May 7, 1971	.30	.05			.50	Unlimited
C83	13¢ red (C79), Dec. 27, 1973	.35	.05			.50	
	Issues of 1972, Perf. 11						
C84	11¢ City of Refuge, May 3	.25	.10	2.75		.65	78,210,000
	Perf. 11x10½						
C85	11¢ Skiing and Olympic Rings,						
	Aug. 17	.25	.10	3.50	(10)	.50	96,240,000
	Issue of 1973						
C86	11¢ De Forest Audions, July 10	.25	.10	1.75		.50	58,705,000
	Issues of 1974, Perf. 11						
C87	18¢ Statue of Liberty, Jan. 11	.40	.30	2.50		.65	Unlimited
C88	26¢ Mt. Rushmore National						
	Memorial, Jan. 2	.55	.10	2.85		.85	Unlimited
	Issue of 1976						
C89	25¢ Plane & Globes, Jan. 2	.55	.15	2.50		.85	
C90	31¢ Plane, Globes & Flag, Jan. 2	.65	.08	3.10		1.10	
	Issues of 1978, Wright Brothers Issue, Sept. 23						
C91	31¢ Orville & Wilbur Wright	.80	.15	3.10		1.15	
C92	31¢ Orville & Wilbur Wright	.80	.15	3.10		1.15	
C92a	Pair, #C91-C92	1.50	.70			2.30	
	Issues of 1979, Octave Chanute Issue, March 29						
C93	21¢ Octave Chanute	.55	.30	2.10		1.00	
C94	21¢ Octave Chanute	.55	.30	2.10		1.00	
C94a	Pair, #C93-C94	1.00	.80			2.00	
	Wiley Post Issue, Nov. 20						
C95	25¢ Wiley Post	.65	.30	2.50		1.00	
C96	25¢ Wiley Post	.65	.30	2.50		1.00	
C96a	Pair, #C95-C96	1.20	.80			2.00	
	Olympic Games Issue						
C97	31¢ High Jump	.90	.30			1.15	4,720,000

C80

C81

C84

C85

C86

C87

C88

C89

C90

C91
C92

C93
C94

C95
C96

C97

C99

C100

CE2

		Un	U	PB	#	FDC		Q
	Issues of 1980							
C98	40¢ Philip Mazzei, Oct. 13	.70	.20					
C99	28¢ Blanche Stuart Scott, Dec. 30	.50	.15	7.75	(12)	1.10		
C100	35¢ Glenn Curtiss, Dec. 30	.65	.15	10.00	(12)	1.25		
	Air Post Special Delivery Stamps							
	Issue of 1934, Perf. 11							
CE1	16¢ dark blue (CE2)	1.20	.90	45.00	(6)	17.50		
	For imperforate variety, see No. 771.							
	Issue of 1936							
CE2	16¢ Great Seal of United States	.30	.20	17.50		12.50		

PIGEON POST

An interesting sidelight to postal history in the area of aerophilately is the story of "pigeon posts."

Pigeons have carried written messages since Biblical times. King Solomon reportedly created the first pigeon post, around 900 B.C. The Sultan of Baghdad established a pigeon post in 1150, and Genghis Khan used the birds to further his conquests 50 years later.

Rumor has it that Nathan Rothschild's fortune began with early advice delivered by pigeon from agents following Napoleon's army. By 1840, pigeons were in regular use to carry stock market news between Holland and France, and Belgium and London.

But it wasn't until the Franco-Prussian War of 1870-71 that pigeon carriers were used extensively. The ingenuity of the French Postal authorities was severely tried during this time, but they proved themselves singularly successful in maintaining correspondence, both inland and foreign, using a form of pigeon post. During the Siege of Paris, pigeons carried 100,000 official messages and a million private ones between Paris and Tours—140 miles as the pigeon flies. Several birds carried identical dispatches, since all would not complete the trip. However, many pigeons eluded the enemy and one pigeon, known as "Gambetta" made four successful flights between Paris and Tours.

The last flight of the Paris-Tours pigeon post carried welcome news: an armistice had been declared.

One pigeon could carry thousands of messages. Letters were printed in ordinary type, then reduced to microscopic dispatches prepared with the aid of early photographic appliances. The films, each measuring but 2" x 1" were extremely light and could be rolled up tightly, placed in a quill, and attached to a bird's tail feathers or leg. Journeys were broken up into relays.

In Belgium, the home of pigeon racing as a sport, nearly every village had a Pigeon Club in the late nineteenth century. In 1881 a 470-mile race from Toulouse to Brussels was inaugurated, with feathered participants reaching speeds of up to 90 miles an hour.

German lighthouse keepers used pigeons in 1876 to announce the arrival of ships and to summon aid during storms. And well into the 20th century, pigeons have served as emergency carriers in times of war. As recently as 1949, pigeons from the Channel Island of Herm were used regularly to fly letters to England.

		Un	U	PB	#	FDC	Q
	Special Delivery Stamps.						
	Unwmkd., Issue of 1885, Perf. 12						
E1	10¢ Messenger Running	335.00	37.50	15,000.00	(8)	8,000.00	
	Issue of 1888						
E2	10¢ blue (E3)	335.00	9.50	15,000.00	(8)		
	Issue of 1893						
E3	10¢ Messenger Running	225.00	17.00	8,500.00	(8)		
	Issue of 1894, Line under "Ten Cents"						
E4	10¢ Messenger Running	850.00	22.50	16,500.00	(6)		
	Issue of 1895, Wmkd. (191)						
E5	10¢ blue (E4)	170.00	3.00	5,500.00	(6)		
	Issue of 1902						
E6	10¢ Messenger on Bicycle	115.00	3.25	3,250.00	(6)		
	Issue of 1908						
E7	10¢ Mercury Helmet and Olive Branch	90.00	37.50	1,300.00	(6)		
	Issue of 1911, Wmkd. (190)						
E8	10¢ ultramarine (E6)	115.00	5.75	3,000.00	(6)		
	Issue of 1914, Perf. 10						
E9	10¢ ultramarine (E6)	250.00	6.25	6,250.00	(6)		
	Unwmkd., Issue of 1916	○					
E10	10¢ ultramarine (E6)	415.00	24.00	8,000.00	(6)		
	Issue of 1917, Perf. 11						
E11	10¢ ultramarine (E6)	26.50	.40	400.00	(6)		
	Issue of 1922						
E12	10¢ Postman and Motorcycle	40.00	.15	625.00	(6)	550.00	
	Issue of 1925						
E13	15¢ Postman and Motorcycle	27.50	1.00	350.00	(6)	275.00	
E14	20¢ Post Office Truck	4.65	2.10	75.00	(6)	150.00	
	Issue of 1927, Perf. 11x10½						
E15	10¢ Postman and Motorcycle	1.10	.08	6.50		100.00	
	Issue of 1931						
E16	15¢ orange (E12)	1.10	.10	6.50		135.00	
	Issue of 1944						
E17	13¢ Postman and Motorcycle	.80	.09	5.00		12.00	
E18	17¢ Postman and Motorcycle	7.75	2.75	30.00		12.00	
	Issue of 1951						
E19	20¢ black (E14)	3.75	.11	12.00		5.00	
	Issue of 1954-57						
E20	20¢ Delivery of Letter	.75	.07	4.50		3.00	
E21	30¢ Delivery of Letter	.85	.05	5.25		2.25	
	Issue of 1969-71, Perf. 11						
E22	45¢ Arrows	2.00	.18	14.50		3.50	
E23	60¢ Arrows	1.10	.10	6.00		3.50	

E1

E3

E4

E6

E7

E12

E13

E14

E15

E17

E18

E20

E21

E22

E23

REGISTRATION
AND CERTIFIED MAIL STAMPS
POSTAGE DUE STAMPS

F1

FA1

JQ1

JQ2

J2

J19

J25

J33

J69

J78

J88

J98

J101

		Un	U	PB	#	FDC	Q
	Registration Stamp						
	Issued for the prepayment of registry; not usable for postage. Sale discontinued May 28, 1913.						
	Issue of 1911, Perf. 12, Wmkd. USPS (190)						
F1	10¢ Bald Eagle	125.00	5.00	2,100.00	(6)		9,000.00
	Certified Mail Stamp						
	For use on first-class mail for which no indemnity value is claimed, but for which proof of mailing and proof of delivery are available at less cost than registered mail.						
	Issue of 1955, Perf. 10½x11						
FA1	15¢ Letter Carrier	.50	.30	6.25			3.25

Postage Due Stamps

For affixing by a postal clerk to any mail to denote amount to be collected from addressee because of insufficient prepayment of postage.

Printed by American Bank Note Company Issue of 1879, Design of J2, Perf. 12, Unwmd.

		Un	U
J1	1¢ brown	25.00	5.00
J2	2¢ Figure of Value	185.00	5.25
J3	3¢ brown	19.50	2.65
J4	5¢ brown	250.00	22.50
J5	10¢ brown	335.00	9.75
J6	30¢ brown	140.00	20.00
J7	50¢ brown	210.00	37.50

Special Printing

		Un	U
J8	1¢ deep brown	—	—
J9	2¢ deep brown	—	—
J10	3¢ deep brown	—	—
J11	5¢ deep brown	—	—
J12	10¢ deep brown	—	—
J13	30¢ deep brown	—	—
J14	50¢ deep brown	—	—

Regular Issue of 1884-89, Design of J19

		Un	U
J15	1¢ red brown	29.50	3.35
J16	2¢ red brown	37.50	3.35
J17	3¢ red brown	415.00	95.00
J18	5¢ red brown	195.00	9.50
J19	10¢ Figure of Value	145.00	5.00
J20	30¢ red brown	100.00	22.50
J21	50¢ red brown	1,000.00	140.00

Issue of 1891-93, Design of J25

J22	1¢ bright claret	9.75	.70
J23	2¢ bright claret	12.50	.60
J24	3¢ bright claret	21.00	3.75
J25	5¢ Figure of Value	25.00	3.75
J26	10¢ bright claret	50.00	8.75
J27	30¢ bright claret	225.00	87.50
J28	50¢ bright claret	250.00	95.00

Parcel Post Postage Due Stamps

For affixing by a postal clerk to any parcel post package to denote the amount to be collected from the addressee because of insufficient prepayment of postage.

Beginning July 1, 1913, these stamps were valid for use as regular postage due stamps.

Issue of 1912, Design of JQ1 and JQ5, Perf. 12

JQ1	1¢ Figure of Value	12.75	3.75
JQ2	2¢ dark green	110.00	19.50
JQ3	5¢ dark green	18.50	4.50
JQ4	10¢ dark green	240.00	45.00
JQ5	25¢ Figure of Value	120.00	4.50

		Un	U	PB	#	FDC	Q
Printed by the Bureau of Engraving and Printing, Issue of 1894, Design of J33, Perf. 12							
J29	1¢ vermilion	415.00	75.00	5,000.00	(6)		
J30	2¢ vermilion	195.00	36.50	2,250.00	(6)		
J31	1¢ deep claret	19.50	3.75	375.00	(6)		
J32	2¢ deep claret	15.00	2.50	325.00	(6)		
J33	3¢ Figure of Value	50.00	16.50	850.00	(6)		
J34	5¢ deep claret	55.00	19.50	950.00	(6)		
J35	10¢ deep rose	50.00	11.00	850.00	(6)		
J36	30¢ deep claret	195.00	50.00				
J37	50¢	375.00	100.00				
Issue of 1895, Design of J33, Wmkd. (191)							
J38	1¢ deep claret	5.00	.40	190.00	(6)		
J39	2¢ deep claret	5.00	.25	190.00	(6)		
J40	3¢ deep claret	29.50	1.25	400.00	(6)		
J41	5¢ deep claret	25.00	.85	450.00	(6)		
J42	10¢ deep claret	31.00	2.25	525.00	(6)		
J43	30¢ deep claret	250.00	20.00	3,500.00	(6)		
J44	50¢ deep claret	140.00	21.00	2,000.00	(6)		
Issue of 1910-12, Design of J33, Wmkd. (190)							
J45	1¢ deep claret	18.00	2.25	400.00	(6)		
J46	2¢ deep claret	18.75	.20	350.00	(6)		
J47	3¢ deep claret	295.00	12.00	3,500.00	(6)		
J48	5¢ deep claret	46.50	3.25	575.00	(6)		
J49	10¢ deep claret	48.50	7.25	1,150.00	(6)		
J50	50¢ deep claret	575.00	65.00	6,250.00	(6)		
Issue of 1914-15, Design of J33, Perf. 10							
J52	1¢ carmine lake	40.00	7.25	550.00	(6)		
J53	2¢ carmine lake	18.50	.20	300.00	(6)		
J54	3¢ carmine lake	325.00	10.50	4,250.00	(6)		
J55	5¢ carmine lake	18.50	1.85	285.00	(6)		
J56	10¢ carmine lake	28.75	1.05	600.00	(6)		
J57	30¢ carmine lake	140.00	15.00	2,350.00	(6)		
J58	50¢ carmine lake	—	350.00	27,500.00	(6)		
Issue of 1916, Design of J33, Unwmkd.							
J59	1¢ rose	800.00	145.00	6,750.00	(6)		
J60	2¢ rose	67.50	3.25	775.00	(6)		
Issue of 1917, Design of J33, Perf. 11							
J61	1¢ carmine rose	1.75	.10	40.00	(6)		
J62	2¢ carmine rose	1.40	.10	35.00	(6)		
J63	3¢ carmine rose	7.50	.11	85.00	(6)		
J64	5¢ carmine	7.50	.10	85.00	(6)		
J65	10¢ carmine rose	10.00	.10	135.00	(6)		
J66	30¢ carmine rose	45.00	.45	525.00	(6)		
J67	50¢ carmine rose	52.50	.15	650.00	(6)		

		Un	U	PB	#	FDC
	Issue of 1925, Design of J33					
J68	½¢ dull red	.60	.10	11.00	(6)	
	Issue of 1930-31, Design of J69					
J69	½¢ Figure of Value	4.25	.90	35.00	(6)	
J70	1¢ carmine	3.00	.18	27.50	(6)	
J71	2¢ carmine	4.25	.18	40.00	(6)	
J72	3¢ carmine	20.00	.90	240.00	(6)	
J73	5¢ carmine	20.00	1.75	225.00	(6)	
J74	10¢ carmine	33.50	.60	375.00	(6)	
J75	30¢ carmine	135.00	1.20	1,000.00	(6)	
J76	50¢ carmine	135.00	.40	1,150.00	(6)	
	Design of J78					
J77	$1 carmine	30.00	.10	250.00	(6)	
J78	$5 "FIVE" on $	45.00	.23	375.00	(6)	
	Issue of 1931-56, Design of J69, Perf. 11x10½					
J79	½¢ dull carmine	1.00	.10	22.50		
J80	1¢ dull carmine	.16	.08	2.00		
J81	2¢ dull carmine	.16	.08	2.00		
J82	3¢ dull carmine	.27	.08	3.00		
J83	5¢ dull carmine	.40	.08	4.00		
J84	10¢ dull carmine	1.00	.08	8.50		
J85	30¢ dull carmine	8.00	.10	45.00		
J86	50¢ dull carmine	9.00	.09	57.50		
	Perf. 10½x11					
J87	$1 scarlet, same design as J78	37.50	.20	325.00		
	Issue of 1959, Perf. 11x10½, Design of J88 and J98					
J88	½¢ Figure of Value	1.15	.65	125.00		
J89	1¢ carmine rose	.05	.05	.50		
J90	2¢ carmine rose	.06	.05	.60		
J91	3¢ carmine rose	.07	.05	.70		
J92	4¢ carmine rose	.08	.05	1.25		
J93	5¢ carmine rose	.10	.05	.75		
J94	6¢ carmine rose	.12	.06	1.40		
J95	7¢ carmine rose	.14	.06	1.60		
J96	8¢ carmine rose	.16	.06	1.75		
J97	10¢ carmine rose	.20	.05	1.25		
J98	30¢ Figure of Value	.55	.06	5.50		
J99	50¢ carmine rose	.90	.06	6.50		
	Design of J101					
J100	$1 carmine rose	1.75	.06	10.00		
J101	$5 Outline Figure of Value	8.75	.14	40.00		
	Design of J88					
J102	11¢ carmine rose	.22	.06	1.10		
J103	13¢ carmine rose	.25	.06	1.30		

OFFICIAL POSTAGE STAMPS

O7   O14   O18   O34   O44

O52   O57   O76   O91

O71

O93   O95   O101   O114   O121

Official Stamps

The franking privilege having been abolished, as of July 1, 1873, these stamps were provided for each of the departments of Government for the prepayment on official matter.

These stamps were supplanted on May 1, 1879 by penalty envelopes and on July 5, 1884 were declared obsolete.

Designs are as follows: Post Office officials, figures of value and department name; all other departments, various portraits and department names.

Issues of 1873
Printed by the Continental Bank Note Co. Thin Hard Paper
Dept. of Agriculture: Yellow

		Un	U
O1	1¢ Franklin	60.00	31.50
O2	2¢ Jackson	37.50	15.00
O3	3¢ Washington	30.00	4.65
O4	6¢ Lincoln	41.50	15.00
O5	10¢ Jefferson	95.00	55.00
O6	12¢ Clay	150.00	75.00
O7	15¢ Webster	95.00	55.00
O8	24¢ Winfield Scott	110.00	62.50
O9	30¢ Hamilton	150.00	95.00

Executive Dept.

		Un	U
O10	1¢ carmine, Franklin	235.00	110.00
O11	2¢ Jackson	150.00	95.00
O12	3¢ carmine, Washington	160.00	75.00
O13	6¢ carmine, Lincoln	295.00	160.00
O14	10¢ Jefferson	230.00	160.00

Dept. of the Interior: Vermilion

		Un	U
O15	1¢ Franklin	12.00	2.95
O16	2¢ Jackson	10.00	2.00
O17	3¢ Washington	22.50	2.00
O18	6¢ Lincoln	16.50	2.00
O19	10¢ Jefferson	12.50	4.65
O20	12¢ Clay	21.00	3.35
O21	15¢ Webster	41.50	9.75
O22	24¢ W. Scott	31.00	7.50
O23	30¢ Hamilton	31.00	8.35
O24	90¢ Perry	85.00	16.50

Dept. of Justice: Purple

		Un	U
O25	1¢ Franklin	29.50	18.50
O26	2¢ Jackson	58.50	25.00
O27	3¢ Washington	67.50	9.00
O28	6¢ Lincoln	55.00	13.00
O29	10¢ Jefferson	62.50	27.50

		Un	U
O30	12¢ Clay	32.50	12.50
O31	15¢ Webster	95.00	50.00
O32	24¢ W. Scott	285.00	125.00
O33	30¢ Hamilton	250.00	97.50
O34	90¢ Perry	415.00	195.00

Navy Dept.: Ultramarine

		Un	U
O35	1¢ Franklin	31.50	12.50
O36	2¢ Jackson	21.00	10.00
O37	3¢ Washington	22.50	3.75
O38	6¢ Lincoln	18.75	5.85
O39	7¢ Stanton	160.00	62.50
O40	10¢ Jefferson	29.50	12.50
O41	12¢ Clay	41.50	11.00
O42	15¢ Webster	70.00	25.00
O43	24¢ W. Scott	70.00	37.50
O44	30¢ Hamilton	60.00	15.00
O45	90¢ Perry	275.00	100.00

Post Office Dept.: Black

		Un	U
O47	1¢ Figure of Value	9.75	3.75
O48	2¢ Figure of Value	8.75	3.35
O49	3¢ Figure of Value	3.25	1.00
O50	6¢ Figure of Value	8.75	2.10
O51	10¢ Figure of Value	41.50	21.00
O52	12¢ Figure of Value	16.75	5.00
O53	15¢ Figure of Value	22.50	8.50
O54	24¢ Figure of Value	26.50	11.00
O55	30¢ Figure of Value	26.50	9.00
O56	90¢ Figure of Value	41.50	12.50

Dept. of State

		Un	U
O57	1¢ dark green Franklin	31.50	12.50
O58	2¢ dark green Jackson	85.00	32.50
O59	3¢ bright green Washington	25.00	9.50
O60	6¢ bright green Lincoln	22.50	9.50
O61	7¢ dark green Stanton	55.00	18.50
O62	10¢ dark green Jefferson	31.00	16.00
O63	12¢ dark green Clay	68.50	36.00
O64	15¢ dark green Webster	47.50	19.00
O65	24¢ dark green W. Scott	150.00	95.00
O66	30¢ Hamilton	145.00	62.50

		Un	U
	1873 continued		
O67	90¢ dark green Perry	300.00	145.00
O68	$2 green and black		
	Seward	600.00	275.00
O69	$5 green and black		
	Seward	4,650.00	2,500.00
O70	$10 green and black		
	Seward	2,900.00	1,650.00
O71	$20 Seward	2,500.00	1,350.00
	Treasury Dept.: Brown		
O72	1¢ Franklin	13.00	2.50
O73	2¢ Jackson	18.75	2.50
O74	3¢ Washington	9.65	1.35
O75	6¢ Lincoln	18.75	1.35
O76	7¢ Stanton	35.00	12.50
O77	10¢ Jefferson	31.50	4.65
O78	12¢ Clay	31.50	2.00
O79	15¢ Webster	36.50	4.15
O80	24¢ W. Scott	165.00	62.50
O81	30¢ Hamilton	46.50	4.35
O82	90¢ Perry	58.50	3.95
	War Dept.: Rose		
O83	1¢ Franklin	50.00	4.15
O84	2¢ Jackson	50.00	6.25
O85	3¢ Washington	47.50	1.35
O86	6¢ Lincoln	185.00	3.35
O87	7¢ Stanton	46.00	25.00
O88	10¢ Jefferson	16.00	3.95
O89	12¢ Clay	47.50	2.75
O90	15¢ Webster	11.75	1.65
O91	24¢ W. Scott	13.00	2.35
O92	30¢ Hamilton	13.00	2.00
O93	90¢ Perry	31.50	12.50

**Issues of 1879
Printed by the American Bank Note Co. Soft, Porous Paper, Dept. of Agriculture: Yellow**

O94	1¢ Franklin, issued		
	without gum	1,350.00	—
O95	3¢ Washington	165.00	27.50
	Dept. of the Interior: Vermilion		
O96	1¢ Franklin	120.00	70.00
O97	2¢ Jackson	3.35	1.00
O98	3¢ Washington	2.50	.85
O99	6¢ Lincoln	3.95	1.35

		Un	U
O100	10¢ Jefferson	35.00	20.00
O101	12¢ Clay	50.00	31.50
O102	15¢ Webster	120.00	75.00
O103	24¢ W. Scott	1,250.00	—
	Dept. of Justice: Bluish Purple		
O106	3¢ Washington	46.50	22.50
O107	6¢ Lincoln	110.00	75.00
	Post Office Dept.: Black		
O108	3¢ Figure of Value	6.25	1.90
	Treasury Dept.: Brown		
O109	3¢ Washington	16.75	3.35
O110	6¢ Lincoln	37.50	19.50
O111	10¢ Jefferson	58.50	16.50
O112	30¢ Hamilton	825.00	165.00
O113	90¢ Perry	825.00	165.00
	War Dept.: Rose Red		
O114	1¢ Franklin	2.25	1.00
O115	2¢ Jackson	3.50	1.35
O116	3¢ Washington	3.50	.90
O117	6¢ Lincoln	3.10	1.00
O118	10¢ Jefferson	15.00	8.00
O119	12¢ Clay	13.00	2.50
O120	30¢ Hamilton	37.50	33.50

Official Postal Savings Mail, Perf. 12
These stamps were used to prepay postage on official correspondence of the Postal Savings Division of the Post Office Department.
Discontinued Sept. 23, 1914.

	Issues of 1911, Wmkd. (191)		
O121	2¢ Official Postal		
	Savings	11.50	1.45
O122	50¢ Official Postal		
	Savings	110.00	45.00
O123	$1 Official Postal		
	Savings	105.00	13.00
	Wmkd. (190)		
O124	1¢ Official Postal		
	Savings	5.25	1.30
O125	2¢ Official Postal		
	Savings	30.00	4.50
O126	10¢ Official Postal		
	Savings	10.50	1.30

CITIZEN'S STAMP ADVISORY COMMITTEE

The U.S. commemorative stamp is just a colorful rectangle with a message. But since each stamp appears in quantities of 140 million or more, these little commemoratives make a very big impression.

In 1971, the Blood Donor stamp helped restock American blood banks for six months. The 1974 Retarded Children's stamp educated millions to the needs of retarded children.

The Citizen's Stamp Advisory Committee, founded in 1957 under Postmaster General Arthur E. Summerfield, guides in the selection of stamp subject and design. Its members are nominated by respected philatelists and interested citizens— anyone can write in. Appointed by the Postmaster General, members meet six times a year to consider thousands of suggestions from organizations and the general public: Register and Vote; Crusade against Cancer; Plan for Better Cities; Law and Order; Support Our Youth; Prevent Drug Abuse; Energy Conservation.

Committee members are chosen to reflect a diversity of educational, geographical and occupational backgrounds. The committee usually includes several philatelists, as well as educators, historians and experts in the graphic arts.

By representing a broad cross-section of American society, the committee can more fairly evaluate the importance, appeal and relevance of each proposed stamp topic.

FEDERATION INTERNATIONALE de PHILATELIE

Today, well over a thousand stamp shows are held annually in the United States. But only once or twice a year do stamp collectors gather from around the world.

The Federation Internationale de Philatelie (F.I.P.), formed in 1926, coordinates international philatelic exhibitions and activities around the world. The F.I.P. is composed of various national federations. The American Philatelic Society, for example, represents the United States.

As a rule, the F.I.P. recognizes only one stamp exhibition a year in an area encompassing Europe, Africa and the Near East. It sanctions another international exhibit for the countries in North and South America, Asia and the Pacific.

F.I.P.-sanctioned International Philatelic Exhibitions are the Olympics of international philately. The finest collections in the world compete for gold, silver and bronze medals. Entries in the Competitive Class are arranged by geographical area and also in special categories, such as youth collections, thematics or philatelic literature.

Most of the collections in the Competitive Class have already won top honors in their home countries or at other international exhibitions.

The highest possible award is the Grand Prix d'Honneur, *given to collections that have won at least two gold nedals at an F.I.P.-sponsored international competition within the past five years.*

The host country usually issues special stamps or souvenir sheets to honor an International Philatelic Exhibition and uses a special postmark and cachet. The occasions also showcase the country's history, culture and social heritage.

The next international exhibit to be held in the United States will be AMERIPEX, which is scheduled to take place in Chicago in 1986.

1632

NEWSPAPER STAMPS
PARCEL POST STAMPS

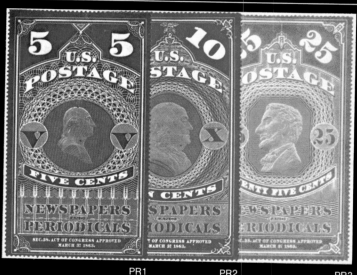

PR1   PR2   PR3

		Un	U
	Newspaper Stamps **Perf. 12, Issues of 1865** **Printed by the National Bank Note Co.,** **Thin, Hard Paper, No Gum, Unwmkd.,** **Colored Borders**		
PR1	5¢ Washington	115.00	—
PR2	10¢ Franklin	55.00	—
PR3	25¢ Lincoln	60.00	—
	White Border, Yellowish Paper		
PR4	5¢ light blue (PR1)	27.50	25.00
	Reprints of 1875 **Printed by the Continental Bank Note** **Co., Hard, White Paper, No Gum**		
PR5	5¢ dull blue (PR1),		
	white border	50.00	—
PR6	10¢ dark bluish green,		
	(PR2), colored border	32.50	—
PR7	25¢ dark carmine		
	(PR3), colored border	—	—
	Issue of 1880 **Printed by the American Bank Note** **Co., Soft, Porous Paper, White Border**		
PR8	5¢ dark blue (PR1)	95.00	—
	Issue of 1875 **Printed by the Continental Bank Note** **Co., Thin, Hard Paper**		
	PR9-PR15; "Statue of Freedom" (PR15)		
PR9	2¢ black	6.50	6.50
PR10	3¢ black	9.00	9.00
PR11	4¢ black	8.00	8.00
PR12	6¢ black	10.00	10.00
PR13	8¢ black	15.00	15.00
PR14	9¢ black	25.00	25.00
PR15	10¢ Statue of Freedom	15.00	12.00
	PR16-PR23: "Justice" (PR18)		
PR16	12¢ rose	27.50	20.00
PR17	24¢ rose	40.00	30.00
PR22	84¢ rose	125000	85.00
PR23	96¢ rose	90.00	75.00
PR24	$1.92 Ceres	110.00	85.00
PR25	$3 "Victory"	145.00	100.00
PR26	$6 Clio	275.00	135.00
PR27	$9 Minerva	350.00	165.00
PR28	$12 Vesta	400.00	200.00
PR29	$24 "Peace"	400.00	225.00
PR30	$36 "Commerce"	450.00	275.00
PR31	$48 red brown Hebe		
	(PR78)	600.00	375.00

		Un	U
PR32	$60 violet Indian		
	Maiden (PR79)	600.00	325.00
	Special Printing, Hard, White Paper, **Without Gum**		
	PR33-PR39: Statue of Freedom (PR15)		
PR33	2¢ gray black	55.00	—
PR34	3¢ gray black	60.00	—
PR35	4¢ gray black	75.00	—
PR36	6¢ gray black	95.00	—
PR37	8¢ gray black	110.00	—
PR38	9¢ gray black	125.00	—
PR39	10¢ gray black	150.00	—
	PR40-PR47: "Justice" (PR18)		
PR40	12¢ pale rose	175.00	—
PR41	24¢ pale rose	210.00	—
PR42	36¢ pale rose	300.00	—
PR43	48¢ pale rose	350.00	—
PR44	60¢ pale rose	400.00	—
PR45	72¢ pale rose	550.00	—
PR46	84¢ pale rose	575.00	—
PR47	96¢ pale rose	700.00	—
PR48	$1.92 dark brown		
	Ceres (PR24)	—	—
PR49	$3 vermilion "Victory"		
	(PR25)	—	—
PR50	$6 ultra. Clio (PR26)	—	—
PR51	$9 yel. Minerva		
	(PR27)	—	—
PR52	$12 bl. grn. Vesta		
	(PR28)	—	—
PR53	$24 dark gray violet		
	"Peace" (PR29)	—	—
PR54	$36 brown rose		
	"Commerce" (PR30)	—	—
PR55	$48 red brown Hebe		
	(PR78)	—	—
PR56	$60 violet Indian		
	Maiden (PR79)	—	—
	All values of this issue Nos. PR33 to PR56 exist imperforate but were not regularly issued.		

		Un	U
Issue of 1879 **Printed by the American Bank Note Co., Soft, Porous Paper**			
PR57-PR62: Statue of Freedom (PR15)			
PR57	2¢ black	4.00	3.50
PR58	3¢ black	5.00	4.50
PR59	4¢ black	5.00	4.50
PR60	6¢ black	10.50	9.00
PR61	8¢ black	10.50	9.00
PR62	10¢ black	10.50	9.00
PR63-PR70: "Justice" (PR18)			
PR63	12¢ red	30.00	20.00
PR64	24¢ red	30.00	18.50
PR65	36¢ red	110.00	85.00
PR66	48¢ red	80.00	50.00
PR67	60¢ red	60.00	50.00
PR68	72¢ red	145.00	90.00
PR69	84¢ red	110.00	75.00
PR70	96¢ red	80.00	55.00
PR71	$1.92 pale brown Ceres (PR24)	60.00	50.00
PR72	$3 red vermilion "Victory" (PR25)	60.00	50.00
PR73	$6 blue Clio (PR26)	110.00	75.00
PR74	$9 org. Minerva (PR27)	70.00	50.00
PR75	$12 yellow green Vesta (PR28)	110.00	70.00
PR76	$24 dark violet "Peace" (PR29)	145.00	100.00
PR77	$36 Indian red "Commerce" (PR30)	185.00	120.00
PR78	$48 Hebe	250.00	140.00
PR79	$60 Indian Maiden	275.00	140.00

All values of the 1879 issue except Nos. PR63 to PR66 and PR68 to PR70 exist imperforate but were not regularly issued.

		Un	U
Issue of 1883 **Special Printing**			
PR80	2¢ intense black Statue of Freedom (PR15)	115.00	—
Regular Issue of 1885			
PR81	1¢ black Statue of Freedom (PR15)	3.50	1.75

		Un	U
PR82-PR89: "Justice" (PR18)			
PR82	12¢ carmine	10.50	6.00
PR83	24¢ carmine	12.00	9.00
PR84	36¢ carmine	17.50	11.00
PR85	48¢ carmine	25.00	18.00
PR86	60¢ carmine	37.50	25.00
PR87	72¢ carmine	47.50	30.00
PR88	84¢ carmine	100.00	65.00
PR89	96¢ carmine	72.50	55.00

All values of the 1885 issue exist imperforate but were not regularly issued.

		Un	U
Issue of 1894 **Printed by the Bureau of Engraving and Printing, Soft Wove Paper**			
PR90-PR94: Statue of Freedom (PR90)			
PR90	1¢ Statue of Freedom	17.50	—
PR91	2¢ intense black	17.50	—
PR92	4¢ intense black	25.00	—
PR93	6¢ intense black	700.00	—
PR94	10¢ intense black	37.50	—
PR95-PR99: "Justice" (PR18)			
PR95	12¢ pink	200.00	—
PR96	24¢ pink	175.00	—
PR97	36¢ pink	—	—
PR98	60¢ pink	—	—
PR99	96¢ pink	—	—
PR100	$3 scarlet "Victory" (PR25)	—	—
PR101	$6 pale blue Clio (PR26)	—	—
Issue of 1895, Unwmkd. **PR102-PR105: Statue of Freedom (PR116)**			
PR102	1¢ black	14.00	4.00
PR103	2¢ black	16.50	4.50
PR104	5¢ black	21.00	7.00
PR105	10¢ black	42.50	20.00
PR106	25¢ carmine "Justice" (PR118)	52.50	20.00
PR107	50¢ carmine "Justice" (PR119)	130.00	65.00
PR108	$2 scarlet "Victory" (PR120)	160.00	35.00
PR109	$5 ultra Clio (PR121)	275.00	120.00

PR15

PR18

PR24

PR25

PR26

PR27

PR28

PR29

PR30

PR78

PR79

PR90

PR116

PR118

PR119

PR120

PR121

PR122

PR123

PR124

PR125

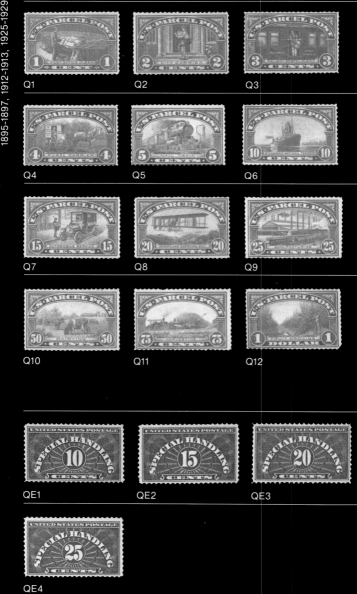

Q1 Q2 Q3
Q4 Q5 Q6
Q7 Q8 Q9
Q10 Q11 Q12

QE1 QE2 QE3

QE4

	Un	U
PR110 $10 green Vesta		
(PR122)	250.00	120.00
PR111 $20 slate "Peace"		
(PR123)	475.00	225.00
PR112 $50 dull rose		
"Commerce" (PR124)	475.00	225.00
PR113 $100 purple Indian		
Maiden (PR125)	550.00	250.00

Issue of 1895-97
Wmkd. (191), Yellowish Gum

PR114-PR117: Statue of Freedom (PR116)

PR114	1¢ black	2.50	2.00
PR115	2¢ black	2.50	1.50
PR116	5¢ black	4.00	3.00
PR117	10¢ black	2.50	2.00
PR118	25¢ "Justice"	4.00	3.75
PR119	50¢ "Justice"	4.25	3.50
PR120	$2 "Victory"	7.50	7.50
PR121	$5 Clio	15.00	16.50
PR122	$10 Vesta	11.50	15.00
PR123	$20 "Peace"	12.50	17.50
PR124	$50 "Commerce"	13.50	17.50
PR125	$100 Indian Maiden	17.50	25.00

In 1899, the Government sold 26,989 sets of these stamps, but, as the stock of the high values was not sufficient to make up the required number, the $5, $10, $20, $50 and $100 were reprinted. These are virtually indistinguishable from earlier printings.

Parcel Post Stamps
Issued for the prepayment of postage on parcel post packages only.

Beginning July 1, 1913, these stamps were valid for all postal purposes.

Issue of 1912-13, Perf. 12

Q1	1¢ Post Office Clerk	5.25	1.15
Q2	2¢ City Carrier	5.65	.90
Q3	3¢ Railway Postal Clerk	13.50	6.00
Q4	4¢ Rural Carrier	36.50	2.40
Q5	5¢ Mail Train	33.50	1.60
Q6	10¢ Steamship and Mail Tender	60.00	2.25
Q7	15¢ Automobile Service	85.00	11.00
Q8	20¢ Airplane Carrying Mail	200.00	21.75
Q9	25¢ Manufacturing	80.00	6.00
Q10	50¢ Dairying	325.00	45.00
Q11	75¢ Harvesting	95.00	32.50
Q12	$1 Fruit Growing	485.00	24.00

Special Handling Stamps
For use on parcel post packages to secure the same expeditious handling accorded to first class mail matter.

Issue of 1925-29, Design of QE3, Perf. 11

QE1	10¢ Special Handling	2.00	.85
QE2	15¢ Special Handling	2.10	.85
QE3	20¢ Special Handling	4.25	2.00
QE4	25¢ Special Handling	35.00	8.00

1

2

3

5

6

8

9

11

13

14

Please detach at perforation.

Official Business
Penalty for Private Use to
Avoid Payment of
Postage, $300

BUSINESS REPLY MAIL

First Class, Permit No. 73026, Washington, DC

Postage Will Be Paid By Addressee

United States Postal Service
Philatelic Sales Division
Washington, DC 20265-9987

WANT TO KNOW ABOUT ALL THE STAMPS AND PRODUCTS YOUR U.S. POSTAL SERVICE OFFERS?

You can "sign up" to receive a **FREE** copy of the Philatelic Catalog. This bimonthly catalog will keep you up-to-date on the currently available stamp issues and philatelic products . . . give you the opportunity to have stamps, postal cards, collecting kits and more delivered right to your home! When you order from it, you will automatically receive copies for the balance of the year.

Your Philatelic Catalog is **FREE** when you send in this card. Neatly print your name and address below and drop this card in the mail. No postage necessary.

Information which you provide will be protected and only disclosed in accordance with the Privacy Act of 1974.

Mr./Mrs./Ms. _____

Initials _____ Last Name _____

Street address _____
(Include P.O. Box, R.D. Route, etc. where appropriate)

City _____ State _____ ZIP CODE _____

Please Print Legibly

Please detach at perforation.

General Issues, All Imperf.
Issue of 1861: Lithographed, Unwatermarked

		Un	U
1	5¢ Jefferson Davis	150.00	95.00
2	10¢ Thomas Jefferson	200.00	150.00

Issue of 1862

3	2¢ Andrew Jackson	500.00	675.00
4	5¢ blue J. Davis (6)	100.00	87.50
5	10¢ Thomas Jefferson	800.00	550.00

Typographed

6	5¢ J. Davis		
	(London print)	12.00	14.50
7	5¢ blue (6) (local print)	15.00	17.50

Issues of 1863, Engraved

8	2¢ Andrew Jackson	60.00	225.00

Thick or Thin Paper

9	10¢ Jefferson Davis	600.00	400.00
10	10¢ blue (9), (with		
	rectangular frame)	3,000.00	1,600.00

Prices of No. 10 are for copies showing parts of lines on at least two sides of frame.

11	10¢ Jefferson Davis,		
	die A	12.00	14.00
12	10¢ blue J. Davis,		
	die B (11)	13.50	16.00

Dies A and B differ in that B has an extra line outside its corner ornaments.

13	20¢ George Washington	37.50	225.00

Issue of 1862, Typographed

14	1¢ John C. Calhoun		
	(This stamp was never		
	put in use.)	130.00	—

Important Dates in Postal History

1639	Fairbanks' tavern named repository for overseas mail
1775	Benjamin Franklin, first Postmaster General under Continental Congress
1789	Samuel Osgood, first Postmaster General under Constitution
1847	Postage stamps
1855	Registered mail
1855	Prepayment of postage compulsory
1860-61	Pony Express
1862	Experimental railway mail service
1863	City delivery service
1863	Uniform letter rate regardless of distance
1863	Domestic mail divided into three classes
1864	Post offices categorized by classes
1864	Railway mail service
1864	Domestic money orders
1869	Foreign or international money orders
1872	Postal cards
1874	Universal Postal Union (originally General Postal Union)
1879	Domestic mail divided into four classes
1885	Special delivery
1887	International Parcel Post
1896	Rural free delivery
1911	Postal Savings
1912	Village Delivery
1913	Parcel post, including insurance and collect-on-delivery service
1918	Air Mail
1920	Metered postage
1920	First Transcontinental Air Mail
1924	Regular Transcontinental Air Mail Service
1925	Special handling service
1927	International Air Mail Service
1935	Trans-Pacific Air Mail
1939	Trans-Atlantic Air Mail
1939	Experimental autogiro service
1941	Highway postal service
1942	V-Mail service
1943	Postal Unit Numbering System
1948	Parcel post international air service
1948	Parcel post domestic air service
1953	Piggy-back mail service by trailers or railroad flatcars
1955	Certified mail service
1959	Official Missile Mail dispatched from submarine to the mainland, Florida
1963	ZIP Code Program and Sectional Center Plan
1964	First 24 hour self-service post office
1965	Optical Scanner (ZIP Code Reader)
1966	Postal Savings terminated
1967	Mandatory presorting by ZIP Code for second- and third-class commercial mailers
1969	First postage stamp cancelled on moon by Apollo 11 mission
1970	Mailgram (Combination letter-telegram)
1970	The Postal Reorganization Act signed into law
1970	Experimental Express Mail Service
1971	U.S. Postal Service began operation
1971	First labor contract in history of Federal Government achieved through collective bargaining
1971	Star Routes became Highway Contract Routes
1972	Stamps By Mail
1972	First U.S. Postal Service bonds sold
1972	Passport applications accepted nationwide
1974	Highway Post Offices terminated
1974	First satellite transmission of Mailgrams
1976	Post Office class categories eliminated
1976	Presort First Class Mail
1977	Air Mail abolished as a separate rate category
1977	Express Mail becomes permanent new class of service
1977	Railway Post Office's final run June 30

SOUVENIR PAGES

With First Day Cancellations

The Postal Service offers Souvenir Pages for new stamps. The series began with a page for the Yellowstone Park Centennial stamp issued March 1, 1972. The pages feature one or more stamps tied by the first day cancel, technical data and information on the subject of the issue. More than just collectors' items, Souvenir Pages make wonderful show and conversation pieces. Souvenir Pages are issued in limited editions. For information on becoming a subscriber, see the postal card following page 256.

1972
1 Yellowstone Park, 60.00
1A Family Planning (sold only with FD cancellation by USPS at ASDA show in NYC) $90.00
2 Cape Hatteras, 60.00
3 Fiorello La Guardia, 60.00
4 City of Refuge, 60.00
5 Wolf Trap Farm, 20.00
6 Colonial Craftsman, 20.00
7 Mount McKinley, 20.00
8 Olympic Games, 12.00
9 Parent Teachers Association, 10.00
10 Wildlife Conservation, 10.00
11 Mail Order, 10.00
12 Osteopathic Medicine, 8.00
13 Tom Sawyer, 8.00
14 Benjamin Franklin, 8.00
15 Christmas, 8.00
16 Pharmacy, 6.00
17 Stamp Collecting, 6.00

1973
18 Eugene O'Neill Coil, 12.00
19 Love, 8.00
20 Pamphleteer, 6.00
21 George Gershwin, 6.00
22 Posting Broadside, 5.00
23 Copernicus, 5.00
24 Postal Service Employees, 8.00
25 Harry S. Truman, 5.00
26 Postrider, 5.00
27 Giannini, 5.00
28 Boston Tea Party, 8.00
29 Progress in Electronics, 7.00
30 Robinson Jeffers, 5.00
31 Lyndon B. Johnson, 5.00
32 Henry O. Tanner, 5.00
33 Willa Cather, 5.00
34 Colonial Drummer, 5.00
35 Angus Cattle, 5.00
36 Christmas, 7.00
37 13¢ Airmail sheet stamp, 4.00
38 10¢ Crossed Flags, 4.00
39 Jefferson Memorial, 4.00
40 13¢ Airmail Coil, 4.00

1974
41 Mount Rushmore, 4.00
42 ZIP Code, 4.00
43 Statue of Liberty, 4.00
44 Elizabeth Blackwell, 4.00
45 Veterans of Foreign Wars, 4.00
46 Robert Frost, 4.00
47 EXPO '74, 4.00

48 Horse Racing, 4.00
49 Skylab, 5.00
50 Universal Postal Union, 8.00
51 Mineral Heritage, 5.00
52 Fort Harrod, 4.00
53 Continental Congress, 5.00
54 Chautauqua, 4.00
55 Kansas Wheat, 4.00
56 Energy Conservation, 4.00
57 6.3¢ Bulk Rate, 4.00
58 Sleepy Hollow, 4.00
59 Retarded Children, 4.00
60 Christmas, two dates, 5.00

1975
61 Benjamin West, 4.00
62 Pioneer, 5.00
63 Collective Bargaining, 4.00
64 Sybil Ludington, 4.00
65 Salem Poor, 4.00

66 Haym Salomon, 4.00
67 Peter Francisco, 4.00
68 Mariner, 5.00
69 Lexington & Concord, both cities, 4.00
70 Paul Laurence Dunbar, 4.00
71 D.W. Griffith, 4.00
72 Bunker Hill, 4.00
73 Military Uniforms, 5.00
74 Apollo Soyuz, 6.00
75 International Women's Year, 4.00
76 Postal Bicentennial, 4.00
77 World Peace Through Law, 5.00
78 Banking & Commerce, 4.00
79 Christmas, 4.00
80 Francis Parkman, 3.00
81 Freedom of the Press, 3.00

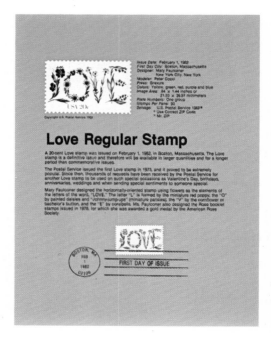

Love Regular Stamp

A 20-cent Love stamp was issued on February 1, 1982, in Boston, Massachusetts. The Love stamp is a definitive issue and therefore will be available in larger quantities and for a longer period than commemorative issues.

The Postal Service issued the first Love stamp in 1973, and it proved to be extremely popular. Since then, thousands of requests have been received by the Postal Service for another Love stamp to be used on such special occasions as Valentine's Day, birthdays, anniversaries, weddings and when sending special sentiments to someone special.

Mary Faulconer designed the horizontally-oriented stamp using flowers as the elements of the letters of the word, "LOVE." The letter "L" is formed by the miniature red poppy, the "O" by painted daisies and "Johnny-jump-ups" (miniature pansies), the "V" by the cornflower or bachelor's button, and the "E" by cornbells. Ms. Faulconer also designed the Rose booklet stamps issued in 1978, for which she was awarded a gold medal by the American Rose Society.

Issue Date: January 30, 1982
First Day City: Hyde Park, New York
Designer: Clarence Holbert
Bureau of Engraving and Printing
Modeler: Clarence Holbert
Engravers: Thomas R. Hipschen (vignette)
Thomas J. Bakos (lettering
& numerals)
Press: Intaglio
Color: Blue
Image Area: 1.075 × 1.075 inches or
27.30 × 27.30 millimeters
Plate Numbers: One
Stamps Per Pane: 48
Selvage: U.S. Postal Service 1981⁰
° Use Correct ZIP Code
° Mr. ZIP

Franklin D. Roosevelt
Commemorative Stamp

A 20-cent commemorative stamp honoring Franklin Delano Roosevelt was issued on the 100th anniversary of his birth, January 30, at Hyde Park, New York, his birthplace. The first day of issue ceremony was held at the Roosevelt estate where he was born and where he and his wife, Eleanor, are buried.

Franklin Delano Roosevelt was the 32nd president of the United States, taking office in March, 1933 during the Great Depression and serving during the New Deal era and World War II. He was the only U.S. president to be elected four times and he died while in office in 1945, less than a month before the end of the fighting in Europe.

The Roosevelt stamp was based on a UPI photograph of the late president in his touring car taking reporters to see tree plantings at Hyde Park on July 4, 1937. This is the third time that President Roosevelt has been the subject of a U.S. postage stamp. A series of four stamps, titled the "Roosevelt Memorial Series," was issued during 1945 and 1946 shortly after his death. He was also honored by the issuance of a 6-cent stamp in 1966.

FIRST DAY OF ISSUE

199 Antique Toys, 2.00
200 19¢ Sequoyah, 2.00
201 28¢ Scott A/M, 2.50
202 35¢ Curtiss A/M, 2.50

1981
203 Everett Dirksen, 2.00
204 Whitney M. Young, 2.00
205 "B" Sheet & Coil, 3.00
206 "B" Booklet Pane, 4.00
207 12¢ Americana S & C, 3.00
208 Flowers Block (4), 3.00
209 18¢ Flag Sheet & Coil, 3.00
210 18¢ Flag Booklet Pane, 4.00
211 American Red Cross, 2.00
212 George Mason, 2.00
213 Savings & Loan, 2.00
214 Animals Booklet Pane, 5.00
215 18¢ Surrey Coil, 2.50
216 Space Achievement (8), 6.00
217 17¢ Rachel Carson, 2.00
218 35¢ Dr. Charles Drew, 2.50
219 Professional Management, 2.00
220 17¢ Electric Car Coil, 2.50
221 Wildlife Habitat (4), 3.00
222 International Year Disabled, 2.00
223 Edna St. Vincent Millay, 2.00
224 Alcoholism, 2.00
225 Architecture (4), 3.00
226 Zaharis, 2.00
227 Bobby Jones, 2.00
228 Frederic Remington, 2.00
229 "C" Sheet/Coil, 3.00
230 "C" Booklet, 4.50
231 18¢/20¢ Hoban, 2.50
232 Yorktown, 2.50
233 Teddybear-Xmas, 2.00
234 Art-Xmas '81, 2.00
235 John Hanson, 2.00
236 20¢ Pumper, 2.50
237 Desert Plant, 3.00
238 9.3¢ Wagon, 2.50
239 20¢ Reg + Coil, 3.00
240 20¢ Booklet, 4.00

1982
241 Sheep Booklet, 4.50
242 20¢ Ralph Bunche, 2.00
243 13¢ Crazy Horse, 2.00
244 37¢ Millikan, 2.00
245 Roosevelt, FD., 2.00
246 20¢ LOVE, 2.00
247 5.9¢ Bicycle, 2.00
248 20¢ Washington, 2.00
249 10.9¢ Cab Coil, 2.00
250 Birds & Flowers, 25.00
251 Netherlands, 2.00
252 Library/Congress, 2.00
253 20¢ Consumer Coil, 2.50
254 World Fair, 3.00
255 Horatio Alger, 2.00
256 2¢ Locomotive Coil, 2.00
257 20¢ Aging, 2.00
258 20¢ Barrymores, 2.00
259 Mary Walker, 2.00
260 Peace Garden, 2.00
261 Libraries, 2.00
262 Jackie Robinson, 2.00
263 Stagecoach, 2.00
264 Touro Synagogue, 2.00
265 Wolf Trap, 2.00
266 Architecture, 3.00
267 Francis of Assisi, 2.00
268 Ponce de Leon, 2.00
269 Snow Scenes, 2.00
270 Art-Christmas, 2.00
271 Igor Stravinsky, 2.00
272 Kitten & Puppy, 2.00

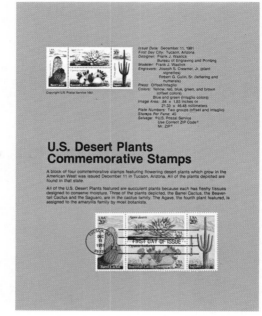

Issue Date: December 11, 1981
First Day City: Tucson, Arizona
Designer: Frank J. Waslick
　　　　　Bureau of Engraving and Printing
Modeler: Frank J. Waslick
Engravers: Joseph S. Creamer, Jr. (plant vignettes)
　　　　　Robert G. Culin, Sr. (lettering and numerals)
Press: Offset/Intaglio
Colors: Yellow, red, blue, green, and brown (offset colors)
　　　　　Blue and green (Intaglio colors)
Image Area: .84 x 1.83 inches or
　　　　　21.33 x 46.48 millimeters
Plate Numbers: Two groups (offset and intaglio)
Stamps Per Pane: 40
Selvage: ©U.S. Postal Service
　　　　　Use Correct ZIP Code®
　　　　　Mr. ZIP®

U.S. Desert Plants Commemorative Stamps

A block of four commemorative stamps featuring flowering desert plants which grow in the American West was issued December 11 in Tucson, Arizona. All of the plants depicted are found in that state.

All of the U.S. Desert Plants featured are succulent plants because each has fleshy tissues designed to conserve moisture. Three of the plants depicted, the Barrel Cactus, the Beavertail Cactus and the Saguaro, are in the cactus family. The Agave, the fourth plant featured, is assigned to the amaryllis family by most botanists.

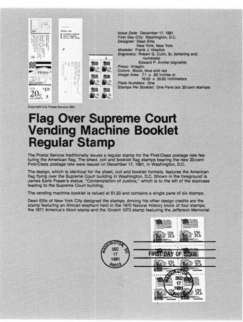

Issue Date: December 17, 1981
First Day City: Washington, D.C.
Designer: Dean Ellis
　　　　　New York, New York
Modeler: Frank J. Waslick
Engravers: Robert G. Culin, Sr. (lettering and numerals)
　　　　　Edward P. Archer (vignette)
Press: Intaglio
Colors: Black, blue and red
Image Area: .71 x .82 inches or
　　　　　18.03 x 20.82 millimeters
Plate Numbers: One
Stamps Per Booklet: One Pane (six 20-cent stamps)

Flag Over Supreme Court Vending Machine Booklet Regular Stamp

The Postal Service traditionally issues a regular stamp for the First-Class postage rate featuring the American flag. The sheet, coil and booklet flag stamps bearing the new 20-cent First-Class postage rate were issued on December 17, 1981, in Washington, D.C.

The design, which is identical for the sheet, coil and booklet formats, features the American flag flying over the Supreme Court building in Washington, D.C. Shown in the foreground is James Earle Fraser's statue, "Contemplation of Justice," which is to the left of the staircase leading to the Supreme Court building.

The vending machine booklet is valued at $1.20 and contains a single pane of six stamps.

Dean Ellis of New York City designed the stamps. Among his other design credits are the stamp featuring an African elephant herd in the 1970 Natural History block of four stamps, the 1971 America's Wool stamp and the 10-cent 1973 stamp featuring the Jefferson Memorial.

COMMEMORATIVE PANELS

The Postal Service offers American Commemorative Panels for each new commemorative stamp and special Christmas stamps issued. The series first began September 20, 1972 with the issuance of the Wild Life Commemorative Panel and will total over 171 panels by the end of 1982. The panels feature stamps in mint condition complemented by reproductions of steel line engravings and stories behind the commemorated subject. For more information about Commemorative Panels, please see postal card following page 256.

1972
1 Wildlife, 12.00
2 Mail Order, 12.00
3 Osteopathic Medicine, 12.00
4 Tom Sawyer, 12.00
5 Pharmacy, 12.00
6 Christmas 1972, 15.00
7 'Twas the Night Before Christmas, 15.00
8 Stamp Collecting, 12.00

1973
9 Love, 12.00
10 Pamphleteers, 15.00
11 George Gershwin, 15.00
12 Posting Broadside, 15.00
13 Copernicus, 12.00
14 Postal People, 15.00
15 Harry S. Truman, 18.00
16 Post Rider, 20.00
17 Boston Tea Party, 40.00
18 Electronics, 12.00
19 Robinson Jeffers, 12.00
20 Lyndon B. Johnson, 18.00
21 Henry O. Tanner, 12.00
22 Willa Cather, 12.00
23 Drummer, 20.00
24 Angus Cattle, 12.00
25 Christmas 1973, 15.00
26 Needlepoint, 15.00

1974
27 Veterans of Foreign Wars, 12.00
28 Robert Frost, 12.00
29 EXPO '74, 15.00
30 Horse Racing, 12.00
31 Skylab, 15.00
32 Universal Postal Union, 18.00
33 Mineral Heritage, 12.00
34 Fort Harrod, 12.00
35 Continental, Congress, 12.00
36 Chautauqua, 12.00
37 Kansas Wheat, 12.00
38 Energy Conservation, 12.00
39 Sleepy Hollow, 12.00
40 Retarded Children, 12.00
41 "The Road-Winter", 15.00
42 Angel Altarpiece, 15.00

1975
43 Benjamin West, 12.00
44 Pioneer, 15.00
45 Collective Bargaining, 12.00

46 Contributors to the Cause, 15.00
47 Mariner, 15.00
48 Lexington & Concord, 15.00
49 Paul Laurence Dunbar, 12.00
50 D. W. Griffith, 12.00
51 Bunker Hill, 15.00
52 Military Services, 15.00
53 Apollo Soyuz, 15.00
54 World Peace Through Law, 12.00
55 International Women's Year, 12.00
56 Postal Bicentennial, 15.00
57 Banking and Commerce, 12.00
58 Early Christmas Card, 15.00

59 Ghirlandaio Madonna, 15.00

1976
60 Spirit of '76, 15.00
61 Interphil 76, 15.00
62 State Flags, 25.00
63 Telephone, Centennial, 12.00
64 Commercial Aviation, 12.00
65 Chemistry, 12.00
66 Benjamin Franklin, 15.00
67 Declaration of Independence, 15.00
68 Olympics, 15.00
69 Clara Maas, 15.00
70 Adolph S. Ochs, 12.00

71 Currier Winter
    Pastime, 15.00
72 Copley Nativity, 15.00

1977
73 Washington at
    Princeton, 18.00
74 Sound Recording, 22.00
75 Pueblo Art, 100.00
76 Lindbergh Flight, 100.00
77 Colorado Centennial, 22.00
78 Butterflies, 25.00
79 Lafayette, 22.00
80 Skilled Hands, 22.00
81 Peace Bridge, 22.00
82 Herkimer at
    Oriskany, 22.00
83 Alta, California, 22.00
84 Articles of
    Confederation, 22.00
85 Talking Pictures, 22.00
86 Surrender at Saratoga,
    22.00
87 Energy Conservation
    & Development, 22.00
88 Washington at
    Valley Forge, 25.00
89 Rural Mailbox, 25.00

1978
90 Carl Sandburg, 15.00
91 Captain Cook, 25.00
92 Harriet Tubman, 15.00
93 American Quilts, 22.00
94 American Dance, 15.00
95 French Alliance, 15.00
96 Dr. Papanicolaou, 15.00
97 Jimmie Rodgers, 15.00
98 Photography, 15.00
99 George M. Cohan, 15.00
100 Viking Missions, 25.00
101 American Owls, 22.00
102 American Trees, 22.00
103 Madonna and Child, 15.00
104 Hobby Horse, 15.00

1979
105 Robert F. Kennedy, 15.00
106 Martin Luther King, Jr.,
    15.00
107 Year of the Child, 15.00
108 John Steinbeck, 15.00
109 Albert Einstein, 25.00
110 Pennsylvania Toleware,
    15.00
111 American Architecture,
    15.00
112 Endangered Flora, 15.00
113 Seeing Eye Dogs, 15.00
114 Special Olympics, 15.00
115 John Paul Jones, 30.00
116 15¢ Olympic Games, 20.00
117 Virgin and Child, 15.00
118 Santa Claus, 15.00
119 Will Rogers, 15.00
120 Vietnam Veterans, 18.00
121 10¢, 31¢ Olympic
    Games, 20.00

1980
122 W.C. Fields, 12.00
123 Winter Olympics, 20.00
124 Benjamin Banneker, 15.00
125 Frances Perkins, 15.00

AMERICAN COMMEMORATIVES

PRESERVATION OF **WILDLIFE HABITATS**

AMERICAN COMMEMORATIVES

Space Achievement

AMERICAN COMMEMORATIVES

AMERICAN ARCHITECTURE

"In— the architectural structure, man's pride, man's triumph over gravitation, man's will to power, assume a visible form. Architecture is a sort of oratory of power by means of forms."
Friedrich Wilhelm Nietzsche

Featuring architecture of enduring beauty, strength and usefulness, this block of four 18-cent stamps is the third issue in the American Architecture Series begun in 1979.

The stamp at upper left depicts the New York University Library. Designed by Stanford White (1853-1906), this building is more commonly known as the Gould Memorial Library. It is located on the campus of the Bronx Community College of the City University of New York.

The upper right stamp shows the Biltmore House in Asheville, North Carolina, designed by Richard Morris Hunt (1826-1895). Designed for George W. Vanderbilt and completed in 1895, this building is sometimes called the "grandest castle in the land".

At the lower left, the stamp features the Palace of Fine Arts in San Francisco, built for the Panama-Pacific Exposition of 1915. Designed by Bernard Maybeck (1862-1957), the Palace is located on the edge of a lagoon to

enhance and reflect its grandeur.

The stamp at lower right shows a bank building in Owatonna, Minnesota designed by Louis Sullivan (1856-1924) in 1906 for the National Farmer's Bank. This design was based on the idea that building forms should interrelate with building functions.

The first-day-of-issue ceremony for these stamps was held on August 28, 1981 at the historic Pension Building in Washington, D.C.

The vignette of the Empire State Building at top left was engraved by E. Krantz and used on a Christmas card by the American Bank Note Company in 1929.

Stamps printed by the Bureau of Engraving and Printing, Washington, D.C.

Copyright 1981 United States Postal Service

No. 150 in a series

August 28, 1981 / Printed in U.S.A.

AMERICAN COMMEMORATIVES

FREDERIC REMINGTON

"I paint for boys, boys from ten to seventy."
Frederic Remington

Known for his paintings and sculptures of Indians, cowboys, soldiers, horses and other aspects of life on the plains, no other artist has ever captured the feeling of the Old West the way Frederic Remington did. His artwork inspired some to refer to him as "America's Rembrandt of the range."

Remington was born on October 4, 1861 in Canton, New York. Even as a young boy, he filled the margins of his school books with drawings of soldiers, horses and Indians. His first "work" was published in 1878 as Yale's student newspaper - a cartoon about college football.

Although he attended the Yale School of Fine Arts and studied briefly at the Art Students' League of New York, Remington was virtually self-taught. Much of his inspiration came from his travels into the American West where, as a young man, he spent five years of his life. Returning to New York in 1885, Remington's struggle for recognition was intense but brief - within a year he was exhibiting paintings and making remarkable strides as an illustrator of Western scenes for leading magazines.

In 1895, Remington tried his hand at sculpture and modeled the most famous of American Western art bronzes - "Bronco Buster."

In all, during his relatively short life - he died in 1909 at the age of 48 - Remington created over 2,700 paintings and drawings and 25 bronze statues ... wrote and illustrated 8 books which enjoyed popularity because of his action sketches of frontier scenes and his dashing journalistic prose ... illustrated 142 other volumes and hundreds of magazine stories. The Remington Art Memorial in Ogdensburg, New York features an extensive collection of his work.

The steel line engraving at the upper left was rendered by engraver C. Brec. Used on the Chile-Banco Credito Bank Note issued October 4, 1888, the scene is of a horse running on a barren plain. The upper right engraving shows two pioneers on horseback pulling a pack mule up a mountainous western slope. The lower engraving pictures two Indians on horseback in pursuit of bison.

Stamps printed by the Bureau of Engraving and Printing, Washington, D.C.

Copyright 1981 United States Postal Service

No. 151 in a series

October 9, 1981 / Printed in U.S.A.

SOUVENIR CARDS

These cards were issued as souvenirs of the philatelic gatherings at which they were distributed by the United States Postal Service, its predecessor the United States Post Office Department, or the Bureau of Engraving and Printing. They were not valid for postage.

Most of the cards bear reproductions of United States stamps with the design enlarged or altered. The U.S. reproductions are engraved except stamps Nos. 914, 1396, 1460-1462 and C85. The cards are not perforated.

For information regarding current availability of souvenir cards, send postal card following page 256.

A forerunner of the souvenir cards is the 1938 Philatelic Truck souvenir sheet which the Post Office Department issued and distributed in various cities visited by the Philatelic Truck. It shows the White House, printed in blue on white paper. Issued with and without gum. Price, with gum, $115, without gum, $20.

United States Post Office & United States Postal Service

1960 Barcelona, 1st International Philatelic Congress, Mar. 26-Apr. 5. Enlarged vignette, Landing of Columbus from No. 231. Printed in black. 400.00

1968 EFIMEX , International Philatelic Exhibition, Nov. 1-9, Mexico City, Card of 1. No. 292, inscribed in Spanish. 6.00

1970 PHILYMPIA, London International Stamp Exhibition, Sept. 18-26. Card of 3. Nos. 548-550. 4.50

1971 EXFILIMA 71, 3rd Inter-American Philatelic Exhibition, Nov. 6-14, Lima, Peru. Card of 3. Nos. 1111 and 1126, Peru No. 360. Card inscribed in Spanish. 3.50

1972 BELGICA 72, Brussels International Philatelic Exhibition, June 24-July 9. Brussels, Belgium. Card of 3. Nos. 914, 1026 and 1104. Card inscribed in Flemish and French. 3.50
OLYMPIA PHILATELIC MÜNCHEN 72, Aug. 18-Sept. 10, Munich, Germany. Card of 4. Nos. 1460-1462 and C85. Card inscribed in German. 3.75
EXFILBRA 72, 4th Inter-American Philatelic Exhibition, Aug. 26-Sept. 2, Rio de Janeiro, Brazil. Card of 3. No. C14, Brazil Nos. C18-C19. Card inscribed in Portuguese. 3.50
NATIONAL POSTAL FORUM VI, Aug. 28-30, Washington, D.C. Card of 4. No. 1396. 3.50

1973 IBRA 73 Internationale Briefmarken Ausstellung, May 11-20, Munich, Germany. With one No. C13. 4.00
APEX 73, International Airmail Exhibition, July 4-7, Manchester, England. Card of 3. Newfoundland No. C4, U.S. No. C3a and Honduras No. C12. 3.50
POLSKA 73, Swiatowa Wystawa Filatelistyczna, Aug. 19-Sept. 2, Poznan, Poland. Card of 3. No. 1488 and Poland Nos. 1944-1945. Card inscribed in Polish. 3.50
POSTAL PEOPLE CARD, Card of 10 (#1489-1498) distributed to Postal Service employees. Not available to public. 14x11". $75.00 (est.)

1974 HOBBY, The Hobby Industry Association of America Convention and Trade Show, February 3-6, Chicago, Illinois. Card of 4. Nos. 1456-1459. 4.00
INTERNABA, International Philatelic Exhibition, June 7-16, Basel, Switzerland. Card of 8, strip of Nos. 1530-1537. Card inscribed in 4 languages. 4.00
STOCKHOLMIA 74, International frimarksutställning, September 21-29, Stockholm, Sweden. Card of 3. No. 836, Sweden Nos. 300 and 765. Card inscribed in Swedish. 4.50
EXFILMEX 74 UPU, Philatelic Exposition Inter-Americana, October 26-November 3, Mexico City, Mexico. Card of 2. No. 1157 and Mexico No. 910. Card inscribed in Spanish and English. 4.50

1975 ESPANA 75, World Stamp Exhibition, Apr. 4-13, Madrid, Spain. Card of 3. Nos. 233, 1271 and Spain No. 1312. Card inscribed in Spanish. 4.00
ARPHILA 75, June 6-16, Paris, France. Card of 3. Nos. 1187, 1207 and France No. 1117. Card inscribed in French. 3.50

1976 WERABA 76, Third International Space Stamp Exhibition, April 1-4, Zurich, Switzerland. Card of 2. Nos. 1434 and 1435 setenant. 4.00
BICENTENNIAL EXPOSITION on Science and Technology, May 30-Sept. 6, Kennedy Space Center, Fla. Card of 1. No. C76. 5.50
COLORADO STATEHOOD CENTENNIAL, August 1, Card of 3. Nos. 743, 288 and 1670. 5.00
HAFNIA 76, International Stamp Exhibition, Aug. 20-29, Copenhagen, Denmark. Card of 2. No. 5 and Denmark No. 2. Card inscribed in Danish and English. 5.00
ITALIA 76, International Philatelic Exhibition, Oct. 14-24, Milan, Italy. Card of 3. No. 1168 and Italy Nos. 578 and 601. Card inscribed in Italian. 4.00
NORDPOSTA 76, North German Stamp Exhibition, Oct. 30-31, Hamburg, Germany. Card of 3. No. 689 and Germany Nos. B366 and B417. Card inscribed in German. 4.00

1977 AMPHILEX 77, International Philatelic Exhibition, May 26-June 5, Amsterdam, Netherlands. Card of 3. No. 1027 and Netherlands Nos. 41 and 294. Card inscribed in Dutch. 4.50

NORDPOSTA 81

Hamburg, Bundesrepublik Deutschland

7.-8. November 1981

Die US-Postverwaltung gibt aus Anlass der NORDPOSTA '81 diese philatelistische Erinnerungskarte heraus. Hamburg ist weltbekannt sowohl als aktive Hafenstadt wie auch als reges Produktionszentrum. Hamburg ist ebenso aufgeschlossen für Besucher wie für Handel und Wandel. Es hat sich als Treffpunkt der Briefmarkensammler aus aller Welt bedeutendes Ansehen erworben.

Für diese Erinnerungskarte wurden die Reproduktionen von zwei Briefmarken gewählt:

Die US-Sondermarke zeigt die "Savannah", die 1819 als erstes Dampfschiff den Atlantischen Ozean überquerte. Das Markenmotiv symbolisiert die festen Verbindungen der USA mit der "Alten Welt".

Die Sondermarke der Deutschen Bundespost ehrt die "WAPEN VON HAMBURG", eines der berühmtesten alten Segelschiffe Deutschlands.

William F. Bolger
Postmaster General

NATIONAL STAMP COLLECTING MONTH

Benefiting Mankind

DISCOVER STAMP COLLECTING—THE HOBBY OF A LIFETIME

The U.S. Postal Service is pleased to issue this special souvenir card in honor of the first observance of National Stamp Collecting Month in October 1981 in cooperation with the Council of Philatelic Organizations.

Stamp collecting, the world's most popular hobby, is an important and worthwhile lifetime endeavor for millions of people. As such, it brings generations together in the joy of discovery and accomplishment.

The two stamps chosen for this card complement the observance theme of discovery and accomplishment. The engraved stamp features the profile of Christopher Columbus and is from the Columbian Exposition Issue of 1893 commemorating the 400th anniversary of the discovery of America in 1492. The other stamp is one of the block of eight Space Achievement stamps issued in May 1981. This stamp depicts the Space Shuttle, *Columbia*, which is leading current United States explorations into space, today's frontier challenge.

William F. Bolger
Postmaster General

PHILATOKYO '81

1981年10月9日〜18日　　　　　　　　　　　　　　東京

PHILATOKYO '81 に対し、米国郵政公社は、記念のカードを送り、祝意を表したいと思います。東京は、1868年以来、日本の首都として、政治・経済・文化の中心であり、東洋のもの、あるいは西洋のもの、ふるきもの、あるいは新しきものがうまくとけあった都です。そこで開催される国際切手展を通じて、各国の切手収集家が一同に会し、友情と相互理解を深めあうことは、すばらしいことだと思います。このカードは、'ふみ'にちなんで、北斎の有名な像に素材を求めた二種の切手を複製したものです。一つは、1963年に日本で発行された北斎の「富嶽三十六景」の一つ、「神奈川沖波裏」であり、もう一つは、1974年に米国で発行された「五美人図」であります。

WFBolger

WILLIAM F. BOLGER
POSTMASTER GENERAL

Universal
Postal Union
1874-1974　　　10c US

© UNITED STATES POSTAL SERVICE 1981

Bureau of Engraving and Printing

1954 POSTAGE STAMP DESIGN EXHIBITION, National Philatelic Museum, Mar. 13, Philadelphia. Card of 4. Monochrome views of Washington, D.C. Inscribed: "Souvenir sheet designed, engraved and printed by members, Bureau, Engraving and Printing. / Reissued by popular request". 625.00

1966 SIPEX, 6th International Philatelic Exhibition, May 21-30, Washington, D.C. Card of 3. Multicolored views of Washington, D.C. Inscribed "Sixth International Philatelic Exhibition / Washington, D.C. / Designed, Engraved, and Printed by Union Members of Bureau of Engraving and Printing". 210.00

1969 SANDIPEX, San Diego Philatelic Exhibition, July 16-20, San Diego, Cal. Card of 3. Multicolored views of Washington, D.C. Inscribed: "Sandipex—San Diego 200th Anniversary—1769-1969". 80.00
A.S.D.A. National Postage Stamp Show, Nov. 21-23, 1969, New York. Card of 4. No. E4. 30.00

1970 INTERPEX, Mar. 13-15, New York. Card of 4. Nos. 1027, 1035, C35 and C38. 65.00
COMPEX, Combined Philatelic Exhibition of Chicagoland, May 29-31, Chicago. Card of 4. No. C18. 20.00
HAPEX, American Philatelic Society Convention, Nov. 5-8, Honolulu, Hawaii. Card of 3. Nos. 799, C46 and C55. 25.00

1971 INTERPEX, Mar. 12-14, New York. Card of 4. No. 1193. Background includes Nos. 1331-1332, 1371 and C76. 5.00
WESTPEX, Western Philatelic Exhibition, Apr. 23-25, San Francisco. Card of 4. Nos. 740, 852, 966 and 997. 4.50
NAPEX 71, National Philatelic Exhibition, May 21-23, Washington, D.C. Card of 3. Nos. 990, 991, 992. 4.50
TEXANEX 71, Texas Philatelic Association and American Philatelic Society conventions, Aug. 26-29, San Antonio, Tex. Card of 3. Nos. 938, 1043 and 1242. 4.50
A.S.D.A. National Postage Stamp Show, Nov. 19-21, New York. Card of 3. Nos. C13-C15. 4.50
ANPHILEX '71, Anniversary Philatelic Exhibition, Nov. 26-Dec. 1, New York. Card of 2. Nos. 1-2. 4.50

1972 INTERPEX, Mar. 17-19, New York. Card of 4. No. 1173. Background includes Nos. 976, 1434-1435 and C69. 4.00
NOPEX, Apr. 6-9, New Orleans. Card of 4. No. 1020. Background includes Nos. 323-327. 3.50
SEPAD 72, Oct. 20-22, Philadelpia. Card of 4. No. 1044. 3.50
A.S.D.A. National Postage Stamp Show, Nov. 17-19, New York. Card of 4. Nos. 883, 863, 868 and 888. 3.00
STAMP EXPO, Nov. 24-26, San Francisco. Card of 4. No. C36. 3.00

1973 INTERPEX, March 9-11, New York. Card of 4. No. 976. 4.00
COMPEX 73, May 25-27, Chicago. Card of 4. No. 245. 4.00
NAPEX 73, Sept. 14-16, Washington, D.C. Card of 4. No. C3. Background includes Nos. C4-C6. 3.50
A.S.D.A. National Postage Stamp Show, Nov. 16-18, New York. Card of 4 No. 908. Foreground includes Nos. 1139-1144. 4.00
STAMP EXPO NORTH, Dec. 7-9, San Francisco. Card of 4. No. C20. 4.00

1974 MILCOPEX, March 8-10, Milwaukee, Wisconsin. Card of 4. No. C43. Background depicts U.P.U. monument at Berne, Switzerland. 5.00

1975 NAPEX 75, May 9-11, Washington, D.C. Card of 4. No. 708. 14.00
INTERNATIONAL WOMEN'S YEAR. Card of 3. Nos. 872, 878 and 959. Reproduction of 1886 dollar bill. 35.00
A.S.D.A. National Postage Stamp Show, Nov. 21-23, New York. Bicentennial series. Card of 4. No. 1003. ". . . and maintain the liberty which we have derived from our ancestors." 57.50

1976 INTERPHIL 76, Seventh International Philatelic Exhibition, May 29-June 6, Philadelphia. Bicentennial series. Card of 4. No. 120. "that all men are created equal." 9.50
STAMP EXPO 76, June 11-13, Los Angeles. Bicentennial series. Card of 4. Nos. 1351, 1352, 1345 and 1348 se-tenant vertically. "when we assumed the soldier, we did not lay aside the citizen". 6.50

1977 MILCOPEX, Milwaukee Philatelic Society, Mar. 4-6, Milwaukee. Card of 2. Nos. 733 and 1128. 5.00
ROMPEX 77, Rocky Mountain Philatelic Exhibition, May 20-22, Denver. Card of 4. No. 1001. 4.00
PURIPEX 77, Silver Anniversary Philatelic Exhibit, Sept. 2-5, San Juan, Puerto Rico. Card of 4. No. 801. 5.00
A.S.D.A. National Postage Stamp Show, Nov. 15-20, New York. Card of 4. No. C45. 4.50

1978 CENJEX 78, Federated Stamp Clubs of New Jersey, 30th annual exhibition, June 23-25, Freehold, N.J. Card of 9. Nos. 646, 680, 689, 1086, 1716 and 4 No. 785. 5.00

1980 NAPEX 80, July 4-6, Washington, D.C. Card of 4. No. 573. $5.00
ASDA National Postage Stamp Show, Sept. 25-28, New York. Card of 4. No. 962. $5.00

1981 STAMP EXPO 81, South International Stamp Collectors Society, Mar. 20-22, Anaheim, CA. Card of 4. No. 1287. 5.00

1982 MILCOPEX, March 5-7, Milwaukee, Wisconsin. Card of 4. No. 1136. $5.00

PHILATELIC CENTERS

In addition to the 13,000 Stamp Collecting Centers at post offices, the U.S. Postal Service also maintains more than 300 Philatelic Centers located in major population centers throughout the country. Each of these Centers carries an extensive range of stamps, stationery and collateral materials issued by the Postal Service.

Philatelic Centers have been developed to serve the collector and make it convenient for you to acquire the U.S. Postal Service philatelic products you require. All centers listed here are located at the Main Post Office unless otherwise indicated.

Alabama
351 North 24th Street
Birmingham, AL 35203

101 Holmes N.W.
Huntsville, AL 35804

250 St. Joseph
Mobile, AL 36601

2256 E.South Blvd.
Montgomery, AL 36104

1313 2nd Avenue
Tuscaloosa, AL 35401

Alaska
College Branch
3350 College Road
Fairbanks, AK 99708

Downtown Station
3rd & C Street
Anchorage, AK 99510

Arizona
Osborn Station
3905 North 7th Avenue
Phoenix, AZ 85013

1501 South Cherrybell
Tucson, AZ 85726

Arkansas
South 6th & Rogers Ave.
Fort Smith, AR 72901

Reserve & Broadway
Hot Springs National
Park, AR 71901

310 East Street
Jonesboro, AR 72401

600 West Capitol
Little Rock, AR 72201

California
Downtown Station
135 East Olive Street
Burbank, CA 91502

1900 E Street
Fresno, CA 93706

313 E. Broadway
Glendale, CA 91209

Hillcrest Station
303 E. Hillcrest
Inglewood, CA 90311

300 Long Beach Blvd.
Long Beach, CA 90801

300 N. Los Angeles St.
Los Angeles, CA 90012

Terminal Annex
900 N. Alameda
Los Angeles, CA 90052

Village Station
11000 Wilshire Blvd.
Los Angeles, CA 90024

El Viejo Station
1125 I Street
Modesto, CA 95354

Civic Center Annex
201 13th Street
Oakland, CA 94612

281 E. Colorado Blvd.
Pasadena, CA 91109

2000 Royal Oaks Drive
Sacramento, CA 95813

Base Line Station
1164 North E Street
San Bernardino, CA
92410

2535 Midway Drive
San Diego, CA 92199

7th and Mission Sts.
San Francisco, CA
94101

1750 Meridian Drive
San Jose, CA 95101

Spurgeon Station
615 North Bush
Santa Ana, CA 92701

Victoria Court Station
State Street at Victoria
Santa Barbara, CA
93101

4245 West Lane
Stockton, CA 95208

15701 Sherman Way
Van Nuys, CA 91408

Colorado
201 E. Pikes Peak
Colorado Springs,
CO 80901

241 Front Street
Grand Junction,
CO 81501

1823 Stout Street
Denver, CO 80202

421 N. Main Street
Pueblo, CO 81003

Connecticut
141 Weston Street
Hartford, CT 06101

11 Silver Street
Middletown, CT 06457

141 Church Street
New Haven, CT 06510

27 Masonic Street
New London, CT 06320

421 Atlantic Street
Stamford, CT 06904

135 Grand Street
Waterbury, CT 06701

Delaware
55 The Plaza
Dover, DE 19801

11th and Market Streets
Wilmington, DE 19801

District of Columbia
L'Enfant Plaza Philatelic
Center
U.S. Postal Service
Headquarters
475 L'Enfant Plaza
West, SW
Washington, DC 20260

Harriet Tubman
Philatelic Center
North Capitol Street and
Massachusetts Avenue
Washington, DC 20013

National Visitors Center
Union Station
50 Massachusetts Ave.,
N.E.
Washington, D.C. 20002

Headsville Station
National Museum of
American History
Smithsonian Institution
Washington, DC 20560

Florida
824 Manatee Ave. West
Bradenton, FL 33506

100 South Belcher Road
Clearwater, FL 33515

1900 West Oakland Park
Boulevard
Fort Lauderdale, FL 33310

401 S.E. 1st Avenue
Gainesville, FL 32601

1801 Polk Street
Hollywood, FL 33022

1110 Kings Road
Jacksonville, FL 32201

210 North Missouri Ave.
Lakeland, FL 33802

118 North Bay Drive
Largo, FL 33540

2200 NW 72nd Avenue
Miami, FL 33101

1200 Goodlette Rd. North
Naples, FL 33940

400 Southwest First Ave.
Ocala, FL 32678

46 East Robinson Street
Orlando, FL 32801

1400 West Jordan Street
Pensacola, FL 32501

3135 First Avenue North
Saint Petersburg,
FL 33730

Open Air Station
76 4th St. N.
Saint Petersburg,
FL 33701

1661 Ringland Blvd.
Sarasota, FL 33578

5201 Spruce Street
Tampa, FL 33602

801 Clematis Street
West Palm Beach,
FL 33401

Georgia
1501 South Slappey Blvd.
Albany, GA 31706

115 Hancock Avenue
Athens, GA 30601

Downtown Station
101 Marietta Street
Atlanta, GA 30304

Downtown Station
120 12th Street
Columbus, GA 31902

364 Green Street
Gainesville, GA 30501

451 College Street
Macon, GA 31201

2 North Fahm Street
Savannah, GA 31401

Hawaii
3600 Aolele Street
Honolulu, HI 96819

Idaho
770 South 13th Street
Boise, ID 83708

Illinois
909 West Euclid Avenue
Arlington Heights,
IL 60004

Moraine Valley Station
7401 100th Place
Bridgeview, IL 60455

433 West Van Buren St.
Chicago, IL 60607

Loop Station
211 South Clark Street
Chicago, IL 60604

1000 East Oakton
Des Plaines, IL 60018

2350 Madison Ave.
Granite City, IL 62040

150 North Scott Ave.
Joliet, IL 60431

901 Lake Street
Oak Park, IL 60301

123 Indianwood
Park Forest, IL 60466

211-19th Street
Rock Island, IL 61201

Edison Square Station
1520 Washington
Waukegan, IL 60085

Indiana

North Park Branch
44923 1st Avenue
Evansville, IN 47710

Fort Wayne Postal
Facility
1501 S. Clinton Street
Fort Wayne, IN 46802

5530 Sohl Street
Hammond, IN 46320

125 West South Street
Indianapolis, IN 46206

2719 South Webster
Kokomo, IN 46901

3450 State Road 26, E
Lafayette, IN 47901

424 South Michigan
South Bend, IN 46624

30 N. 7th Street
Terre Haute, IN 47808

Iowa

615 6th Avenue
Cedar Rapids, IA 52401

1165 Second Avenue
Des Moines, IA 50318

320 6th Street
Sioux City, IA 51101

Kansas

1021 Pacific
Kansas City, KS 66110

434 Kansas Avenue
Topeka, KS 66603

Downtown Station
401 North Market
Wichita, KS 67202

Kentucky

1088 Nadino Blvd.
Lexington, KY 40511

St Mathews Station
4600 Shelbyville Road
Louisville, KY 40207

Louisiana

750 Florida Street
Baton Rouge, LA 70821

705 Jefferson Street
Lafayette, LA 70501

3301 17th Street
Metairie, LA 70004

501 Sterlington Road
Monroe, LA 71201

701 Loyola Avenue
New Orleans, LA 70113

Vieux Carre Station
1022 Iberville Street
New Orleans, LA 70112

2400 Texas Avenue
Shreveport, LA 71102

Maine

40 Western Avenue
Augusta, ME 04330

202 Harlow Street
Bangor, ME 04401

125 Forest Avenue
Portland, ME 04101

Maryland

900 E. Fayette Street
Baltimore, MD 21233

201 East Patrick Street
Frederick, MD 21701

6411 Baltimore Avenue
Riverdale, MD 20840

U.S. Route 50
and Naylor Road
Salisbury, MD 21801

Massachusetts

Post Office and
Courthouse Bldg.
Boston, MA 02109

120 Commercial Street
Brockton, MA 02401

7 Bedford Street
Burlington, MA 01803

330 Cocituate Road
Framingham, MA 01701

385 Main Street
Hyannis, MA 02601

212 Fenn Street
Pittsfield, MA 01201

Long Pond Road
Plymouth, MA 02360

Quincy Branch
47 Washington Street
Quincy, MA 02169

2 Margin Street
Salem, MA 01970

74 Elm Street
West Springfield,
MA 01089

4 East Central Street
Worcester, MA 01603

Michigan

2075 W. Stadium Blvd.
Ann Arbor, MI 48106

26200 Ford Road
Dearborn Heights,
MI 48127

1401 West Fort Street
Detroit, MI 48233

250 East Boulevard Dr.
Flint, MI 48502

225 Michigan Avenue
Grand Rapids, MI 49501

200 South Otsego
Jackson, MI 49201

Downtown Station
315 West Allegan
Lansing, MI 48901

200 West 2nd Street
Royal Oak, MI 48068

30550 Gratiot Street
Roseville, MI 48066

Minnesota

2800 West Michigan
Duluth, MN 55806

1st and Marquette Ave.
Minneapolis, MN 55401

The Pioneer Postal
Emporium
133 Endicott Arcade
St. Paul, MN 55101

Mississippi

Highway 49 North
Gulfport, MS 39501

245 East Capitol
Jackson, MS 32905

500 West Miln Street
Tupelo, MS 38801

Missouri

315 Pershing Road
Kansas City, MO 64108

Northwest Plaza Station
500 Northwest Plaza
St. Ann, MO 63074

8th and Edmond
St. Joseph, MO 64501

Clayton Branch
7750 Maryland
St. Louis, MO 63105

Montana

841 South 26th
Billings, MT 59101

Nebraska

700 R Street
Lincoln, NE 68501

204 W. South Front St.
Grand Island, NE 68801

1124 Pacific
Omaha, NE 68108

Nevada

1001 Circus Circus Dr.
Las Vegas, NV 89114

200 Vassar Street
Reno, NV 89510

New Hampshire

South Main Street
Hanover, NH 03755

80 Daniel Street
Portsmouth, NH 03801

955 Goffs Falls Road
Manchester, NH 03103

New Jersey

1701 Pacific Avenue
Atlantic City, NJ 08401

3 Miln Street
Cranford, NJ 07016

Bellmawr Branch
Haag Ave. & Benigno
Boulevard
Gloucester, NJ 08031

Route 35, & Hazlet Ave.
Hazlet, NJ 07730

150 Ridgedale
Morristown, NJ 07960

Federal Square
Newark, NJ 07102

86 Bayard Street
New Brunswick,
NJ 08901

194 Ward Street
Paterson, NJ 07510

171 Broad Street
Red Bank, NJ 07701

76 Huyler Street
South Hackensack,
NJ 07606

680 Highway √130
Trenton, NJ 08650

155 Clinton Road
West Caldwell,
NJ 07006

41 Greenwood Avenue
Wykoff, NJ 07481

New Mexico

Main Post Office
1135 Broadway NE
Albuquerque, NM 87101

New York

General Mail Facility
30 Old Karner Road
Albany, NY 12212

Empire State Plaza
Station
Albany, NY 12220

115 Henry Street
Binghampton, NY 13902

Bronx General Post Office
149th Street & Grand
Concourse
Bronx, NY 10401

Parkchester Station
1449 West Avenue
Bronx, NY 10462

Riverdale Station
5951 Riverdale Avenue
Bronx, NY 10471

Throggs Neck Station
3630 East Tremont Ave.
Bronx, NY 10465

Wakefield Station
4165 White Plains Rd.
Bronx, NY 10466

Bayridge Station
5501 7th Avenue
Brooklyn, NY 11229

Brooklyn General
Post Office
271 Cadman Plaza East
Brooklyn, NY 11201

Greenpoint Station
66 Meserole Avenue
Brooklyn, NY 11222

Homecrest Station
2002 Avenue U
Brooklyn, NY 11229

Kensington Station
421 McDonald Avenue
Brooklyn, NY 11218

1200 William Street
Buffalo, NY 14240

Rte. 9
Clifton Park, NY 12065

1836 Mott Avenue
Far Rockaway, NY 11691

41-65 Main Street
Flushing, NY 11351

Ridgewood Station
869 Cypress Avenue
Flushing, NY 11385

Old Glenham Road
Glenham, NY 12527

16 Hudson Avenue
Glens Falls, NY 12801

185 West John Street
Hicksville, NY 11802

88-40 164th Street
Jamaica, NY 11431

Ansonia Station
1980 Broadway
New York, NY 10004

Bowling Green Station
25 Broadway
New York, NY 10004

Church Street Station
90 Church Street
New York, NY 10007

Empire State Station
350 Fifth Avenue
New York, NY 10001

F.D.R. Station
909 Third Avenue
New York, NY 10022

Grand Central Station
45th St. & Lexington Ave.
New York, NY 10017

Madison Square Station
149 East 23rd Street
New York, NY 10010

New York General
Post Office
33rd and 8th Avenue
New York, NY 10001

Rockefeller Center
Station
610 Fifth Avenue
New York, NY 10020

Times Square Station
340 West 42nd Street
New York, NY 10036

Franklin & S. Main Sts.
Pearl River, NY 10965

55 Mansion Street
Poughkeepsie, NY 12601

1335 Jefferson Road
Rochester, NY 14692

Rockville Centre Main
Post Office
250 Merrick Road
Rockville Centre,
NY 11570

25 Route 111
Smithtown, NY 11787

550 Manor Road
Staten Island, NY 10314

New Springville Station
2843 Richmond Ave.
Staten Island, NY 10314

5640 East Taft Road
Syracuse, NY 13220

10 Broad Street
Utica, NY 13503

143 Grand Street
White Plains, NY 10602

North Carolina

West Asheville Station
1300 Patton Avenue
Asheville, NC 28806

Eastway Station
3065 Eastway Drive
Charlotte, NC 28205

301 Green Street
Fayetteville, NC 28302

Fort Bragg Branch
Main Post Shopping
Area
Riley Road
Fayetteville, NC 28307

310 New Bern Avenue
Raleigh, NC 27611

North Dakota

657 2nd Avenue North
Fargo, ND 58102

Ohio

675 Wolf Ledges Pkwy.
Akron, OH 44309

2650 N. Cleveland Ave.
Canton, OH 44701

Fountain Square Station
5th and Walnut Street
Cincinnati, OH 45202

301 W. Prospect Ave.
Cleveland, OH 44101

850 Twin Rivers Drive
Columbus, OH 43216

1111 East 5th Street
Dayton, OH 45401

200 North Diamond St.
Mansfield, OH 44901

200 North 4th Street
Steubenville,
OH 43952

435 S. St. Clair Street
Toledo, OH 46301

99 South Walnut Street
Youngstown,
OH 44503

Oklahoma

101 East First
Edmond, OK 73034

115 West Broadway
Enid, OK 73701

102 South 5th
Lawton, OK 73501

525 West Okmulgee
Muskogee, OK 74401

129 West Gray
Norman, OK 73069

76320 SW 5th
Oklahoma City,
OK 73125

333 West 4th
Tulsa, OK 74101

12 South 5th
Yukon, Ok 73099

Oregon

520 Willamette Street
Eugene, OR 97401

751 N.W. Hoyt
Portland, OR 97208

Pennsylvania

Lehigh Valley Branch
Airport Rd. & Route 22
Betlehem, PA 18001

Main Post Office
Beaver Drive Industrial
Park
Dubois, PA 15801

442-456 Hamilton St.
Allentown, PA 18101

Griswold Plaza
Erie, PA 16501

238 S. Penn-
sylvania Ave.
Greensburg, PA 15601

10th and Market Sts.
Harrisburg, PA 17105

111 Franklin Street
Johnstown, PA 15901

Downtown Station
48-50 W. Chestnut St.
Lancaster, PA 17603

1 W. Washington Street
Kennedy Square
New Castle, PA 16101

30th and Market Sts.
Philadelphia, PA 19104

B. Free Franklin Station
316 Market Street
Philadelphia, PA 19106

William Penn Annex
Station
9th and Chestnut Sts.
Philadelphia, PA 19107

Seventh Avenue
& Grant Street
Pittsburgh, PA 15219

450 N. Center Street
Pottsville, PA 17901

59 North 5th Street
Reading, PA 19603

North Washington Ave.
& Linden St.
Scranton, PA 18503

237 South Frazer Street
State College, PA 16801

200 S. George Street
York, PA 17405

Puerto Rico

San Juan General
Post Office
Roosevelt Avenue
San Juan, PR 00936

Plaza Las Americas
Station
San Juan, PR 00938

Rhode Island

24 Corliss Street
Providence, RI 02904

South Carolina

85 Broad Street
Charleston, SC 29401

1601 Assembly Street
Columbia, SC 29201

600 West Washington
Greenville, SC 29602

South Dakota

320 S. 2nd Avenue
Sioux Falls, SD 57101

Tennessee

9th and Georgia
Chattanooga, TN 37401

Tom Murray Station
133 Tucker Street
Jackson, TN 38301

501 West Main Avenue
Knoxville, TN 37901

555 South Third
Memphis, TN 38101

Crosstown Finance Unit
1520 Union Street
Memphis, TN 38104

901 Broadway
Nashville, TN 37202

Texas

2300 South Ross
Amarillo, TX 79105

300 East South Street
Arlington, TX 76010

300 East 9th
Austin, TX 78710

307 Willow Street
Beaumont, TX 77704

809 Nueces Bay
Corpus Christi,
TX 78408

Bryan & Ervay Streets
Dallas, TX 75221

5300 East Paisano Dr.
El Paso, TX 79910

Jennings & Lancaster
Streets
Fort Worth, TX 76101

408 Main Street
Hereford, TX 79045

401 Franklin Avenue
Houston, TX 77201

1515 Avenue "G"
Lubbock, TX 79408

100 East Wall
Midland, TX 79702

615 East Houston
San Antonio, TX 78205

2211 North Robinson
Texarkana, TX 75501

221 West Ferguson
Tyler, TX 75702

800 Franklin
Waco, TX 76701

1000 Lamar Street
Wichita Falls, TX 76307

Utah

1760 West 2100 South
Salt Lake City, UT 84119

Vermont

1 Elmwood Avenue
Burlington, VT 05401

Virginia

1155 Seminole Trail
Charlottesville, VA 22906

Merrified Branch
8409 Lee Highway
Fairfax, VA 22116

600 Granby Street
Norfolk, VA 23501

Tyson's Corner Branch
Tyson's Corner
Shopping Center
McLean, VA 22102

Thomas Corner Station
6274 East Virginia
Beach Blvd.
Norfolk, VA 23502

1801 Brook Road
Richmond, VA 23232

419 Rutherford Ave. NE
Roanoke, VA 24022

London Bridge Station
550 1st Colonial Road
Virginia Beach, VA 23454

Washington

Crossroads Station
15800 N.E. 8th
Bellevue, WA 98008

301 Union Street
Seattle, WA 98101

West 904 Riverside
Spokane, WA 99210

1102 A Street
Tacoma, WA 98402

West Virginia

301 North Street
Bluefield, WV 24701

Lee and Dickinson St.
Charleston, WV 25301

500 West Pike Street
Clarksburg, WV 26301

1000 Virginia Street
Huntington, WV 25704

217 King Street
Martinsburg, WV 25401

Wisconsin

325 East Walnut
Green Bay, WI 54301

345 West St. Paul Ave.
Milwaukee, WI 53203

Wyoming

2120 Capitol Avenue
Cheyenne, WY 82001

STAMP COLLECTING KITS

Sometimes the biggest hurdle to stamp collecting is the dilemma of "where to start." So, the next time you visit your local post office, ask about the exciting U.S. Postal Service Stamp Collecting Kits! They're the perfect way to introduce yourself (or a friend) to the fascinating world of stamps. USPS Collecting Kits get you involved from the minute you open them. Before you know it, you're over the hurdle—you've begun collecting!

USPS Stamp Collecting Kits are fun and inexpensive. They're one of the best values available to a beginning collector of any age. And if at some point you become interested in beginning a topical collection, you can expand easily from one of these Kits.

Every USPS Kit contains four basic collecting tools: a color-illustrated album with background information and display space for each stamp; a selection of genuine, colorful stamps ready for mounting; a convenient packet of mounting hinges; and The Introduction to Stamp Collecting, a 24-page booklet containing all the guidelines you need to start your own collection.

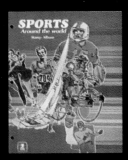  

Your local post office may have additional Stamp Collecting Kits beyond those shown here. Be sure to ask. Since availability may vary, you may also wish to check more than one post office.

USPS Stamp Collecting Kits to be issued during the next months include: Outer Space, Sports, Spirit of America, Science and Scientists, Animals, Famous Persons, Transportation, 30 Stamps from 30 Countries and a 1982 U.S. Collecting Kit. To request additional information, use the postal card following page 256.

COMMEMORATIVE MINT SETS

Each year the U.S. Postal Service issues a new Commemorative Mint Set that includes all the commemorative stamps and Christmas stamps issued for that year, along with a handy album for displaying them. Of interest to both beginning and experienced collectors, these mint sets are a fascinating and convenient way to capture the spirit and history of this country in a format that continues to offer high value over the years. (For details on values of past mint sets and other philatelic products, see page 276.) Commemorative Mint Sets are an excellent way to start a specialty collection in commemoratives, or if you missed purchasing certain issues through your post office, you can fill the gap in your collection from that year's mint set. Each colorfully illustrated album includes an interesting background story for each stamp and its subject, plus a display area supplied with acetate strips to keep your stamps mint fresh.

1980

1981

1982

The 1982 Mint Set contains 20 issues with a total of 29 spectacular stamps, including a random single from the pane of 50 State Birds and Flowers issue, and three colorful blocks of four on the World's Fair, Architecture and Christmas (contemporary). A sampling of additional themes for the 1982 Set includes International Peace Garden, Wolf Trap, American Libraries and numerous well known Americans. $6.50.

The 1981 Mint Set contains 21 issues with a total of 41 individual stamps. In addition to two colorful Christmas stamps which feature both contemporary and traditional designs, the 1981 set includes the Space Achievement block of eight along with four stamp blocks of Flowers, Wildlife Habitats, American Architecture, and Desert Plants. $8.25

The 1980 Mint Set of Commemorative and Special Stamps contains 16 commemoratives. In addition to colorful, four-stamp blocks of Coral Reefs, American Architecture, Northwest Indian Masks and Winter Olympics, this set includes two Christmas stamps in both contemporary and traditional designs. $5.00

1981 DEFINITIVE MINT SETS

Offered for the first time in 1980, Definitive Mint Sets have quickly become a popular addition to the list of philatelic items made available by the U.S. Postal Service. As a companion piece to the 1981 Commemorative Mint Set, the 1981 mint set of definitive stamps and postal stationery offers collectors an opportunity to acquire one of every postal item issued by the Postal Service during 1981. With a limited edition printing of 350,000 (compared to a production of 1.2 million for the Commemorative Mint Set) Definitive Mint Sets hold obvious interest for the serious collector.

Stamp enthusiasts will find the 1981 Definitive Mint Set a fascinating package. The 16-page, full color definitive album contains intriguing stories and photographs relating to all the regular stamps and stationery items issued throughout the year. Individual plastic mounts offer improved protection for all items in the set.

The 1981 Definitive Mint Set (Part A) is available at more than 13,000 post offices nationwide, through all philatelic centers, and by mail order through the Postal Service's Philatelic Sales Division, Washington, DC, 20265-9997. Parts B and C of the set may be purchased by mail order only. For additional information, send postal card following page 256.

For the 1981 set, the U.S. Postal Service is offering the package in three parts to permit customers to purchase by mail order only those items they wish to acquire. The $5.00 minimum purchase and service charge normally associated with mail orders will also be waived for these orders. The album and Part A offer 46 mint denominated stamps and mounts (face value $7.89) for $8.50; Part B contains 10 "B" and "C" nondenominated stamps and mounts (face value $1.90) for $2.00; and Part C consists of 14 pieces of postal stationery plus mounts (face value $2.56) for $3.00.

AMERICAN COMMEMORATIVE PANEL SERIES

When special occasions arise, the U.S. Postal Service can be your best source for a distinctive gift. Limited edition Commemorative Panels have been offered annually by the Postal Service since 1972, in honor of each new commemorative issue for that year, including Christmas stamps. The Wildlife Commemorative Panel became the first in the series, and it remains a valued collector's item today (values for Panels are listed on pages 261-263).

Commemorative Panels combine the finest examples of stamp art with quality reproductions of the engraver's craft. Each consists of a professionally designed, 8½ x 11¼" page that features four or more newly-issued commemorative stamps in mint condition. Accompanying them are lovely, intaglio-printed reproductions of fine, steel line engravings (many more than a century old), and thoughtful articles on each commemorative stamp subject. The resulting panels are elegant philatelic keepsakes and gifts of lasting value appropriate for almost any occasion. As gifts, awards, or a simple gesture of appreciation, American Commemorative Panels convey a unique message of thoughtfulness. And, of course, their value as collector's items is well-founded. Future yearly subscriptions which include every panel issued throughout the year, are available through the Philatelic Sales Division. For additional information, send postal card following page 256.

Battle of Virginia Capes

Let independence be our boast,
Ever mindful what it cost;
Ever grateful for the prize,
Let its altar reach the skies!
From Hail Columbia, Stanza I
Joseph Hopkinson

The battle of Virginia Capes took place in the Chesapeake Bay channel between Cape Charles and Cape Henry on September 5, 1781. It was the last naval battle of the American Revolution and is considered by many historians to be a critical turning point in the fight for freedom.

With French ships blocking the passage of British ships up the Chesapeake Bay channel, Lord Cornwallis, the British Commander at Yorktown, was sealed off from receiving much needed supplies and reinforcements. After a three day sea battle, the British, under the command of Admiral Sir Thomas Graves, were unable to gain access to the channel and retreated to New York.

Sea and cut off, the British forces under Cornwallis were in trouble. The American and French armies under Washington, LaFayette and Rochambeau surrounded and laid siege to Cornwallis and his 7,000 men. After a three week assault and two attempts to escape with his army, Cornwallis finally surrendered on October 19, 1781.

While this final battle practically assured independence, it was not until September 6, 1783 that a definitive peace treaty between the United States and England was signed in Paris.

The event line engraving at the upper left depicts the end of the Revolutionary War — the British General Charles O'Hara handing over his sword to General Lincoln. George Washington's deputy. The engraving at the middle right shows a line of ships similar to those used throughout the war. General LaFayette is shown in the bottom left vignette.

AMERICAN RED CROSS

"After all, there is but one race — humanity."
George Moses

FIRST 100 YEARS

To her grave she believed she was her brother's keeper, and during the ninety-one years of her remarkable life she sought to convince her countrymen that they too have a shared responsibility for others — regardless of race, creed or nationality.

Her name is Clara Barton, founder and first president of the American Red Cross Society in the United States.

Honoring the woman and the organization she initiated, the 1981 Red Cross Commemorative stamp pays tribute to the humanitarian and selfless ideals that have become hallmarks of the movement's efforts over the last nine decades.

Born in Oxford, Massachusetts, Miss Barton first gained notoriety when she began distributing supplies for the relief of wounded Civil War soldiers and helped organize a bureau of records in Washington to aid in the search for missing men. In 1871, she superintended the distribution of relief to the poor in Strasbourg and in 1872 performed a like service in Paris for which she was decorated with the Iron Cross by the German empress.

On returning to the United States Miss Barton began a twelve crusade to have the United States included in the Geneva Treaty — the international Cross-Bridge alliance organized by Henri Dunant several years earlier. Her efforts finally bore fruit in 1881.

More than a year relief agency, the Red Cross has been particularly active in times of such other calamities as the Johnstown flood (1889), the famine in Russia (1891), the hurricane at Galveston, Texas (1900), the earthquake in Italy (1908). The Red Cross blood donor program has been responsible for saving countless thousands of lives. And the list goes on and on.

The motif line engraving featured on this Red Cross Commemorative panel illustrates the need for such an organization as well as the basic altruistic philosophy it has come to epitomize. The Arms of the City of Marseilles appeared on an engraving issued by the American Bank Note Company. The rendering of the wounded Civil War soldier was engraved by artists J.S. Davis and James Smillie.

Everett Dirksen

Everett Dirksen's long and illustrious career as a U.S. Senator from Illinois brought him the well-deserved admiration and respect of his peers and constituents. A forceful and eloquent speaker, Senator Dirksen now receives much-deserved recognition and Postal honor in the form of a commemorative stamp in legislative detail.

Dirksen (1896-1969) was born in Pekin, Illinois, near Peoria, then a farm belt community, about 5,000 people. His parents, Johann Frederick and Antje Conrady Dirksen, were from Germany.

Senator Dirksen was a pre-law student at the University of Minnesota from 1914 to 1917, when he left school to enlist in the Army at the start of the U.S. involvement in World War I. He was sent to France in May 1918, and discharged in October 1919, having been commissioned a second lieutenant in the field.

Dirksen returned to civilian life in Pekin and got in business there until 1927, when he was elected to a part-time position as city commissioner of finance. This election fueled his interest in politics, and he went on to be elected as Illinois Congressman in 1932. He completed his legal education in Washington, and was admitted to the Illinois bar in 1936.

As a Congressman, Dirksen was re-elected by his constituents regularly, by large margins. At the end of 1948 he was forced to retire because of a serious eye ailment.

In 1950, having regained his eyesight, Dirksen ran for the U.S. Senate in Illinois, and won. As a Senator, he served on the Appropriations and Judiciary committees, and was minority whip (1957-59) and virtually leader (1960-69). Dirksen served his government and his fellow congressmen honorably in the Senate for almost twenty years. He died on September 9, 1969.

This commemorative stamp honoring Senator Dirksen was issued on January 4, 1981, in Pekin, Illinois, his hometown. It was designed by Ron Adair, whose pencil sketch was based on a photograph taken about 1968 by David Douglas Duncan.

The top engraving on the panel, originally the property of Western Bank Note Company, Chicago, shows the State Capitol of Illinois. The middle engraving was originally the property of Continental Bank Note Company, New York. The bottom engraving is the Illinois State Seal.

INTERNATIONAL YEAR OF DISABLED PERSONS

"Poetry is what Milton saw when he went blind."
Donald Robert Perry Marquis
From The Sun Dial

Several years ago, the United Nations General Assembly designated 1981 as the International Year of Disabled Persons.

The Assembly urged all nations to give attention to measures and programs designed to aid the 450 million handicapped people in the world today. It also proclaims education for the prevention of impairments and the encouragement of rehabilitation.

More importantly, the goal of the International Year is to promote awareness — to note that disabled people can think and have made tremendous contributions to the world in spite of their handicaps. To recognize that the disabled can feel, feeling and productive lives with only minor accommodations on the part of society. And to recognize that a handicap is just that—something that shouldn't affect a person's ability to perform many other functions unrelated to his handicap.

That message is perhaps best summed up with the U.S.A. 18-cent Disabled Persons commemorative stamp, which depicts a man in a wheelchair, working alone intently, using a sophisticated microscope. This stamp was designed by Martha Perske of Darien, Connecticut following a series of interviews with disabled persons as well as people who worked with them. The legend across the bottom of the stamp says it all—"Disabled doesn't mean Unable."

The engraving in the upper right-hand corner commemorating Science and Commerce was rendered by engraver Sydney Smith and has been used on a number of stock certificates. The vignette on the bottom right which was used by the American Bank Note Company in 1943 was originally drawn by and engraved by William Adolph.

VALUES FOR OTHER USPS PHILATELIC PRODUCTS

Over the years, the U.S. Postal Service has published a number of limited edition philatelic products. These products include hardcover books issued to commemorate the Bicentennial, the 1980 Olympics, the Prominent Americans Series and, most recently, the Americana Series. The U.S. Postal Service Commemorative Stamp Mint Sets also fall into this special limited edition category, now joined by the 1980 and 1981 Definitive Stamp Mint Sets. These current market values were determined through various dealers who carry these products.

Commemorative Mint Sets	Original Price	Current Market Value
1968	$ 2.50	$22.50
1969	2.50	28.50
1970	2.50	14.95
1971	2.50	7.95
1972	3.00	7.95
1973	3.00	7.95
1974	3.50	7.95
1975	3.50	7.95
1976	3.50	7.95
1977	4.50	7.95
Bicentennial Mint Set With Souvenir Sheets	$11.80	$25.00
Without Souvenir Sheets	7.50	9.95
1980 Olympics Mint Set	6.50	9.95
Prominent Americans Series Mint Set	12.00	22.50
Americana Series Mint Set	14.00	19.50

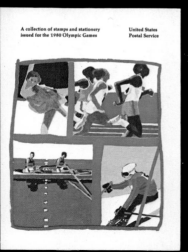

A collection of stamps and stationery issued for the 1980 Olympic Games

United States Postal Service

INDEX OF COMMEMORATIVE STAMPS & STORIES

Stamps having related stories are indicated in **boldface** type. The numbers in this index are the Scott numbers of the stamps.